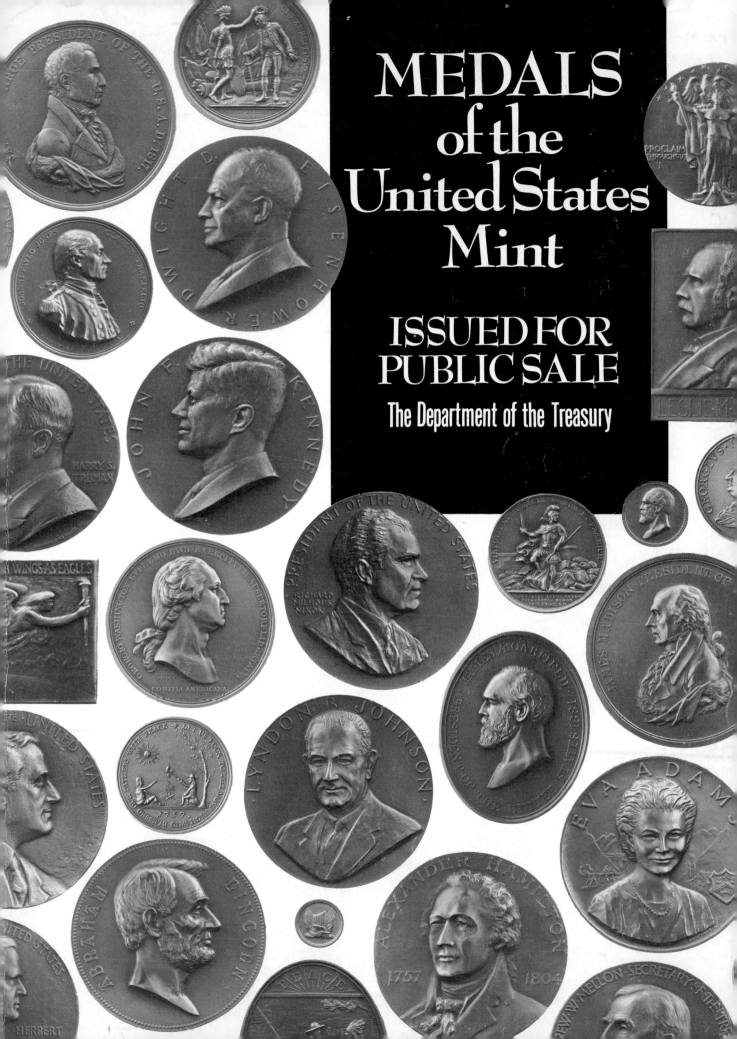

MEDALS
of the
United States
Mint

ISSUED FOR PUBLIC SALE

The Department of the Treasury

MEDALS
of the
United States
Mint

Prepared under the direction of the
Honorable Eva Adams Director of the Mint

By Captain Kenneth M. Failor, USNR,
Consultant to the Director of the Mint and
Eleonora Hayden, Bureau of the Mint

Library of Congress Catalog Card No. 74–602460

For sale by the Superintendent of Documents, U.S. Government Printing Office
Washington, D.C. 20402   -   Price $3.50 cents

FOREWORD

A nation reveals itself not only by the men it produces
but also by the men it honors, the men it remembers.

JOHN F. KENNEDY, Address at Amherst College,
Amherst, Mass., October 26, 1963.

This catalogue of Medals of the U.S. Mint has been compiled as a memorial to the Nation's great, who have left their imprint on the course of American history. It is being issued in conjunction with the opening of the new U.S. Mint at Philadelphia, which will be not only the most modern coinage mint in the world, but will also have extensive facilities for one of its lesser known activities, the manufacture of national medals which it has produced for the past century.

All of the medals listed in this catalogue are offered for purchase by the public. An order form appears in the appendix; additional copies are available upon request from the Superintendent, U.S. Mint, Philadelphia, Pa. 19106.

The sizes of the medals are not listed in this catalogue because the medals are here reproduced in approximately their exact size. The medals are made of bronze and are boxed for mailing. Most of the medals will be carried in stock and will be readily available, although in some cases delays in filling orders may be occasioned.

The series of official medals of the Presidents of the United States is complete. A short history of these medals appears in the appendix. Miniatures of Presidential medals, bearing the portrait on one side and the Seal of the President on the other, will be released as soon as the dies for this series have been completed. Not all of the Secretaries of the Treasury and the Directors of the Mint are included in the series currently available for these officials.

A supplement, or revision of this catalogue, will be published in the future, as new medals are added to the list and additional material has been compiled to round out the biographies already contained in this document.

August, 1969.

Table of Contents

V

2312

Presidents of the United States

GEORGE WASHINGTON

First President of the United States
April 30, 1789 to March 3, 1797
(No. 101)

OBV. George Washington, President of the United States, 1789. Bust of the President.

By Pierre Simon Duvivier.

REV. Peace and Friendship. Two hands clasped in token of amity; on the cuff of the left wrist three stripes with buttons, each button carrying the American eagle; the other wrist is bare; above the hands, crossed, the pipe of peace and the tomahawk.

By John Reich.

GEORGE WASHINGTON

1732—Born on February 22, at "Wakefield," Westmoreland County, Va.; the son of Augustine and Mary Ball Washington.
Self-educated; principal studies were geometry and trigonometry, establishing a foundation for his occupation as a surveyor.

1748—Moved to Mount Vernon, the home of his half-brother, Lawrence; helped survey the lands of Thomas, Lord Fairfax, in the Shenandoah.

1749—Was appointed public surveyor of Culpeper County, Va.; his income from this pursuit enabled him to purchase large tracts of land.

1751—Appointed adjutant-general by Governor Robert Dinwiddie, with the rank of major, with the mission of protecting the Southern District of Virginia against French and Indian attacks. This gave Washington experience in the exercise of military strategy and tactics—a field in which he had a particular interest.

1752—After death of Lawrence Washington, he acquired Mount Vernon by inheritance.

1753—Carried ultimatum from Lieutenant Governor Dinwiddie of Virginia to the French, warning them against encroaching on English lands in the Ohio Valley. War followed.

1754—Commissioned lieutenant colonel by Governor Dinwiddie; his regiment was sent out to reinforce a British post on the forks of the Ohio River (site of today's modern city of Pittsburgh). This post, occupied and renamed Fort Duquesne by the French, was so firmly established that Washington took up his position at Great Meadows, Pa., naming his new post Fort Necessity. On May 28, he defeated a French scouting party; later Fort Necessity was put under 10 hours of siege by the main French forces and it was necessary to capitulate. Despite this defeat, on July 3, the expedition enhanced Washington's combat experience.

1755—As a colonel, joined the staff of General Braddock for an expedition of regular British troops against Fort Duquesne. The attack met with failure; Braddock was mortally wounded, and the command passed to Washington. During this French and Indian onslaught, two horses were shot out from under Washington, and his coat showed four bullet holes.

Was appointed commander in chief of all the Virginia forces with the rank of colonel. For the following 3 years he had the responsibility for the defense of 350 miles of mountainous frontier, with a force of 300 troops, against French and Indian raids. The engagements, which averaged two a month, gave Washington considerable opportunity to develop his skill in conducting warfare over an extensive range of territory.

1758—He had the satisfaction this year of joining the British forces as they moved into the burning ruins of Fort Duquesne, abandoned by the French. Resigned his command and withdrew to Mount Vernon.

1759—Married Mrs. Martha (Dandridge) Custis on January 6, a Virginia widow.

Took his seat in the Virginia House of Burgesses, serving continuously with that body until 1774.

1765—Supported Virginians protesting against the Stamp Act, which made mandatory the use of stamps on commercial and legal documents, newspapers, pamphlets, almanacs, cards and dice; also supported the grievance against the British prohibition of colonial paper money.

1769—Drew up a Nonimportation Act, providing for the imposition of an embargo on various British articles. This act was ratified by the Virginia House of Burgesses.

1773—Was a delegate to the Williamsburg Convention which resolved that taxation and representation were inseparable. Was among the foremost advocates for colonial self-government.

1774—Was elected a Virginia delegate to the First Continental Congress, which met in September.

1775—Was a member of the Second Continental Congress beginning in May; served on the committee for drafting Army regulations and planning the defense of New York City.

Was elected commander in chief of the Continental Army and took command on July 2, at Cambridge, Mass.

Although an American attempt to take Quebec and Montreal was not successful, it revealed Washington to be a brilliant tactician and a great soldier.

1776—On March 17, caused the British to evacuate Boston, for which he was awarded a medal by the Congress. (This medal is shown in the Army Series of Mint Medals.) The Continental Army was transferred to New York.

Was defeated on August 27, at the Battle of Long Island.

On Christmas night, he crossed the Delaware and crushed the Hessians at the Battle of Trenton.

1777—Expelled the British from Princeton, on January 3.

The battles at Trenton and Princeton were decisive; had it not been for them, the impetus to carry on with the Revolutionary War might have died out. In these actions, as well as in other engagements undertaken, it was evident that Washington knew how and when to retreat and how and when to take the initiative.

Attempting to prevent British forces from reaching the Chesapeake Bay, Washington intercepted them at Brandywine Creek, Chester County, Pa., on September 11. Although defeated, this engagement prevented British forces from reaching Philadelphia for a period of 2 weeks.

Fought a gallant, but unsuccessful battle at Germantown on October 3–4. This action is believed to have damaged British morale and to have convinced the French of the determination of the Americans to persist in the War for Independence.

1777—With his troops, he endured the hardships of winter encampment at Valley Forge.

1778—By authority of the Congress, Washington was given power to build a permanent army, one involving 3-year enlistments, or for the duration of the war; was given assistance by Baron von Steuben who undertook intensive troop training. In March the French entered into an alliance with the Americans.

On June 28, American forces overtook the British at Monmouth and held the field while the British retreated from Philadelphia to New York City.

1780—The treason of Benedict Arnold was a severe blow.

1781—Though Washington's preliminary plans were for a joint American-French attack against the British-held city of New York, he made the decision to utilize the French fleet under Admiral de Grasse, to attack Cornwallis at Yorktown. Bottled up and cut off from a sea escape by the French, Cornwallis surrendered on October 19.

After Yorktown, the American forces drew back to quarters at Newburgh, N.Y.

1783—Held the Army together until November 25, when the British evacuated New York City, and he led the American troops into the city.

On December 4, Washington said farewell to his officers at Fraunces Tavern in New York City; on December 23, at Annapolis, he resigned his commission; and he returned to his home at Mount Vernon.

1785—Held a meeting at Mount Vernon on navigation rights on the Potomac River, which indirectly led to the convening of the United States Constitutional Convention at Philadelphia.

1787—Was a delegate to, and President of, the National Convention which met in Philadelphia in May and adopted a new Constitution, greatly increasing the power of the Federal Government.

1788—Washington was unaminously elected the first President of the United States.

1789—On April 30, 1789, Washington took his oath of office on the balcony of Federal Hall, Broad and Walnut Streets, New York City. (This is now the site of the Washington statue in front of the old Sub-Treasury Building.) At the end of his first term, he was unaminously reelected. In his Cabinet, Jefferson was Secretary of State; Hamilton, Secretary of the Treasury; Knox, Secretary of War; and Randolph, Attorney General.

Washington's accomplishments as President were substantial, and proved to be of lasting value.

The Neutrality Proclamation of April 22, 1793, promulgated by Washington after the outbreak of war between France and Great Britain, was a milestone in American diplomatic history. When it was enacted into law the following year, it established the basic principles of international law and neutral rights and obligations of U.S. citizens in trading with belligerent countries.

The full force and effect of the authority of the U.S. Government was first put to the test in domestic affairs, and successfully so, in suppressing opposition to excise taxes on liquor (known as the Whiskey Rebellion) and in dealing with Indian intrusions.

The public credit was established, at home and abroad, by Washington's support of monetary principles espoused by his Secretary of the Treasury, Alexander Hamilton.

Washington made considerable progress in ironing out western and southern boundary problems which existed with Spain and were the subject of the Pinckney Treaty of 1795. Likewise, issues relating to commerce and neutral rights with Great Britain were brought closer to solution through negotiation of the Jay Treaty.

There evolved, during Washington's administration, rules-of-the-road governing the independence of each of the three branches of Government—the Legislative, the Executive, and the Judicial. Washington, for example, laid down the basic principle requiring the approval of the President for the release of controversial Executive documents desired for examination by the Congress.

Though Washington did not favor political parties, they did come into existence during his administration.

1796—On September 19, 1796, declining a third term, Washington delivered his "Farewell Address" to the Congress. Notwithstanding his intention of spending his remaining years in private life, he was appointed lieutenant general and Commander in Chief of the armies of the United States, to meet a possible war with France, which did not materialize.

1799—Died on December 14 and was buried at Mount Vernon, Virginia.

IMPORTANT LEGISLATION*

Bill of Rights (first 10 amendments)—December 15, 1791, 1 Stat. 97.
Judiciary Act—September 4, 1789, 1 Stat. 73.
Tariff Act—July 4, 1789, 1 Stat. 24.
District of Columbia Act (first)—July 16, 1790, 1 Stat. 130.
Bank of Columbia Act (first)—February 25, 1791, 1 Stat. 191.
Eleventh Amendment—February 7, 1795, 1 Stat. 402.

---

*(The lists of "Important Legislation" which follow the presidential biographies are meant to be selective rather than all-inclusive, since the term "important" is subject to varied interpretation by different authorities. With certain exceptions, declarations of war, conclusions of treaties, routine and appropriation legislation have been omitted. Some subsidiary legislation under certain existing acts has also been omitted.)

JOHN ADAMS

Second President of the United States
March 4, 1797 to March 3, 1801
(No. 102)

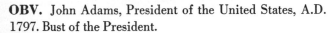

OBV. John Adams, President of the United States, A.D. 1797. Bust of the President.

By Moritz Furst.

REV. Peace and Friendship. Two hands clasped in token of amity; on the cuff of the left wrist three stripes with buttons, each button carrying the American eagle; the other wrist is bare; above the hands, crossed, the pipe of peace and the tomahawk.

By John Reich.

JOHN ADAMS

1735—Born on October 30, in the village of Braintree (Quincy), Mass. He was the fourth in descent from Henry Adams who fled from persecution in England and settled in Massachusetts about 1630. Another of his ancestors was John Adams, a founder of Plymouth Colony in 1620.

1755—Graduated from Harvard College; taught school at Worcester, Mass., and studied law.

1758—Admitted to the bar of Suffolk County and commenced the practice of law in Boston. He soon acquired prominence for his writings which were spirited, terse, clear and pungent.

1761—Already identified with the patriot cause, he evidenced his growing interest in constitutional law by reporting on the action brought by the merchants of Boston, questioning the legality of general search warrants. Known as "writs of assistance",

these documents were issued to the customs officers by the superior courts of several colonies.

Joined the Sons of Liberty, an energetic and forceful organization which served as the extralegal arm of a movement for colonial self-government.

1764—Married Abigail Smith, the daughter of a minister.

1765—Appeared before Governor Hutchison to oppose the Stamp Act on the basis that it constituted taxation without representation. This legislation required the use of stamps on all legal papers, pamphlets, newspapers, almanacs, cards and dice. Adams' protest served as a model for other New England colonies.

1768—Moved to Boston where he won distinction at the bar. Became the father of John Quincy Adams, destined to become the sixth President of the United States.

1770—Exhibited great moral courage in defending and winning acquittal of a British officer he felt was unjustly charged with responsibility for the Boston Massacre, an incident in which four citizens were killed.

1771—Represented Boston in the Massachusetts Legislature (General Court).

1774—Condemned the act which closed the Port of Boston until the townspeople paid for the cargoes of taxed tea they had dumped into the harbor, and otherwise demonstrated to the satisfaction of the crown that they would be peaceful subjects. The "Tea

Party" is said to have been "the boldest stroke which had yet been struck in America for its independence."

1774–78—Became a vigorous delegate to the First and Second Continental Congresses, during which time he emerged a leader in the movement for American independence.

Seconded the nomination of Washington as commander in chief of the army; advocated creation of a naval force; formulated foreign policy principles; and helped write the resolution of May 10, 1776, declaring American independence. Jefferson wrote that during congressional debate on the Declaration of Independence, Adams was "its ablest advocate and defender against the multifarious assaults it encountered."

1776—As Chairman of the Board of War and Ordnance, he helped to develop and equip an army.

1778–88—Entered the Diplomatic Service, first as a commissioner to the Court of France, where he served with Benjamin Franklin; later, as a minister to England and then to Holland. In 1782 he won recognition of American Independence by The Hague. Together with Jay and Jefferson, he negotiated the Treaty of 1783 with Great Britain, which ended the Revolutionary War.

In 1785, he was appointed the first American minister to the Court of St. James, a post he held until his return to America in 1788.

1788—In the first election held under the Constitution, Adams was elected the first Vice President of the United States; he was reelected in 1792.

During his administration as Vice President, policy differences led to the formulation of two political parties—the Federalist (of which Adams had been a leader) and the Democratic Republicans.

Like Washington, Adams withdrew from partisan politics, leadership of the Federalist Party passing to Alexander Hamilton. By 1792, the followers of Jefferson called themselves Republicans, but the Republican Party of today had its beginning in the 1850's.

1796—On the retirement of Washington, Adams was elected President; Jefferson, the leader of the opposition party, became Vice President.

1797—Following his inauguration on March 4, Adams' approach to the problems of his office was one of moderation. The Hamiltonians felt he was too conciliatory to the opposition; the Jeffersonians became increasingly hostile. Adams' attempts to achieve political harmony and end partisan politics at home met with little success.

American policy was to remain neutral in the war between the British and the French. The Directory in France, feeling that the United States was pro-British because of the Jay Treaty, broke off commercial relations and refused to accept an American envoy except by payment of a bribe. Despite the war fever which broke out for an all-out showdown, Adams began to formulate what later proved to be a prudent course of action—intensive preparation for war but at the same time he gave equal attention to a program designed to settle the issues peacefully through negotiation.

1798—Although the President did not ask the Congress for a declaration of war, he did ask for, and was given, funds to establish a provincial army. Authority was given the President to arm merchant ships, as well as to establish a Department of the Navy. Included in the naval authorization were funds to build three new frigates. One of these ships, the CONSTITUTION, whose decks "once red with heroes' blood" still remains commissioned in the U.S. Navy. It is berthed at the Boston Navy Yard.

As a means of coping with and driving out hostile foreign agents and sympathizers, Adams supported the Alien and Sedition Acts which authorized imprisonment of aliens whose motherland was at war with the United States, and which made it a high misdemeanor to unlawfully combine and conspire against the Government of the United States.

1799—Notwithstanding the strong opposition in the Congress and in his own Cabinet, Adams appointed a minister to the French Republic, proposing a peace commission.

1800—As the sea lanes were cleared by U.S. warships and armed merchantmen, the long period of diplomatic negotiation and cautious action on the part of the President, led to a peace with the French Government on September 30, 1800. It was an honorable peace, one which preserved the neutrality of the United States.

Adams arrived in Washington on November 1, 1800. He took up residence in the still unfinished presidential residence later to be known as the White House. The following day he closed a letter to his wife with the words which now appear on a mantle in the White House: "I pray Heaven to bestow the best of Blessings on this House and all men that shall hereafter inhabit it. May none but honest and wise men ever rule under this roof."

1801—Defeated for a second term in office by Thomas Jefferson, Adams retired to his home, the Old House, which is now a historic site in Quincy,

Mass. In retirement he wrote much on public affairs, past and current. He became reconciled with Jefferson.

1816—Headed the list of presidential electors of his party in the State; was a member of the State Convention to revise the Constitution of Massachusetts.

1826—Just before he died, Adams is said to have whispered: "Thomas Jefferson survives." Jefferson had died a few hours earlier, on the same day, July 4—the 50th Anniversary of the American Declaration of Independence.

Adams lies buried in the Old First Congregational Church in Quincy, Mass.

Naturalization Act—March 26, 1790, 1 Stat. 103.
Naval establishment—April 30, 1798, 1 Stat. 553.
Construction of 12 naval vessels—April 27, 1798, 1 Stat. 552.
Alien and Sedition Acts—June 25, 1798, 1 Stat. 570; July 6, 1798, 1 Stat. 577.

THOMAS JEFFERSON

Third President of the United States
March 4, 1801 to March 3, 1809
(No. 103)

OBV. Th. Jefferson, President of the United States, A.D. 1801. Bust of the President.

REV. Peace and Friendship. Two hands clasped in token of amity; on the cuff of the left wrist three stripes and as many buttons; the other wrist bears a wristband ornamented by an eagle; above the hands, a pipe of peace and a tomahawk crossed.

By John Reich.

THOMAS JEFFERSON

"I HAVE SWORN UPON THE ALTAR OF GOD ETERNAL HOSTILITY AGAINST EVERY FORM OF TYRANNY OVER THE MIND OF MAN"

1743—Born on April 13, at Shadwell (Albermarle County), Va.; the oldest son of Peter Jefferson who died in 1757.

1760—After private tutoring in the classics, he attended the College of William and Mary at Williamsburg, Va.

Studied law under George Wythe who, in his generation, was Virginia's greatest jurist.

1767—After admission to the bar, Jefferson commenced the practice of law which he continued until 1774 when the courts were closed by the American Revolution.

1769—Became a member of the Virginia House of Burgesses, where he served until 1775. This early public service developed in Jefferson a lifelong interest in the rights of an individual to have a voice in government. Jefferson's activity in the House of Burgesses, and in later public posts, was as a writer rather than as a speaker.

8

1770—Began to build "Monticello", his new home, located near Charlottesville, Va.

1772—Married Mrs. Martha Wayles Skelton, daughter of John Wayles, an eminent Virginia lawyer. Of the six children born of this marriage, only two survived infancy.

1773—Chosen a member of the first Committee of Correspondence established by the Colonial Legislature.

1774—Prepared *A Summary View of the Rights of America* for the use of the Virginia delegates to the Continental Congress, in which he made a notable contribution to the patriot cause by presenting his views on natural rights, including that of emigration. This document attacked the supremacy of Parliament over the colonies and recognized no tie with England except through its King. This treatise won for Jefferson the chairmanship of the committee selected to draft the Declaration of Independence which, in great measure, is a restatement of the principles set forth in the "Summary."

1775—Member of the Continental Congress. As a member of the Committee of Five, Jefferson wrote the basic draft of the Declaration of Independence. This basic charter of American liberty, was adopted July 4, 1776, after minor changes by John Adams, Benjamin Franklin and the Congress.

1776—Resigned his seat in the Congress and returned to Monticello, partly for personal reasons, but also for the purpose of revising the laws of Virginia so as to reflect his own philosophy of human rights. For this reason, he served in the Virginia Legislature from 1776 until his selection as Governor of Virginia in 1779, a post he held until 1781.

As Governor of Virginia, Jefferson was called upon to resist the British invasion of that State.

Jefferson's service in the legislature and as Governor of Virginia was marked by his outstanding success in obtaining legislation in broad areas. Foremost in this respect was a statute establishing religious freedom, including the right of each to worship according to his own conscience, and to discontinue State support of an established church through taxation. Other reforms served to broaden the electorate through a system of more equitable representation, and to eliminate feudal vestiges of land laws relating to primogeniture and entail. While the mood of the time did not favor abolishment of slavery, legislation was enacted to prevent the further importation of slaves into Virginia.

1782—Appointed by Congress as minister plenipotentiary to act with others in Europe in negotiating a treaty of peace with Great Britain.

1783–85—Member of the Continental Congress. Drew up an ordinance which prohibited slavery in the North West Territory after 1800; though it failed of passage, it did become the basis for the famous North West Ordinance of 1787. Performed notable services connected with the adoption of the decimal system of coinage, with the dollar as a unit of value. (The mint was placed under Jefferson when he became Secretary of State.)

1785–88—Together with Benjamin Franklin and John Adams, was sent to Paris to negotiate commerce treaties; then served as Franklin's successor as minister to the King of France. Was able to win important commercial concessions, and submitted reports on events related to the development of the French Revolution.

1789—Washington appointed Jefferson as the first Secretary of State. Jefferson's strong faith in the principle that a government derives its power from the consent of the governed brought him into conflict with the Secretary of the Treasury, Alexander Hamilton, an exponent of executive control based on the doctrine of "implied powers." With reluctance, Washington accepted Jefferson's resignation as Secretary of State on December 31, 1793, when the latter returned to Monticello.

1797—Recalled from private life, he made himself available as a presidential candidate, running on the Republican ticket. A difference of three electoral votes resulted in the election of John Adams as President; whereupon Jefferson became Vice President, an office he held until 1801. Utilizing his experience as President of the Senate, he compiled and published a "Manual of Parliamentary Practice."

Jefferson also became president of the American Philosophical Society, a post which he occupied for many years. Founded by Benjamin Franklin in 1743, this is the oldest learned society in America.

Jefferson was a strong opponent of the Alien and Sedition Acts (which, nonetheless became law) on the basis that they attempted to suppress freedom of speech and destroy political opposition.

1800—In the presidential election this year, the Federalists were defeated, and the Republican candidates—Thomas Jefferson and Aaron Burr received identical electoral votes. The contest was thrown into the House of Representatives where, after 36 roll calls, Jefferson (with the aid of Hamilton) was elected as President of the United States. He was the first President to be inaugurated in Washington.

The defeat of the Federalists dispelled in Jefferson's mind such fears as he had of the establishment of a monarchy in the United States.

His inaugural address extended the olive branch to the opposition party and proved to be effective in establishing his leadership over the Congress. In his Cabinet, Madison was Secretary of State; Gallatin, Secretary of the Treasury; Dearborn, Secretary of War; Robert Smith, Secretary of the Navy; and Lincoln, Attorney General.

1803—The major achievement of Jefferson's first term was the purchase of Louisiana from Napoleon for $15 million. This was the beginning of a program which eventually extended the boundaries of the United States to the Pacific. The negotiations leading to the purchase of Louisiana were handled by the American Minister to Paris, Robert R. Livingston together with James Monroe who was appointed by Jefferson as a special envoy.

Jefferson was less successful in his efforts to curb what he felt was partisanship on the part of judges in the U.S. courts. As one of his last acts in office, Adams had appointed John Marshall as Chief Justice of the U.S. Supreme Court. A strong Federalist, Marshall had the support of a number of judges of his own party (the "midnight judges") who were also appointed by Adams on the eve of his departure from the White House. In the famous opinion of *Marbury* v. *Madison*, handed down by Chief Justice Marshall, the Court established its authority to declare invalid any Federal legislation which it deemed to be in conflict with the Constitution.

Placed Commodore Edward Preble in command of the CONSTITUTION, to lead the Mediterranean squadron against the pirates of Tripoli. Unprotected by naval strength, American commerce had fallen prey to marauding Barbary corsairs.

Selected his personal secretary, Meriwether Lewis, and William Clark, to head an expedition for the exploration of the West. When Lewis and Clark departed, they carried with them medals bearing the likeness of Jefferson for presentation to the Indian Chiefs.

1804—Reelected to the Presidency. Jefferson's new administration was beleaguered with problems caused by the English-French wars on the continent. Jefferson maintained American neutrality, in large degree, by resort to economic measures such as the Non-Importation Act of 1806, and the Embargo Act of 1807. Economic distress led to a partial lifting of the embargo restrictions in 1809.

1809—Retired to Monticello where the last years of his life were absorbed with the establishment of the University of Virginia, a milestone in higher public education.

1826—Died on July 4 at Monticello. For his tomb he chose the inscription:

"Here was buried Thomas Jefferson, author of the Declaration of Independence, of the statute of Virginia for religious freedom, and father of the University of Virginia."

Louisiana Purchase Treaty—April 30, 1803, 8 Stat. 200.
Embargo Act—December 22, 1807, 2 Stat. 451.
Bank of the United States Act—March 23, 1804, 2 Stat. 274.
Twelfth Amendment—June 15, 1804, 2 Stat. 306.

JAMES MADISON

Fourth President of the United States
March 4, 1809 to March 3, 1817
(No. 104)

OBV. James Madison, President of the United States, A.D. 1809. Bust of the President.

REV. Peace and Friendship. Two hands clasped in token of amity; on the cuff of the left wrist three stripes and as many buttons; the other wrist is bare; above the hands, a pipe of peace and a tomahawk crossed.

By John Reich.

JAMES MADISON, *"Father of the Constitution"*

1751—Born on March 16, at Port Conway, King George County, Va.; the son of James Madison, the family being of English descent and among the early settlers of Virginia.

1771—Graduated from the College of New Jersey (now Princeton University); took 1 year of postgraduate work in theology. While still young, was distinguished for sound judgment, industry, and patriotism.

1774—Began his public career by serving as a member of the Committee of Safety for Orange County, Va.—one of many such committees which sprang up throughout the colonies for the purpose of kindling and keeping alive the revolutionary spirit. These committees, in turn aided in the formulation of provincial congresses which were the revolutionary governing bodies of the colonies concerned. The First Continental Congress which met in 1774 was organized as a result of the efforts of the revolutionary committees and provincial congresses.

1776—Delegate to the Virginia Convention; served on a committee to draft a constitution for the State of Virginia; worked with Thomas Jefferson to achieve a Declaration of Rights (not adopted) to make the free exercise of religion a matter of right rather than one of toleration.

1777—Was a leader in the first General Assembly of Virginia; appointed the following year by Governor Patrick Henry to the Executive Council of the Assembly.

1780–83—Elected a delegate from Virginia to the Continental Congress, he proved to be one of its most vocal and effective leaders in working for the establishment of a central government. He advocated extension of the powers of Congress, authority of the Government to impose import duties as a means of paying the public debt, American navigation of the Mississippi without interference from Spain, and opposed the further issuance of paper money by the States.

1783—Returned to Virginia; studied law; was a delegate to the Virginia House of Delegates.

1786—Appointed as one of the delegates to a convention at Annapolis, Md., to devise a system of commercial regulations for all the States. Upon their recommendations, a convention of delegates from

335-478 O - 69 - 2

all the States was held in Philadelphia the following year.

1787—Delegate from Virginia to the Constitutional Convention at Philadelphia. The proposals Madison offered to the Convention met with such favor as to earn for him the appellation "Father of the Constitution," a term which he modestly declined to acknowledge on the basis that the Constitution was the product of "many heads and many hands." The notes taken by Madison during this Convention were preserved and represent one of the basic sources of American constitutional history of the period.

1788—Coauthored, with Alexander Hamilton and John Jay, a series of articles on political theory which appeared as *The Federalist Papers*. These writings are credited as having been the major force in offsetting opposition to the new government and in achieving ratification of the Constitution.

1789–97—Elected to the U.S. House of Representatives, defeating James Monroe. Feeling that too much centralization in the Federal Government could jeopardize the democratic rights of people, Madison became a strong ally of Jefferson. They both became leaders of a new party, the Democratic Republicans, who opposed the Federalists headed by Hamilton.

Married Mrs. Dolly Paine Todd of Philadelphia in 1794, widow of a Pennsylvania lawyer. Madison declined a diplomatic assignment as well as an opportunity to serve as Secretary of State in the Cabinet of President Washington, feeling perhaps that he could be more useful in the Congress. Practically all the major legislation of this period bears the imprint of Madison. This includes the first 10 amendments to the Constitution, otherwise known as the Bill of Rights; revenue legislation, and statutes creating the Departments of State, War, and the Treasury.

Madison joined Jefferson in opposing the Alien and Sedition Acts, as an infringement on civil liberties, and he upheld the rights of States to oppose unconstitutional power assumed by the Federal Government.

1797—Retired from Congress and accepted a seat in the Virginia Assembly.

1800—Served as a presidential elector on the Democratic ticket, voting for Jefferson and Burr.

1801—Was appointed by President Jefferson as Secretary of State. Holding this post for 8 years, he had the complete confidence of Jefferson in handling affairs of state. Most of his problems stemmed from the Anglo-French wars on the continent. He earnestly sought peace with both countries; he did what he could to protest the impressment of American seamen and the seizure of American vessels by the British. He supported Jefferson's Embargo Act which denied France and England access to American raw materials and products. This embargo was later modified because of its depressing effect on the U.S. economy.

1808—Elected to the Presidency on the Democratic-Republican ticket by a strong majority, Madison inherited all of the problems, and more, that he had patiently and judiciously handled as Secretary of State. He was a "strict constructionist" in utilizing his constitutional authority as Chief Executive, as opposed to the Federalists who were inclined to freely interpret the Constitution. Was reelected to the Presidency in 1812.

With great patience, he endeavored to protect the sovereign rights of the United States notwithstanding the continuing difficulties with England and France. Legislation was enacted during his administration, again terminating trade with these two countries and, later, giving Madison the option of establishing trade with either or both of these two countries if they agreed to respect American rights. Napoleon made a pretense of complying, whereupon Madison declared a nontrade policy with England. The continuing belligerence on the part of the British caused Madison to ask Congress for a declaration of war, which was enacted on June 18, 1812.

The lack of preparation for a war with England initially met with American military failures; the British burned the White House; and the conflict, in some parts of the country, met with such dissatisfaction (particularly on the part of the Federalists) that it became known as "Mr. Madison's War." American sentiment changed, however, after our military and naval forces met with success. A chronicle of many of these events appears in the sections of this catalogue relating to Army and Navy Medals.

1814—The signing of the Treaty of Ghent signaled the close of the War of 1812. It also marked the repudiation of the Federalist Party and its disappearance from the national scene.

With the end of Federalism and the existence of only one party in the United States, the Democratic-Republicans, lessons of war caused a resurgence of nationalism. A stronger military organization was proposed by Madison. He advocated a tariff to protect industry, and though he had opposed the First Bank of the United States, he signed a bill creating the Second Bank of the United States.

1817—Retired to his home at Montpelier in Orange County, Va. Succeeded Thomas Jefferson as rector of the University of Virginia at Charlottesville, and also interested himself as "visitor" to the College of William and Mary at Williamsburg.

Even in retirement, Madison continued to speak out against disruptive States' rights influences which threatened the perpetuation of the Federal Union.

1829—Chosen a member of the State Convention to revise the Constitution of Virginia.

1836—Died on June 28 at Montpelier and was buried on his estate.

Macon's Bill No. 2 (restoring commercial intercourse with England and France) May 1, 1810, 2 Stat. 605.
Protective Tariff Act (first)—February 5, 1816, 3 Stat. 253.
Second Bank of the United States—April 10, 1816, 3 Stat. 266.

JAMES MONROE

Fifth President of the United States
March 4, 1817 to March 3, 1825
(No. 105)

OBV. James Monroe, President of the United States, A.D. 1817. Bust of the President.

By Moritz Furst

REV. Peace and Friendship. Two hands clasped in token of amity; on the cuff of the left wrist three stripes and as many buttons; the other wrist is bare; above the hands, a pipe of peace and a tomahawk crossed.

By John Reich

JAMES MONROE

1758—Born on April 28, Westmoreland County, Va.; the son of Spence and Elizabeth (Jones) Monroe, both natives of Virginia.

1774—Attended William and Mary College.

1776–80—Enlisted in the Continental Army, appointed a lieutenant in the Third Virginia Regiment and later promoted to major. Served in the battles of Brandywine, Germantown, Harlem Heights, Monmouth, White Plains, and Trenton (where he was wounded).

1780—Studied law under Thomas Jefferson, then Governor of Virginia; became his close friend and political protege.

1782—As an anti-Federalist, he served as a member of the Virginia Assembly; again in 1786 and 1810.

1783–86—Served in the Congress of the Confederation where he strongly opposed Jay's proposal of relinquishing Mississippi navigation rights in exchange for a commercial treaty with Spain; opposed ratification of the Constitution because it lacked a bill of rights; and argued for a strengthening of congressional authority to regulate commerce.

1786—Resumed the study of law; was admitted to the bar, and engaged in practice in Fredericksburg, Va.

Married Eliza Kortright of New York City, the daughter of a British Army officer.

Participated in the Annapolis Convention (predecessor of the Constitutional Convention) for the purpose of forming recommendations relating to reform of limitations placed by various States on interstate commerce.

1788—Member of the Virginia State Convention which was convened to consider ratification of the Federal Constitution.

1790-94—Elected to the U.S. Senate, filling the vacancy caused by the death of William Grayson; reelected in 1791 and served until his resignation in 1794.

1794-96—Appointed by Washington as U.S. Minister Plenipotentiary to France.

1799-1802—Elected Governor of Virginia; again in 1811.

1803—Appointed as Minister Plenipotentiary to France to work with Robert R. Livingston in arranging for the purchase of the territory at the mouth of the Mississippi and the island of New Orleans. By the time Monroe arrived in Paris, Livingston had been offered all the territory ceded by the Spanish to the French. Though the extent of the territory was far in excess of what Monroe was authorized to negotiate, he is to be credited for his willingness to have associated himself with this daring transaction— one which secured all of Louisiana for the United States.

1804—Proceeded to Madrid where he faced difficult diplomatic tasks for his country in negotiating settlements with Spain. Later, he was sent as Minister to London, where he remained until 1807.

1808—Upon his return home, Monroe was defeated by Madison in his bid for the Presidency.

1810-11—Elected a member of the State Assembly, then as Governor of Virginia.

1811-17—Served as Secretary of State in the Cabinet of President Madison and, in addition, took on the duties of Secretary of War (1814-15) after the British captured the city of Washington.

1816-25—Elected to the Presidency, defeating the Federalist candidate, Rufus King; reelected in 1820, receiving all the electoral votes but one.

Monroe regarded the Presidency as an office which should leave the initiation of legislation to the Congress. He did, however, prove to be an outstanding administrator. He gathered about him one of the strongest cabinets ever formed: John Quincy Adams, Secretary of State; John C. Calhoun, Secretary of War; William H. Crawford, Secretary of the Treasury; and William Wirt, an eminent lawyer of his day, Attorney General.

Monroe's administration, popularly known as the "Era of Good Feeling," was eventful. Florida became part of the United States; agreement was reached with the British, limiting naval armaments on the Great Lakes and eliminating the necessity for border forts; the Missouri Compromise was effected, whereby that State agreed that on the issue of slavery nothing in its constitution would be construed to abridge the privileges and immunities of U.S. citizens. A longstanding dispute on American fishing rights in British territorial waters was settled.

The President's message of December 2, 1823 declared: "The American continents, by the free and independent conditions which they have assumed and maintained, are henceforth not to be considered as subject for future colonization by any European Powers." This pronouncement became known as *The Monroe Doctrine*.

1825—Retired to his farm, Ash Lawn, in Loudon County, Va., 5 miles from Charlottesville. He inherited another estate, Oak Hill, in the same county, from an uncle. The mansion he built on the latter estate was designed by Jefferson and executed by the White House Architect, James Hoban.

1828—Member of the board of visitors, University of Virginia.

1829—Member and president of the Virginia Constitutional Convention.

1830—Moved to New York City to be with his daughters; died there on July 4, 1831; interment was in Marble Cemetery on Second Street in New York City; reinterred in Hollywood Cemetery, Richmond, Va., in 1858.

Missouri Compromise—March 6, 1820, 3 Stat. 545; March 2, 1821, 3 Stat. 645.

JOHN QUINCY ADAMS

Sixth President of the United States
March 4, 1825 to March 3, 1829
(No. 106)

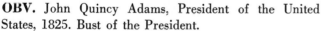

OBV. John Quincy Adams, President of the United States, 1825. Bust of the President.

By Moritz Furst.

REV. Peace and Friendship. Two hands clasped in token of amity; on the cuff of the left wrist three stripes and as many buttons; the other wrist is bare; above the hands, a pipe of peace and a tomahawk crossed.

By John Reich.

JOHN QUINCY ADAMS, *"The Old Man Eloquent"*

1767— Born in Braintree (now Quincy), Mass., July 11, the son of John Adams, second President of the United States, and Abigail Adams.

1778—Traveled abroad with his father, then on a mission to France.

1780—Attended the University of Leyden, where he learned Latin and Greek.

1781—Was appointed private secretary to Francis Dana, Minister to Russia. Remained in St. Petersburg until October 1782, after which he resumed his studies at The Hague.

1783—Was present at the signing of the definitive treaty of peace in Paris.

1786—Entered Harvard College; graduated in 1788.

1791—Having concluded his studies in law under Theophilus Parsons of Newburyport, he was admitted to the Massachusetts bar and commenced practice at Boston.

Wrote series of articles for the *Boston Centinel*, under the signatures of "Publicola" and "Marcellus," on questions of the day which attracted national and international attention. Defended President Washington's policy of neutrality in the conflict between England and France.

1794–97—Appointed by President Washington as U.S. Minister to the Netherlands.

1797—Married Louisa Catherine Johnson, daughter of the American consul at London.

1797–1801—In a letter dated February 20, 1797, Washington commended young Adams to his father, then President-elect, and advised him not to withhold promotion from him because he was his son. He was eventually appointed to serve as U.S. Minister to Berlin. While there he negotiated a treaty of amity and commerce with the Prussian Government.

1802—Was elected to the Massachusetts State Senate.

1803–08—Elected as a Federalist, he served in the U.S. Senate. While in this post he acted with independence and without regard to party lines. He voted with the Republicans for the Louisiana Purchase; he voted with the Democrats in vigorously supporting Jefferson's Embargo and Non-Importation Acts of 1807 though they were strongly opposed by the commercial interests of New England. Two years before his term was due to expire, the Federalists called a special election for a candidate

15

to replace him, whereupon he resigned his Senate seat in 1808.

Adams also held a professorship in rhetoric and belles-lettres at Harvard College (1805–09).

1809–14—Appointed by President Madison as the first U.S. Minister to the Court of St. Petersburg. He chronicled the events leading to Napoleon's invasion of Russia, the latter's defeat and downfall. In 1813, Adams, Bayard, Clay, Russell, and Gallatin were appointed commissioners to negotiate a treaty of peace with Great Britain. They met the British diplomats at Ghent, and after a protracted negotiation of 6 months, signed a treaty of peace December 24, 1814.

1815—Assisted in concluding a commercial agreement with Great Britain; was later appointed U.S. Minister to Great Britain, a post he held until 1817.

1817–25—Secretary of State in the Cabinet of President Monroe. The major role he played in laying down basic tenets of U.S. foreign policy, including principal authorship of the Monroe Doctrine, established him as one of the greatest Secretaries of State in American history. He led the negotiations which resulted in the purchase of the Floridas from Spain. He also conducted the negotiations which resulted in the fisheries convention of 1818 with Great Britain. By this agreement, the United States renounced its right to fish in British waters in North America—a right which was established by his father, the President, in 1783.

1824—The presidential election of this year fell into the House of Representatives because none of the candidates received a majority of the electors' votes. In addition to Adams, the other candidates were Andrew Jackson, Henry Clay, William H. Crawford, and John C. Calhoun. Not being among the three candidates with the highest number of electoral votes, Clay threw his support to Adams and thus helped achieve the latter's election by the House, as President of the United States.

1825–28—Adams' administration as President was not the most productive period of his public service. Strong political opposition developed in the Congress resulting in the pigeonholing of legislative proposals. There was enacted, however, legislation for the protection of New England industries, which was referred to as the "Tariff of Abominations" by the agricultural South which wanted free trade.

Adams did achieve a measure of success in obtaining some "internal improvements" which he recommended in his first inaugural address. Notwithstanding the opposition of the South and New England, Congress appropriated $14 million for public roads and canals. With State aid, the Erie Canal was completed in 1825. In 1826, the first railroad in the United States went into operation, hauling stone from the old Adams' home in Quincy, Mass., to Charlestown, for the construction of the Bunker Hill Monument.

The antagonism between the Adams and Jackson forces led to the emergence of a group which later became the Whig Party, the party of Adams. The Jackson people took on the name Democratic Republican Party, which was later shortened to Democratic Party.

1828—Shunning political patronage and organization Adams was defeated for reelection by Gen. Andrew Jackson.

1831–48—Elected to the U.S. House of Representatives, as a Whig, to the 22d and to the eight succeeding Congresses, where he served with distinction and independence until his death.

When asked if he felt it to be humiliating to serve as a Congressman after having been President, his forthright reply was that no person could be degraded by serving the Nation as a representative in the Congress or, for that matter, as a selectman of his town.

As a parliamentarian and debater, Adams had no peer in the Congress. He came by the nickname conferred on him by his associates—"Old Man Eloquent."

The House of Representatives adopted a rule in 1836, which, in effect, prevented a flood of antislavery petitions from reaching the floor for debate. For the following 10 years, Adams was the chief voice and champion in the House for the right of petition. He met with success on December 3, 1844, when the gag rule was repealed.

1846—Adams was instrumental in getting a favorable vote in the Congress for the establishment of the Smithsonian Institution in Washington, D.C.

1848—Died of a stroke while in the Speaker's Room, U.S. House of Representatives, Washington, on February 23. Interment was made in the family burial ground at Quincy, Mass.

Tariff Act—May 19, 1828, 4 Stat. 270–5.

ANDREW JACKSON

Seventh President of the United States
March 4, 1829 to March 3, 1837
(No. 107)

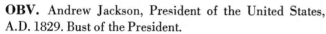

OBV. Andrew Jackson, President of the United States, A.D. 1829. Bust of the President.

By Moritz Furst.

REV. Peace and Friendship. Two hands clasped in token of amity; on the cuff of the left wrist three stripes and as many buttons; the other wrist is bare; above the hands, a pipe of peace and a tomahawk crossed.

By John Reich.

ANDREW JACKSON

"OUR FEDERAL UNION! IT MUST AND SHALL BE PRESERVED"

1767—Born on March 15, in the Waxhaw Settlement, Lancaster County, S.C., the son of Andrew Jackson, an Irishman who emigrated to America in 1765, and died in 1767.

Had little opportunity and disposition to undertake formal schooling. One source reported: "He learned to read, to write, and cost accounts—little more."

1780—At the age of 13, Jackson participated in the Revolutionary War battle of Hanging Rock. A year later was taken prisoner after an unsuccessful effort to capture a body of British troops at Waxhaw Church; received a saber blow, which marked him for life, when he refused to clean the boots of a British officer.

1784–87—Studied in the law offices of Spruce Macay in Salisbury, N.C.; was admitted to the bar, and commenced practice in McLeanville, Guilford County, N.C.

1788—Appointed prosecuting attorney for the western district of North Carolina, the region now forming the State of Tennessee.

1791—Married Rachel (Donelson) Robards, remarried her in 1794, when it was found that the earlier marriage was not valid.

1796—Delegate to the convention which formed a constitution for the new State of Tennessee.

1797—Elected to fill an unexpired term in the U.S. Senate; served until he resigned the following year.

1798–1804—Served as a judge, Tennessee State Supreme Court. His biographer, James Parton, wrote: "Tradition reports that he maintained the dignity and authority of the bench * * * that his decisions were short, untechnical, unlearned, sometimes ungrammatical, and generally right." Was appointed a major general in the Tennessee Militia (1802).

After his resignation from the bench, he engaged in agricultural pursuits.

1813—Was ordered to lead the Tennessee Militia to support General Wilkinson in New Orleans. After reaching Natchez, Jackson received orders to disband his troops, which he refused to carry out. During the march he had displayed such courage and

17

endurance, as well as concern for the welfare and privations of his militia, he earned the sobriquet of "Old Hickory," which his troops conferred on him.

1814—Commanding the Tennessee Militia, he defeated the Creek Indians on March 27, at Horshoe Bend, Ga.; this was in retaliation for their massacre at Fort Mims in the Mississippi Territory. Was commissioned major general, U.S. Army, with command of the Seventh Southwestern Military District. In November of this year he captured Pensacola, Fla., then owned by Spain but used by the British as a base of operations.

Led the U.S. Army to New Orleans where he was successful in two engagements with the British and afterwards gained his famous victory on January 8, 1815. His conquest was so overwhelming as to make him an outstanding hero of the War of 1812. The Congress memoralized his success by awarding him a gold medal.

1817—Because of Seminole and outlaw harassment of U.S. citizens on the Florida frontier, Jackson headed an expedition which was so successful, he virtually seized Florida. He executed Arbuthnot and Ambrister, two British subjects who were accused of inciting the Indians to hostile acts. He stood accused of exceeding his orders when this action brought the United States to the verge of a war with Great Britain and Spain. Diplomatic action on the part of President Monroe prevented an outbreak of war. The later purchase of Florida by the United States, Jackson felt, justified his action.

1821—Served as the first governor of Florida, from March 10 to July 18.

1823–25—Elected to the U.S. Senate and served from March 4, 1823, to October 14, 1825, when he resigned.

1823—Nominated as candidate for the Presidency, Jackson ran against Henry Clay, John Quincy Adams, and William Crawford. Though he had the most votes in the electoral college, they did not constitute a majority. When the election was thrown into the House of Representatives, Jackson lost to Adams.

1828–36—Defeated Adams in the election of 1828, to become the seventh President of the United States; won 178 of the 261 electoral votes. Reelected in 1832, defeating Henry Clay.

"To the victors belong the spoils." Jackson was the first president to exercise, on a large scale, his prerogative of replacing Federal employees appointed by previous administrations, with those of his own choosing.

The constitutional authority of a State to nullify Federal laws was one of the chief issues which came to a head during Jackson's administration. South Carolina threatened to secede from the Union if the Federal Government used force to collect customs duties to which the State objected. At a "Jefferson Day Dinner" on April 13, 1830, Jackson gave a warning by his famous toast "Our Union! It must be preserved." Troops and warships were dispatched to Charleston Harbor. Hostilities were avoided, however, through compromise legislation which was passed by the Congress, due largely to the efforts of Henry Clay.

In May 1830, Jackson vetoed a bill for construction of a road in Kentucky on the basis that he was determined to withstand raids on the Treasury for purely internal items within the States, such as roads, canals, and dams.

Jackson obtained an agreement from the French in 1831, whereby they undertook to make restitution for seizures made during the Napoleonic Wars.

An innovation of the campaign in 1832 was Jackson's influence in achieving a national party convention for choosing the presidential and vice presidential candidates, in preference to the congressional caucus which previously served as the nominating body.

A dispute between Jackson and the President of the Second Bank of the United States, led to the withdrawal of Government deposits from this bank in 1833 and, 3 years later, to this institution ceasing to function as a national bank. Like the First Bank of the United States, it functioned under a time-limited charter to carry on a commercial banking business as well as to provide a fiscal service for the U.S. Government.

In July 1836, Jackson issued his famous "Species Circular" which required the payment of gold and silver for public lands sold. Its purpose was to curtail wildcat speculation in public lands for which the Government received bank notes of doubtful value. This led to a money crisis at the close of the Jackson administration and as a very real problem with the incoming administration of Van Buren.

1837—Retired to private life.

1845—President Jackson died on June 8, at the age of 78, in his family home "The Hermitage." He is buried in the garden on that estate.

Tariff Acts—July 14, 1832, 4 Stat. 583.
Compromise Tariff Act—March 2, 1833, 4 Stat. 632.
Force Bill—March 2, 1833, 4 Stat. 632.

MARTIN VAN BUREN

Eighth President of the United States
March 4, 1837 to March 3, 1841
(No. 108)

OBV. Martin Van Buren, President of the United States, A.D., 1837. Bust of the President.

By Moritz Furst.

REV. Peace and Friendship. Two hands clasped in token of amity; on the cuff of the left wrist with three stripes and as many buttons; the other wrist is bare; above the hands, the pipe of peace and a tomahawk crossed.

By John Reich.

MARTIN VAN BUREN, *"Little Magician"*

1782—Born December 5, at Kinderhook, Columbia County, N.Y., the eldest son of Abraham and Mary (Hoes) Van Buren, of Dutch descent.

Attended district schools and Kinderhook Academy.

1796—Studied law under Francis Silvester, later under William Peter Van Ness; completed his preparation in 1802, and was admitted to the New York bar in 1803; commenced practice at Kinderhook.

1807—Married his distant cousin, Hannah Hoes, who died 12 years later. Van Buren did not remarry.

Admitted to practice before the Supreme Court of the State of New York.

1808–13—Served as surrogate of Columbia County, N.Y.

1813–20—Member of the New York State Senate, became a regent of the University of the State of New York (1815). While still a member of the State Senate, he also served as Attorney General (1815–19).

1821—Delegate to the New York State Constitutional Convention. Serving as chairman of the Committee on Appointments, he successfully challenged the power of the old Council of Appointment and achieved wider distribution of appointive authority at all levels of State government.

Van Buren organized and headed "The Albany Regime," which was one of the first powerful political machines in the country. This organization controlled party politics in New York State until the late 1840's and made the "spoils system" a standard appointments procedure, followed by later administrations, at all levels of government.

1821–28—Served in the U.S. Senate from March 4, 1821, to December 20, 1828, when he resigned because of his election as Governor of the State of New York.

While a U.S. Senator, Van Buren continued to head the "Albany Regime;" he served on the Judiciary and Finance Committees of the U.S. Senate during which time he was regarded as a "constructionist" in strictly interpreting the Constitution. He supported States' rights and opposed the Bank of the United States. He at first supported tariff legislation which had as its purpose the protection of "infant industry" but later favored tariff for reve-

19

nue only. During his early years in the U.S. Senate he supported legislation for internal improvements at national expense, though in later years he regarded this as being an improper use of Federal funds.

In 1827, Van Buren became one of the managers for Andrew Jackson's campaign for the Presidency, and was influential in swinging eastern support to win the election.

1829—Elected Governor of New York; served from January to March, when he resigned because of his appointment to the Cabinet of President Andrew Jackson.

In his short period as Governor, Van Buren urged upon the New York State Legislature a "safety fund" banking system, whereby the banks would mutually insure each other.

1829–31—Served as Secretary of State, and as chief policy adviser to President Jackson. He reopened trade with the British West Indies which the British had prohibited since the close of the American Revolution; secured French agreement to pay damages done to Americans during the Napoleonic wars; wrote the Maysville Road veto which voiced the administration's opposition to internal improvements at Federal expense; and investigated the possibility of purchasing Texas from Mexico. Political opposition on the part of followers of Vice President John C. Calhoun in the Cabinet of President Jackson led to a reorganization. This was brought about through mutual agreement between Jackson and Van Buren, in having the latter resign, thus forcing the resignation of the other Cabinet members.

In 1831, Calhoun, as President of the Senate, cast the deciding vote which rejected President Jackson's nomination of Van Buren as U.S. Minister to Great Britain.

1832—Elected Vice President of the United States; served from March 4, 1833, to March 3, 1837, during which time he was a consummate politician, and helped President Jackson strengthen his party organization on national, State, and local levels.

1835–36—Nominated for the Presidency; defeated William Henry Harrison, the Whig candidate.

1837–41—As President of the United States, Van Buren continued almost all the Cabinet appointments of his predecessor.

A financial panic developed early in Van Buren's administration because of previous overexpansion of bank credit, huge State debts for internal improvements, land speculation, an unfavorable trade balance, poor crops, and an economic crisis in England which caused the British to call in loans made in America. Van Buren met this crisis, and the depression which followed, with skill and firmness, even though his efforts did not meet with popular approval, and finally led to his defeat for reelection in 1840.

Nothwithstanding the obstacles encountered, Van Buren's major achievement while in office was the establishment of the independent Treasury System to manage the collection, safekeeping, transfer, and disbursement of public moneys without recourse to the services of private banks. It also served as the agency for marketing Government securities independently of the banks until the establishment of the National Banking System in 1863. By the acts of 1846 and later, the various mints were also made public depositories.

Because of the slave issue and the fact that Texas was at war with Mexico, Van Buren blocked its annexation. He directed the use of Federal troops in the Seminole War (in Georgia and Alabama), and he issued an executive order which provided that no person should labor more than 10 hours a day on Federal works.

1840—Van Buren lost the Democratic nomination for the Presidency to Polk, because he continued to oppose annexation of Texas.

1862—Died at his country home, "Lindenwald," at Kinderhook, N.Y., on July 24.

Independent Treasury Act—July 4, 1840, 5 Stat. 385; (repealed in 1841, 9 Stat. 59; later reenacted).

WILLIAM HENRY HARRISON

Ninth President of the United States
March 4, 1841 to April 4, 1841
(No. 109)

OBV. William H. Harrison. Bust of the President.

REV. Within a pearled ring, a laurel wreath. Inaugurated President of the United States March 4, 1841. Died April 4, 1841.

By George T. Morgan, Mint engraver, who executed this medal some 40 years after President Harrison's death.

WILLIAM HENRY HARRISON, *"Old Tippecanoe"*

1773—Born February 9, at Berkeley Plantation, Charles City County, Va., the youngest son of Benjamin Harrison, one of the signers of the Declaration of Independence.

Majored in classical studies at Hampden-Sidney College, Virginia; studied medicine under Dr. Benjamin Rush, American patriot, at the College of Physicians and Surgeons, Philadelphia.

1791—Commissioned as an ensign in the First Regiment, U.S. Army; stationed at Fort Washington (Cincinnati) and served on frontier duty. Was commissioned as a lieutenant the following year. For his services in the expedition, in December 1793, that erected Fort Recovery, he was thanked by name in general orders.

1794—Fought gallantly, with Gen. Anthony Wayne, at the Battle of Fallen Timbers, a region of northwest Ohio at the Rapids of the Maumee.

1795—Given command of Fort Washington, with the mission of preventing the French from moving military supplies down the Mississippi.

Married Anna Symmes, daughter of John Cleves Symmes, from which union six sons were born; their grandson, Benjamin Harrison, became 23d President of the United States.

1798—Resigned his commission as a captain in the Army, peace having been made with the Indians, and was appointed by President John Adams as Secretary of the Northwest Territory.

1799—Member of the Sixth U.S. Congress, as a territorial delegate. While serving as chairman of the Committee on Public Lands he devised a plan for homesteading, which was adopted by the Congress, making it possible for settlers to procure land which they could not otherwise afford to purchase.

1801–12—As Indian Commissioner and also Territorial Governor, Harrison negotiated a number of treaties with the Indians and was instrumental in bringing together practically all the Territory of Indiana—a region now represented by the States of Indiana, Illinois, much of Wisconsin, and part of Michigan. The tremendous land acquisitions from the Indians led to increasing opposition from the Shawnee Chieftain, Tecumseh and his brother, known as the "Prophet." With continuing out-

21

breaks and violence, Harrison decided to move. With a force of militia and regulars, he engaged in battle with Tecumseh and the latter's forces at a point on the Tippecanoe River which is near the present city of Lafayette, Ind. The victory which he achieved on November 7, 1811, made him a national figure, and gave birth to his sobriquet "Old Tippecanoe" which became a major factor, later, in his successful campaign for the presidency.

1812—Upon the outbreak of hostilities with the British in 1812, Harrison was appointed a major general in the Kentucky Militia; was later made a brigadier general in the regular U.S. Army and placed in command of the Northwestern Army, with instructions to act in all cases according to his own discretion and judgment. No latitude as great as this had been given to any commander since Washington. Harrison then took action to regain Detroit and the Michigan Territory, which had been surrendered to the British a year earlier.

One wing of Harrison's forces, garrisoned at Fort Meigs, consisted of about 2,500 regulars. This was augmented by 3,000 Kentucky volunteer infantry led by Governor Isaac Shelby, and by a Kentucky mounted regiment organized by Congressman Richard M. Johnson. The latter received a commission as colonel of Kentucky Volunteers.

Harrison was in command of Fort Meigs when General Proctor, with a force of British troops and Indians, laid unsuccessful siege to it from April 28 to May 9, 1813.

On September 24, 1813, Harrison transferred his main forces into Canada, to a point about 3 miles below the British Fort Malden. The British commander, Col. Henry Proctor, had evacuated Malden because he realized he could not hold it with Lake Erie in the possession of the American Navy. With his army of 800 regulars and 1,200 Indians, Proctor fell back by the road up the Thames River.

Harrison's forces followed, and on the 5th of October they engaged the enemy at a point near Moravian Village in what is now known as the Battle of the Thames. The British were routed, losing 12 killed, 22 wounded, and 600 captured. American losses were seven killed and 22 wounded, five of whom soon died. Tecumseh, the famous Indian leader serving with Proctor, was among the slain; his northwestern confederacy was broken up, and

as a result of the battle, the Indians abandoned their dependence on England.

The victory of Harrison on the Thames, coupled with that of Perry on Lake Erie, ended the British power on the Great Lakes, crushed the Indians, and regained the Territory of Michigan, with the exception of Fort Mackinac, for the United States.

In recognition of the country's appreciation, the U.S. Congress, by resolution of April 4, 1818, authorized the presentation of a gold medal to General Harrison.

1814—Resigning his commission in the U.S. Army, Harrison accepted an appointment from President Madison to negotiate with the Indians in the Northwest, the second Treaty of Greenville (July 22, 1814). This treaty of alliance with the Indians, against the British, marked a new epoch in American policy.

1816–19—While serving as a member of the U.S. House of Representatives from Ohio, Harrison worked for a stronger Army, for liberal pension laws, improvements in navigation of the Ohio River, relief for purchasers of public lands, and for bringing the territories under the full power of the Congress, especially with regard to the slavery issue.

1819—Served in the Ohio State Senate, and in 1822 was an unsuccessful candidate for Congress.

1824—Was a presidential elector, voting for Henry Clay, and in the same year was sent to the U.S. Senate.

1825–28—While in the U.S. Senate, Harrison succeeded Andrew Jackson as Chairman of the Committee on Military Affairs.

1828–29—Appointed by President John Quincy Adams as U.S. Minister to Colombia, South America.

1836—Running as a Whig candidate for the Presidency, Harrison was defeated by Martin Van Buren.

1839—The Whig convention again put Harrison before the country. Van Buren was the opposing candidate.

1840—In the campaign of 1840 the "log cabin and hard cider" charged against his early record by his opponents became a tower of strength to him; a "campaign ball" was set rolling across the country; and "Tippecanoe and Tyler too" were fairly "sung into the White House."

1841—Caught pneumonia during his inauguration and died April 4, 1841, the first U.S. President to expire while in office. After temporary interment in the Congressional Cemetery in Washington, his body was removed to the Harrison Tomb, opposite Congress Green Cemetery, North Bend, Ohio.

JOHN TYLER

Tenth President of the United States
April 6, 1841 to March 3, 1845
(No. 110)

OBV. John Tyler, President of the United States, 1841. Bust of the President.

By F. Pettrich.

REV. Peace and Friendship. Two hands clasped in token of amity; on the cuff of the left wrist three stripes with buttons, each button carrying the American eagle; the other wrist is bare; above the hands, crossed, the pipe of peace and the tomahawk.

By John Reich.

JOHN TYLER

1790—Born on March 29, in Greenway, Charles City County, Va.; son of Judge John Tyler, Governor of Virginia from 1808 to 1811, and Mary (Armistead) Tyler.

1802–7—Studied at the College of William and Mary, Williamsburg, Va., where he evidenced especial interest in ancient history, poetry, and music.

1809—After graduation from William and Mary, Tyler studied law, was admitted to the bar, and commenced practice in Charles City County.

1811–16—Served in the Virginia House of Delegates; was chosen in 1815 as a member of its Council of State.

While in the Virginia Legislature, Tyler identified himself as a strict constructionist with respect to interpretation of the Constitution of the United States and he strongly supported President Madison in his conduct of the war then current.

In 1813, Tyler married Letitia Christian and a few weeks later he left for duty as captain of the militia company organized for the defense of Richmond, then threatened by the British.

1816–21—Elected to the U.S. House of Representatives, 15th and 16th Congresses. Tyler did not hesitate to assert his independence and constructionist views by opposing a considerable amount of proposed Federal legislation: internal improvements at Federal expense, the National Bankruptcy Act, recharter of the Bank of the United States, increased tariff duties for protection of home industry, and a bill to raise congressional salaries to $1,500. Though Tyler's personal views reflected consistent opposition to the slave trade, he opposed the Missouri Compromise of 1820 on the basis that the Congress had no authority to legislate for or against slavery in any Territory.

1821—Returned to private life because of ill health.

1823—Again served as a member of the Virginia State Legislature; was an unsuccessful candidate for the U.S. Senate in 1824.

1825–27—As Governor of Virginia, Tyler supported the development of public roads and schools.

1827—Elected as a Democrat, and reelected in 1833, to the U.S. Senate, where he served until his resignation in 1836.

1828—Believing it to be unconstitutional, Tyler voted against the "Tariff of Abominations"—protection which was afforded to practically everything that could be protected.

1829–30—Participated in the Virginia Constitutional Convention.

1832—Again voted against a tariff bill, on constitutional grounds. The tariff bill proposed a lowering of previous tariffs, because of increased Federal receipts and lack of need to protect infant industry. Notwithstanding his position on the Tariff Act, Tyler condemned the action of South Carolina in declaring Federal legislation null and void.

Although opposed ideologically to Andrew Jackson, he supported him for election in 1832, because he considered him the least objectionable of all the candidates.

Although opposing the abolition of slavery in the District of Columbia without the approval of Maryland and Virginia which had ceded the land which made possible the Nation's Capital, Tyler sought to incorporate a prohibition of slave trade in a new code for the District of Columbia.

1833—Tyler cast the only dissident vote in the Senate against the Force Act obtained by President Jackson—legislation which gave the President authority to use the Army, and the Navy if necessary, to collect customs duties. Open conflict with South Carolina was avoided through a compromise tariff which met with general approval of all concerned. Strongly as he opposed the Bank of the United States, Tyler disapproved of the means resorted to by President Jackson in bringing about its downfall—ordering the Government's deposits removed and placed in private banks.

The bank issue caused Tyler to break with the administration and to associate himself with the opposition, the Whig Party.

Tyler's popularity in Virginia, notwithstanding his independence of party discipline, was such as to win him reelection to his Senate seat in 1833.

1835—Elected President pro tempore of the U.S. Senate, March 3.

1836—Tyler resigned his Senate seat, rather than follow instructions from his State legislature to support a resolution in the U.S. Congress to expunge from the record a previous resolution criticizing President Jackson for his removal of Federal deposits from the Bank of the United States.

This same year, running on the "States-Rights-Whig" ticket, Tyler was defeated in his bid for the Vice-Presidency.

1838–40—In this interim period, Tyler became president of the Virginia Colonization Society, returned to the State legislature, and was unsuccessful in a campaign to regain his seat in the U.S. Senate. In 1840, Tyler was elected, on the ticket with William Henry Harrison, as Vice President of the United States.

1841–45—Tyler served as Vice President of the United States from March 4, 1841, until the death of President Harrison who died on April 4. Two days later, Tyler took his oath of office as President of the United States. He thereby became the first President to assume this office by right of succession.

The Cabinet appointed by the late President Harrison continued to serve under President Tyler until September, 1841, when all the members, save Webster, resigned. This was done in protest of 2 vetoes submitted by Tyler, of legislation to reestablish the Bank of the United States.

Van Buren, who continued to head the Democratic Party after his defeat by Harrison, refused to recognize Tyler as a Democrat. The Whigs, led by Clay, parted company with Tyler over the bank issue.

Though President without a party, Tyler nonetheless achieved a substantial record for his administration. This included settlement of the northeastern boundary of the United States by the signing of the Webster-Ashburton Treaty with Great Britain in 1842; the annexation of Texas in 1845; negotiation of our first trade agreement with China (1844); approval of a bill to improve the navigation on the Mississippi River "to serve the commerce of the whole country"; reorganization of the Navy, including establishment of an agency for naval scientific work (which later became the U.S. Naval Observatory).

Tyler favored measures to enable settlers to have access to public lands; he refused to use the spoils systems, continuing Federal employees with ability in their office. He brought the Indian war in Florida to a close, and wisely refused to use Federal troops when a crisis arose in Rhode Island related to that State's constitution.

His first wife having died in 1842, Tyler married Miss Julia Gardiner of New York on June 26, 1844, from which union 14 children were born.

In 1844, Tyler withdrew his name from the nomination for the Presidency and retired to private life.

1859—Chancellor of William and Mary College.

1861—On the outbreak of civil war, Tyler proposed a series of compromises which he felt might save the Union. He served as president of a peace congress which met in Washington. After its failure and while a delegate to the Virginia State Convention, he advocated the passage of an ordinance of secession.

In May 1861, Tyler was elected a member of the provisional Congress of the Confederate States.

1862—Though elected to the House of Representatives of the permanent Confederate Congress, he did not take his seat. His death occurred in Richmond, Va., on January 18, 1862, before the assembling of the Congress.

Interment was made in Hollywood Cemetery, Richmond, Va., where a monument was erected over his remains in 1915 by the Congress of the United States.

Texas Annexation Resolution—March 1, 1845, 5 Stat. 797.

JAMES KNOX POLK

Eleventh President of the United States
March 4, 1845 to March 3, 1849
(No. 111)

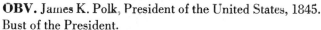

OBV. James K. Polk, President of the United States, 1845. Bust of the President.

By John Gadsby Chapman.

REV. Peace and Friendship. Two hands clasped in token of amity; on the cuff of the left wrist three stripes with buttons, each button carrying the American eagle; the other wrist is bare; above the hands, crossed, the pipe of peace and the tomahawk.

By John Reich.

JAMES KNOX POLK

1795—Born on November 2, 1795 in Mecklenburg County, N.C., the son of Samuel and Jane Polk.

1815—After private tutoring, he entered the sophomore class at the University of North Carolina; was graduated 3 years later, having shown an aptitude for the classics and mathematics.

1819—Entered the law office of Felix Grundy, then at the head of the Tennessee bar. While pursuing his legal studies, he attracted the attention of Andrew Jackson, the beginning of a close friendship.

1820—Polk was admitted to the bar and established himself at Columbia, the county seat of Maury County.

1821–23—Chief Clerk of the Tennessee Senate.

1823–25—Served as a member of the Tennessee House of Representatives.

Married Sarah Childress, daughter of a Tennessee merchant, in 1824.

1825–39—Served in the U.S. House of Representatives, where he was prominently connected with every leading question and upon all he struck what proved to be the keynote for the action of his party. His maiden speech was in defense of the proposed amendment to the Constitution giving the choice of the President and Vice President directly to the people.

In December 1827, he was placed on the Committee on Foreign Affairs and afterwards was also appointed Chairman of the Select Committee to which was referred that portion of President Adams' message calling attention to the probable accumulation of a surplus in the Treasury after the anticipated extinguishment of the national debt. As the head of the latter committee he made a report denying the constitutional power of Congress to collect from the people, for distribution, a surplus beyond the wants of the Government, and maintaining that the revenue should be reduced to the requirements of the public service.

During the whole period of President Jackson's administration he was one of its leading supporters, and at times its chief reliance.

Early in 1833 as a member of the Ways and Means Committee, he made a minority report unfavorable to the Bank of the United States. During the entire contest between the bank and President Jackson, caused by the removal of the deposits in October 1833, Polk as chairman of the Ways and Means Committee, supported President Jackson.

Elected Speaker of the U.S. House of Representatives in 1835; he held that office until 1839.

Polk gave to the administration of Martin Van Buren the same unhesitating support he had given President Jackson.

1839–41—Governor of Tennessee; failed to win when he ran for reelection in 1841 and 1843.

Was nominated by the legislatures of Tennessee and other States for Vice President of the United States in 1839 but lost the nomination to Richard M. Johnson of Kentucky who was the choice of the great body of the Democratic party.

1844—Elected as President of the United States on the Democratic ticket. Favoring reannexation of Texas and other expansionist moves, he ran on the slogan "Fifty-four forty or fight."

1845—Soon after his inauguration, and in a conversation with George Bancroft, his Secretary of the Navy, Polk stated, "There are four great measures which are to be the measures of my administration: one,

a reduction of the tariff; another, the independent treasury; a third, the settlement of the Oregon boundary question; and lastly, the acquisition of California." His administration was successful in accomplishing all these aims.

The Walker Tariff of 1846 used import duties to a great extent as a means of raising revenue, rather than for protection of segments of home industry.

The Independent Treasury bill of 1846 reestablished a financial system which continued with slight modification until supplemented by the Federal Reserve System.

The Oregon Question was settled by the 1846 Treaty with Great Britain; the dispute over the northwest boundary was solved by dividing the area along the 49th parallel.

Polk wanted to force Mexico to give or sell to the United States, California and New Mexico as payment for longstanding damage claims debt owed to the United States by Mexico. But, before he could force this to happen, war broke out between these two countries and the United States received Upper California and New Mexico from Mexico in the Peace Treaty of 1848.

Polk reaffirmed and extended the scope of the Monroe Doctrine, taking the position that *any* foreign intervention in the Americas would be prohibited.

Other accomplishments of Polk's administration were establishment of the U.S. Naval Academy, the Smithsonian Institution, and the Department of the Interior consummation of the annexation of Texas; and the admission of Texas, Iowa, and Wisconsin as States.

1849—Declining to run for reelection Polk returned to his home at Nashville. He died on June 15, only a few months after leaving office. He was buried in the garden of his Nashville residence, "Polk's Place," but in 1893 his remains along with those of his wife, were removed to the grounds of the State Capitol.

Walker Tariff Act—July 30, 1846, 9 Stat. 42.

Independent Treasury (restored—usually listed as first act of this kind)—August 6, 1846, 9 Stat. 59.

Wilmot Proviso (introduced as an amendment to an appropriation bill, did not pass).

ZACHARY TAYLOR

Twelfth President of the United States
March 4, 1849 to July 9, 1850
(No. 112)

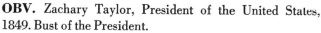

OBV. Zachary Taylor, President of the United States, 1849. Bust of the President.

By Henry Kirke Brown.

REV. Peace and Friendship. Two hands clasped in token of amity; on the cuff of the left wrist three stripes with buttons, each button carrying the American eagle; the other wrist is bare; above the hands, crossed, the pipe of peace and the tomahawk.

By John Reich.

ZACHARY TAYLOR *"Old Rough and Ready"*

1784—Born near Montebello in Orange County, Va., on November 24, the third son of Mary (Strother) and Richard Taylor, the latter having been a Colonel in the War of the Revolution. Zachary Taylor's only formal education came from a tutor, Elisha Ayres of Connecticut.

1808—Appointed first lieutenant in the 7th Infantry, he reported to Gen. James Wilkinson at New Orleans. Yellow fever forced him temporarily out of service.

1810—On June 18, married Margaret Marshall Smith; six children were born. Promoted to captain in his same regiment, was placed under Gen. William Harrison, and was assigned to Fort Knox, Indiana Territory. His company, numbering not more than 50 men, was soon transferred to Fort Harrison on

the Wabash River which he successfully defended against 400 Indians under Tecumseh, on September 4, 1812. As a result of this action he was brevetted major.

1814—Commanded in a campaign against hostile Indians and their British allies on Rock River.

1815—When the Army was disbanded on June 15, he was retained as a captain.

1816—President Madison restored Taylor to his former rank of major and ordered him to join the 3d Infantry at Green Bay, Wis. He spent 2 years in command of Fort Winnebago.

1818—Was granted a year's furlough which he spent at his Kentucky home.

1819—Taylor was promoted to lieutenant colonel of the 1st Infantry, and later was assigned to the 4th Infantry in New Orleans. In the next 4 years he was transferred to four different regiments. His final assignment returned him to the 1st Infantry.

1822—Taylor built Fort Jesup on the Louisiana Frontier.

1824–32—Filled various administrative posts from Louisville to Washington, D.C.

1832—On April 4, Zachary Taylor was promoted to the rank of colonel and given command of the 1st Regiment at Fort Crawford. In the Indian War he commanded 400 men and received Black Hawk's surrender.

1837—His regiment was ordered to Fort Jesup. However, Colonel Taylor received new orders while he was traveling with his men. His new destination—Florida.

Through December he followed the Seminoles with 1,100 men and defeated them at Lake Okeechobee on December 25, 1837 (given nickname "Old Rough and Ready"). As a result of this action he was brevetted brigadier general.

1838—In May of 1838 Taylor was appointed to the Chief Command in Florida.

1840—Was transferred to the Southwest Frontier. About this time he made his family home at Baton Rouge, La.

1844—General Taylor was ordered to Fort Jesup in anticipation of the annexation of Texas. Collecting an army of 4,000 at Corpus Christi, Taylor was ordered to keep in contact with the Texan authorities and to defend Texas against invasion once it was annexed.

1846—General Taylor advanced to the Rio Grande and established a base at Point Isabel.

On May 8 Taylor met the Mexicans under General Arista at Palo Alto and defeated a force three times the size of his own army. He accredited this victory to his regular artillery. On May 9, he again defeated the Mexicans at Resaca de la Palma. Upon receiving the news of these victories, President Polk promoted him to the rank of major general. Taylor was then given command of the Army of the Rio Grande. In September, after setting up Camargo as a supply depot, Taylor departed with 6,000 men. His primary destination was Saltillo. On September 21st he attacked Monterey. After 4 days of fierce fighting, the Mexicans surrendered. An 8 weeks' armistice was signed subject to the approval of both governments. Polk's administration did not approve and 5 days before the armistice was to end, Taylor received orders to terminate it.

1847—General Taylor was then ordered to remain on the defensive. Disregarding these orders he marched south to meet Santa Anna and 20,000 Mexican troops. At Buena Vista the 5,000 Americans fortified and awaited the attack. At two points in the 2-day battle, the Mexicans turned the American left flank and threatened their rear positions. However, after 2 days of fighting, the Mexicans retreated leaving the Americans the victor. Thus ended the fighting in the Northern Provinces and Zachary Taylor's military career.

In November 1847, Taylor left Mexico for his Louisiana home. It was at his Louisiana home that he was asked to run for President as the Whig candidate.

1848—When the Whig nominating convention met in Philadelphia on June 7, Taylor was nominated on the fourth ballot winning over Clay, Scott, and Webster.

The Whig Party did not adopt a platform and Taylor had to run on his own policy and statements. Taylor's "Allison" letters demonstrated his views to the public. In his first Allison letter, Taylor, explaining his political position said: "I am a Whig, but not an Ultra Whig. If elected, I would not be the mere President of a Party. I would endeavor to act independent of party domination. I should feel bound to administer The Government untrammeled by party schemes." In November 1848, Taylor was elected to the Presidency.

1849—Taylor's main problems during his term in office as President were slavery and the sectional conflicts arising over the proposed statehood of California and New Mexico. He sent Thomas Butler King as a special emissary to California to encourage them to form a state government and apply for statehood. New Mexico was also encouraged to act rapidly.

1850—President Taylor went before the House and Senate on January 21 and 23 to urge the immediate acceptance of California and suggested statehood for New Mexico. The Southern representatives organized a filibuster that ended in the Clay's compromise of 1850.

Before the Compromise of 1850 passed, President Taylor had died. In foreign affairs the most notable achievement of his short term was the Clayton-Bulwer Treaty of 1850. This treaty insured joint control to the United States and Great Britain of any canal built across the Isthmus of Panama. This treaty remained in effect until the Hay-Paucefote Treaty of 1902.

President Taylor died in Washington on July 9, 1850, after a severe attack of cholera brought on by exposure in the hot sun. He lies buried on his estate near Louisville, Ky.

(See legislation under Fillmore.)

MILLARD FILLMORE

Thirteenth President of the United States
July 10, 1850 to March 3, 1853
(No. 113)

OBV. Millard Fillmore, President of the United States, 1850. Bust of the President.

By Salathiel Ellis.

REV. A farmer, leaning upon a plow, and conversing with an Indian Chief, an American flag in the background, and above it three links: Labor, Virtue, Honor.

By J. Willson.

MILLARD FILLMORE

1800—Born on a farm in Locke Township (now Summerhill), Cayuga County, N.Y., on January 7, the son of Nathaniel and Phoebe (Millard) Fillmore, whose ancestors served with distinction in the French and Revolutionary Wars.

Was of limited education and self-instructed. At 18 he began to read law in the office of a Cayuga County judge, Walter Wood.

Taught school until 1823 in Buffalo while studying law.

1823—Admitted as an attorney to the Court of Common pleas of Erie County. He opened a successful law office in East Aurora, N.Y., and remained there until 1830.

1826—Married Abigail Powers of Moravia, N.Y., on February 5, 1826, daughter of a clergyman. She died in 1853.

1827—Was admitted as an attorney and 2 years later as Counselor before the Supreme Court.

1828–31—Was elected to the New York State Legislature as a member of the Anti-Masonic Party; served three terms. While there he was distinguished by his advocacy of the act to abolish imprisonment for debt, which passed in 1831.

1832—Elected as a Whig to the 23d Congress, serving from 1833 to 1835. His political career coincided almost precisely with the rise and fall of the ill-fated Whig Party.

1834—Did not try for reelection.

1836—Elected again to Congress and served for three consecutive terms, declining renomination in 1842. In Congress he was a Clay-Whig though in his decisionmaking he was very independent; he refused to join Clay's fight for the reestablishment of a national bank. He opposed the annexation of Texas as slave territory, was an advocate of internal improvements and a protective tariff, supported J. Q. Adams in maintaining the right of offering antislavery petitions, advocated the prohibition by Congress of the slave trade between the States and favored the exclusion of slavery from the District of Columbia.

1840—When the Whigs gained a majority in the House, Fillmore was made Chairman of the House Ways and Means Committee and in that capacity took a leading role in framing the tariff of 1842 which he favored because of his belief in protectionism. Also, he obtained an appropriation of $30,000 for Morse's telegraph against strong opposition.

1844—Was an unsuccessful candidate for the vice-presidential nomination; and later, for the Governorship of New York.

1847—Elected Comptroller of the State of New York.

1848—Introduced as a friend of Henry Clay and Daniel Webster at the Whig Convention at Philadelphia, he secured the vice presidential nomination on the ticket with General Zachary Taylor.

1849—Inaugurated on March 2. As Vice President, Fillmore presided over the Senate with strict impartiality during the exciting debates on the compromise measures of 1850 and Webster's 7th of March speech.

1850—The sudden death of President Zachary Taylor on July 9, placed Fillmore in the Presidency. His appointments of Webster as Secretary of State and Crittenden of Kentucky as Attorney General, gave evidence that his stand on the slavery question was on the side of those favoring compromise.

Signed the Fugitive-Slave Act (Sept. 18, 1850), one of the compromise measures. By signing this measure, he lost much of his popularity in the North and gained the displeasure of the abolitionists. Fillmore placed the preservation of the Union above any specific settlement of the slavery question.

Commodore Matthew Calbraith Perry's expedition, which resulted in the opening of diplomatic relations with Japan in 1854, started near the end of his term. Before leaving office, Fillmore approved a treaty which opened Japan to Western commerce.

1852—He was a candidate for the Whig presidential nomination, but without Webster's support he could not gain it. Webster was a candidate himself. Fillmore led in the early voting, but after the 53d ballot, Gen. Winfield Scott was nominated.

In November, the Whig Party was defeated and never actively participated in an election again. Most members moved to the new Republican Party and some conservative members moved over to the American or "Know-Nothing Party."

1855—Declined to accept an honorary degree of D.C.L. from Oxford University on the ground that he possessed no literary or scientific attainments to entitle him to such an honor.

1856—A nominee of the National American Party, he was unsuccessful in achieving reelection to the Presidency.

1858—Remarried, to Caroline Carmichael McIntosh, a widow from Albany, on February 10.

1858–74—Fillmore was the first Chancellor of the University of Buffalo, one of the founders of the Buffalo Historical Society and its first president, and a founder of the Buffalo General Hospital.

1874—Died on March 8. Buried in Forest Hill Cemetery, Buffalo, N.Y.

"Comprise of 1850"—September 9–20, 1850, 9 Stat. 446, 452, 453, 462, 467. (These are five statutes known collectively by this name.)

FRANKLIN PIERCE

Fourteenth President of the United States
March 4, 1853 to March 3, 1857
(No. 114)

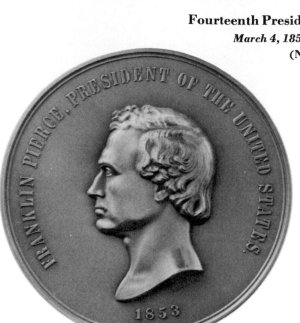

OBV. Franklin Pierce, President of the United States, 1853. Bust of the President.

By Salathiel Ellis.

REV. A farmer, leaning upon a plow, and conversing with an Indian Chief, an American flag in the background, and above it three links: Labor, Virtue, Honor.

By J. Willson.

FRANKLIN PIERCE

1804—Born on November 23, 1804, at Hillsborough, N.H., the son of Benjamin Pierce and Anna Kendrick, of English ancestry.

Pierce's father, a Revolutionary War Officer, was Governor of the State of New Hampshire. From him Pierce received a firm grounding in politics and law.

1824—Having attended the academies of Hancock, Francestown and Philip Exeter, Pierce graduated third in his class at Bowdoin College. Among his classmates were Nathaniel Hawthorne and Henry W. Longfellow.

1827—Pierce studied law under Levi Woodbury at Portsmouth, under Judge Howe at Northampton, and under Judge Edmund Parker at Amherst. In 1827, he was admitted to the bar of Hillsborough County in New Hampshire.

1829–33—Immediately after becoming a lawyer, Pierce entered local politics and in 1829 was elected to the New Hampshire State Legislature. Pierce was an extremely loyal party man, working all of his life for the development of the Democratic Party. He was elected speaker of the legislature in 1831 and 1832.

1833–37—Elected to and served two terms in the U.S. House of Representatives. He rarely made a speech, but did very impressive work in committee. He became known as a moderate; above all he was a champion of personal liberties.

In 1834, married Jane Means Appleton, daughter of a former president of Bowdoin College. They had three sons, all of whom died in childhood.

1837—Elected to the U.S. Senate in 1837; served until 1842. Again he made few speeches, preferring to do his main work in committee.

1842—Numerous reasons, among them his wife's ill health and his financial position, forced Pierce to resign from the Senate and return to his native New Hampshire. Establishing his practice in Concord, Pierce soon became famous for his ability and also his personality as a trial lawyer.

1842–47—Managed local Democratic campaigns, but his firm support for annexation of Texas led to the defeat of the Democratic Party in New Hampshire in 1846.

During these years also, Pierce refused appointments to Attorney General and to the Senate. President Polk had appointed him District Attorney of New Hampshire.

1846—Enlisted in the Army as a private during the Mexican War. Soon promoted to brigadier general, and served with General Scott in Mexico City Was injured in September 1847 while taking part in the Battle of Contreras. He resigned his commission in 1848, when the war was over.

1850—Was a member of the Constitutional Convention which met at Concord to amend the Constitution of New Hampshire, and was chosen to preside over its deliberations.

1852—Four men: Buchanan, Douglass, Marcy, and Cass competed for the Democratic Presidential nomination; none received the required two-thirds majority. Finally, after the convention was deadlocked, Pierce came forward as a "dark horse" candidate and on the 49th ballot captured the nomination. The platform of his party pledged to uphold all of the compromise measures of 1850.

Pierce won the election, carrying every State but four, though his popular vote margin was much narrower than the electoral vote margin; the Whig Party collapsed.

After the election, and before the inauguration, Pierce's only remaining son, 11 years old, was killed before his father's eyes in a railroad accident.

To restore unity in his party, Pierce named a Cabinet consisting of men from all sections of the country, among which were Marcy in the State Department, Jefferson Davis as Secretary of War, and Cushing as Attorney General. Pierce's foreign policy was a defense against all foreign intervention in American affairs. At home, he greatly favored expansion.

1853—Pierce sent James Gadsden to Mexico where he concluded the "Gadsden Purchase," insuring an American right-of-way for a rail route to the Pacific.

At home also, Pierce favored a "strict construction" of the Constitution. He called for a reduction of the Treasury surplus by lowering the tariff; he recommended subsidizing the Pacific Railroad and the Post Office and strengthening the Office of the Attorney General.

1854—A reciprocity treaty with Canada, concerning the use of the Newfoundland fishing banks, was ratified.

Attempts were also made to purchase Cuba and Hawaii, and to secure a coaling station on Santa Domingo.

The Kansas-Nebraska Act of 1854 abandoned the Compromise of 1850 and left the issue of slavery in Kansas and Nebraska to the vote of the settlers. An overwhelming number of Southern emigrants, as well as the proximity of Kansas to the slave State of Missouri caused the legislature to go proslavery in the election of 1854.

The Kansas-Nebraska Act aroused such strong pro- and anti-slavery sentiments as to cause a general realinement in American politics. Many antislavery Democrats, Whigs, Free Soilers, and others, who opposed this legislation and took a strong stand against slavery, moved to form a new party—the Republican Party. Strong resolutions directed against slavery emanated from this new political party which first met at Ripon, Wis., on February 28, 1854, and again at Jackson, Mich., on July 6, 1854.

The "Ostend Manifesto," calling for forcible seizure of Cuba by America if Spain refused to sell it, was signed by the U.S. ministers to Spain, England, and France respectively. The premature release of this document fired deep resentment of the North against Pierce.

Commodore Perry succeeded in establishing diplomatic and trade relations with Japan.

1855—Pierce persuaded Britain to withdraw from all of Central America except Honduras.

Pierce's first Kansas Governor, A. Reeder, was dismissed after being involved in illegal land grafts; civil war erupted in the State; the free-soil group set up a second government in the State. Pierce ordered this illegal government disbanded and ordered Missourians not to interfere.

1856—Pierce's second Governor was unable to resolve the conflict. Finally, in the fall of 1856 the third Governor of the technically proslavery legal government, John W. Geary, reported that law and order had been restored in Kansas.

Pierce was refused renomination for the Presidency.

1859—After a long tour of Europe, Pierce returned to his native New Hampshire.

1869—Pierce died on October 8, and was buried in Concord, N.H. He was 64.

Kansas-Nebraska Act—May 30, 1854, 10 Stat. 277.

JAMES BUCHANAN

Fifteenth President of the United States
March 4, 1857 to March 3, 1861
(No. 115)

OBV. James Buchanan, President of the United States, 1857. Bust of the President.

By Salathiel Ellis.

REV. A farmer, leaning upon a plow, and conversing with an Indian Chief, an American flag in the background, and above it three links: Labor, Virtue, Honor.

By J. Willson.

JAMES BUCHANAN

1791—Born April 23, 1791, at Cove Gap in Franklin County, Pa., the son of James Buchanan and Elizabeth (Speer) Buchanan.

1807–09—Attended, and was graduated from Dickinson College, Pa.; later, studied law.

1812—Although a Federalist and with his party opposed to the War of 1812, he urged the enlistment of volunteers for the defense of Baltimore, and was one of the first to enroll his name.

Admitted to the bar and commenced practice at Lancaster.

1814—Served in the House of Representatives of the Pennsylvania Legislature.

1820—Elected to the U.S. House of Representatives, serving until 1831.

1822—Buchanan's first speech in Congress was made in January 1822, supporting the Administration of

President Monroe, in maintaining an adequate military establishment.

1828—Became Chairman of the Committee on Judiciary of the House of Representatives.

1831—In June he accepted President Jackson's appointment of U.S. Minister to Russia though he contemplated retirement from politics. While in Russia he negotiated a commercial treaty.

1834—Elected as a Democrat to the U.S. Senate. Remained in the Senate until 1845 and was known as one of the prime supporters of Jackson and Van Buren.

1839—Declined the office of Attorney General tendered by Van Buren.

1844—After losing the Democratic presidential nomination to James K. Polk, he accepted the position of Secretary of State under Polk.

The situation in Texas was the major interest of the Polk administration. Mexico would not recognize the independence of Texas and hoped that the Oregon question would strengthen her position. President Polk wanted the Oregon question settled as swiftly as possible. Polk placed Buchanan in charge of negotiations and he claimed all of Oregon for the United States and refused to arbitrate; though he finally reached an agreement with Great Britain on a boundary along the continental line of the 49th parallel.

1846—In order to discourage suspected British designs on California, Buchanan advised President Polk to make a stern restatement of the Monroe Doctrine in his message to Congress.

1848—Made an offer of $120 million to Spain for the purchase of Cuba. The offer was rejected.

1849—Buchanan retired from office and purchased "Wheatland," a country estate near Lancaster, Pa.

1853—After losing the presidential nomination in 1852 to Franklin Pierce, Buchanan accepted the post of Minister to Great Britain.

1856—Unanimously nominated on the 17th ballot as the Democratic candidate for President, and on November 4, 1856, was elected.

In selecting his Cabinet, he gave equal representation to slave and non-slave-holding States calling it "The Sacred Balance." He wanted his administration to be known for its vigorous foreign policy.

He concluded the arrangements between Great Britain, Nicaragua, and Honduras in order to check the activity of the British fleet in searching vessels suspected of participating in slave trade in American waters. He obtained reparation from Paraguay for the firing on the WATER WITCH, and he improved U.S. relations in the Far East by receiving ambassadors from Japan and Siam.

An attempt of the opposition to convict Buchanan of maladministration failed to reveal any condition of unusual laxity in the administration.

Supported the LeCompton constitution causing a split between the two factions of the Democratic Party. The LeCompton constitution identified the administration with the southern wing and incited the revolt of the supporters of Stephen A. Douglas. During his administration, the slavery question became more acute. Proslavery in his own views, Buchanan had surrounded himself with a Cabinet which also strongly supported the maintenance of slavery. As Buchanan's administration was closing, it became apparent that an armed conflict was pending. Notwithstanding the advice of General Scott to reinforce troops in Southern ports, Buchanan took no action. The election of Lincoln to the Presidency in November 1860 was followed by resignations of most of the Cabinet.

1868—President Buchanan died on June 1, 1868, at "Wheatland," near Lancaster, Pa. Buchanan was the only President who never married.

Tariff Acts—March 3, 1857, 11 Stat. 192; March 2, 1861, 12 Stat. 178.

ABRAHAM LINCOLN

Sixteenth President of the United States
March 4, 1861 to April 15, 1865
(No. 116)

OBV. Abraham Lincoln. Bust of the President.

REV. A wreath of oak and laurel. Inaugurated President of the United States March 4, 1861. Second term March 4, 1865. Assassinated April 14, 1865. Within wreath, a spray of pine and cedar, circled by serpent with tail in its month, the Egyptian symbol of eternity and immortality.

By George T. Morgan.

ABRAHAM LINCOLN

1809—Lincoln was born in a log cabin near Hodgenville, in Hardin County, Ky., on February 12, 1809, the son of Thomas and Nancy (Hanks) Lincoln.

1816—The Lincoln family moved to Indiana and settled on Little Pigeon Creek, on the Ohio River, where Abraham grew to manhood. At the age of 9, Lincoln's mother died. His father soon remarried, to a Mrs. Sarah Bush Johnson, who was destined to play a strong role in developing Lincoln's character and interest in study.

1830—The Lincolns moved to Macon County, Ill. By this time Abraham had attained the unusual stature of 6 feet 4 inches and was of great muscular strength. He joined with his father in building a cabin, clearing the fields, and splitting rails for fencing the farm. When the job was completed, Lincoln left his father's home and hired himself to Denton Offutt in Sangamon County, whom he assisted in building a flatboat and navigating it on a trading voyage to New Orleans.

1831—Lincoln settled at New Salem, where he managed a mill. His leisure time was spent in constant reading and study, mostly in the field of English grammar, surveying, and the principles of law.

1832—When an Indian war began, Lincoln volunteered in a company raised in Sangamon County and was immediately elected captain. His company was organized in Richmond on April 21, 1832, but his service in command of it was brief, for it was mustered out on May 27. Lincoln reenlisted as a private and served for several weeks, finally being mustered out on June 16 by Lt. Robert Anderson, who afterwards commanded Fort Sumter at the beginning of the civil war.

Returning home after his brief military career, Lincoln made a try for the legislature, but was defeated. At this time he thought seriously of learning the blacksmith's trade. An opportunity was offered him to buy a store, which he did, giving his notes for the purchase money. He was unfortunate in his selection of a partner. The business soon went to wreck, leaving him burdened with a heavy debt, which he finally paid in full, earning him the nickname "Honest Abe." He then applied himself earnestly to the study of law.

1833—Was appointed postmaster of New Salem and filled the office for 3 years. At the same time he was appointed deputy county surveyor.

1834—Lincoln was elected to the State legislature, and was reelected in 1836, 1838, and 1840, after which he declined further election. In his last two terms he was the candidate of the Whig Party for the speakership of the House of Representatives.

1835—Courted Ann Rutledge, who died of "brain fever" before their marriage could take place.

1837—Moved to Springfield, where he entered into partnership with John T. Stuart and began the practice of law.

1842—Married Mary Todd of Lexington, Ky. They had four sons, but only the eldest, Robert Todd, lived past childhood.

1846—Was elected to Congress as a Whig. Served only one term, until 1849, and was not a candidate for reelection. While a Member, he advocated the abolition of slavery in the District of Columbia.

Was an unsuccessful applicant for Commissioner of the General Land Office under President Taylor.

Was tendered the office of Governor of Oregon Territory, which he declined.

1849—Successful law cases in the State supreme court, circuit court, and Federal courts, brought Lincoln fame in his home State.

1854—Campaigned for the U.S. Senate, denounced Stephen Douglas' "popular sovereignty" doctrine. Unable to secure nomination, Lincoln yielded his votes to another candidate.

1856—Joined the new Republican Party, and at the Illinois State Republican Convention on May 29, 1856, delivered his famous "Lost Speech," uniting both abolitionists and moderates, making himself a leader of the new party.

At the Republican National Convention, Lincoln received 110 ballots for the vice-presidential nomination.

1858—Was nominated by the Republicans to serve as the U.S. Senator from Illinois. At the State convention, June 16, 1858, he delivered his famous "House Divided" speech. During the campaign, he challenged his opponent, Stephen Douglas, to a series of seven debates. These debates gained Lincoln popularity and respect nationally. He forced Douglas to modify his "popular sovereignty" doctrine, thus costing the Democratic leader the votes of the South in the 1860 presidential election. The legislature chosen was favorable to Mr. Douglas and he was elected.

1858–60—Lincoln made speeches defining his and the Republican Party's position in many States. On February 27, 1860, Lincoln delivered a speech at Cooper Union, in New York, where he clearly outlined the principles for which his party stood.

1860—On November 6, Lincoln won the Republican presidential nomination after a low-key, no speeches campaign, over William H. Seward, his close rival. Lincoln was elected over Douglas, Breckenridge, and Bell.

1861—Between the election and the inauguration, Lincoln was silent. He left Springfield February 11, 1861, for Washington. In the interim, the Confederacy was established. Lincoln made it clear that secession would not be tolerated, but his inaugural address was moderate and conciliatory.

In the Cabinet, William H. Seward headed the Department of State, Salmon P. Chase, the Treasury; Simon Cameron, and soon afterward, Edwin M. Stanton, War; Gideon Wells, the Navy; Caleb B. Smith, the Interior; Edward Bates was Attorney General, and Montgomery Blair was Postmaster General.

Lincoln made the decision to send food and other provisions to the Union garrison at Fort Sumter. He notified the Governor of South Carolina that this would be a peaceful mission, that neither men nor ammunition would be carried. The Government of the Confederacy regarded Lincoln's message as a declaration of war. Early in the morning of April 12, 1861, General Beauregard's forces opened fire in Charleston Harbor—the first shots of the Civil War. Two days later the flag of the Confederacy flew over Fort Sumter.

Immediately offer the fall of Fort Sumter, the President called for 75,000 volunteers to put down the rebellion. He soon issued a call for additional troops, instituted a blockade, and summoned Congress to meet in extra session July 4. Congress recognized a state of war July 13, 1861. "War President" Lincoln is identified with the history of the prolonged struggle which ensued.

Foreign complications, military and naval movements, domestic politics, as well as routine administrative duties, all claimed the attention of the President. To the people and the armies he was endeared as "Father Abraham"; numerous anecdotes are related bearing on his humor, strong common sense, and sympathy.

1862–63—On September 22, 1862, profiting by the partial success of Antietam, Lincoln issued a preliminary proclamation fixing the following January 1 as the date for freeing slaves in the insurgent States; there followed the great Emancipation Proclamation to that effect at the opening of 1863.

Victory of the Union forces at Gettysburg and Vicksburg signaled the turning point of the war.

On November 19, 1863, Lincoln pronounced, on the battlefield of Gettysburg, his short but classic eulogy.

1864–65—Two military successes, Adm. David C. Farragut's Mobile Bay victory, and Sherman's capture of Atlanta in the late summer and fall of 1864 assured, and secured, Lincoln's reelection to the Presidency. "Malice toward none, charity for all" was the burden of his second inaugural.

Lincoln and Seward met three Confederate commissioners on board a warship to discuss the terms for surrender: That the States reunite into the Union and that they sign the Emancipation Proclamation.

General Lee surrendered to General Grant at Appomattox Court House on April 9, 1865. On April 11, Lincoln read his intentions for reconstruction to a wildly cheering crowd at the White House.

On the morning of April 14, Lincoln held a long Cabinet meeting to discuss plans for a general reconstruction. That evening, while attending a performance at Ford's Theater in Washington, Lincoln was fatally wounded. Carried to a house across the street, he died the next morning at 7:22.

The measure of this great man is perhaps best expressed by the words of Secretary Stanton: "Now he belongs to the ages."

After lying in state in Washington, and a long, sad funeral journey, Lincoln was buried in Oak Ridge Cemetery in Springfield, Ill.

Emancipation Proclamation—January 1, 1863, 12 Stat. 1268.
Homestead Act—May 20, 1862, 12 Stat. 392.
Habeas Corpus Act—March 3, 1863, 12 Stat. 755.
Income Tax Act (first)—August 5, 1861, 12 Stat. 292.
National Bank Act(s)—January 30, 1863, 12 Stat. 665; February 25, 1863, 12 Stat. 665.
Greenback Act—February 25, 1862, 12 Stat. 345.
Thirteenth Amendment—February 1, 1865, 13 Stat. 567.
Immigration Act—July 4, 1864, 13 Stat. 385.

ANDREW JOHNSON

Seventeenth President of the United States
April 15, 1865 to March 3, 1869
(No. 117)

OBV. Andrew Johnson, President of the United States, 1865. Bust of the President.

REV. Columbia is giving her hand to an Indian Chief, before a tomb surmounted by a bust of Washington. At the feet of the Indian are the attributes of native life, and behind him a buffalo hunt; at the feet of Columbia and behind her are the emblems of maritime and industrial progress.

By Anthony C. Paquet.

ANDREW JOHNSON

1808—Born December 29, 1808, in Raleigh, N.C., the son of Jacob and Mary (McDonough) Johnson.

Fatherless at the age of 4; apprenticed to a tailor at the age of 10; Johnson's early education was almost entirely neglected.

1827—Married Eliza McCardle, a woman of refinement, who taught him writing and arithmetic, and read to him while he worked.

1828–33—Elected alderman; was reelected in 1829; elected mayor of Greenville in 1830.

1831—Appointed by the county court as a trustee of Rhea Academy, and participated in a debating society at Greenville College.

1835—Represented Green and Washington Counties in the legislature; was defeated in 1837, but in 1839 was reelected.

1841—Was an elector for the State at large on the Van Buren ticket and made a State reputation by the force of his oratory.

Elected to the State Senate.

1843—Was elected to the U.S. House of Representatives. His first speech was in support of the resolution to restore to General Jackson the fine imposed on him at New Orleans; he also supported the annexation of Texas. Was regularly reelected to Congress until 1853. During this period he opposed all expenditures for internal improvements that were not general; made a celebrated defense of the veto power; urged the adoption of the homestead law; supported the compromise measures of 1850 as a matter of expediency, but opposed compromises in general as a sacrifice of principle.

1853—Elected Governor of Tennessee; reelected in 1855.

1857–62—Elected to the U.S. Senate. Here, he was one of the main proponents of the Homestead Bill, which was vetoed by President Buchanan. During his tenure Johnson advocated such amendments to the Constitution as the popular election of U.S. Senators and Federal judges, and the abolition of the electoral college for the election of the President. In the 1860 session of the Congress, he took decided and unequivocal grounds in opposition to secession.

1862—A strong unionist, Johnson was appointed by President Lincoln as Military Governor of Tennessee; he organized a provisional government for the State; raised 25 regiments for service in the State and ordered congressional elections. Reconstruction and an end to slavery in the western secessionist part of the State were completed by January 1865.

1864—Won election as Vice President on the Republican ticket. In his letter accepting the nomination, Johnson virtually disclaimed any departure from his principles as a Democrat but placed his acceptance upon the ground of "the higher duty of first preserving the Government."

1865—The Presidency passed to Andrew Johnson, following the death of Abraham Lincoln on April 15.

President Johnson moved rapidly to restore the country to a peacetime basis. By executive and general orders he diminished the Army, rescinded the naval blockade, and took measures to reestablish governments in those States which had seceded.

During the summer and autumn of 1865, southern States were reorganized, elections were held for State conventions, new constitutions were drafted and new governments were formed by the legislatures. The ordnances of secession were repealed, slavery was abolished, the 13th amendment to the Constitution was ratified, and the Confederate debt was repudiated.

Johnson urged, unsuccessfully, that the States grant the vote to qualified Negroes. However, the extension of suffrage to the Negro was left a power belonging exclusively to the States.

The problems of reconstruction were approached by Johnson in a conciliatory spirit. However, strong factions developed in the Congress which advocated the use of military force to achieve reconstruction reforms.

1867—The main foreign achievement of Johnson's administration was the purchase of Alaska for $7.2 million.

On March 2, 1867, the Congress passed the Tenure of Office Act which prohibited the removal of any officeholder, including a Cabinet member, without the consent of the Senate. This act was passed to prevent the removal of Secretary of War, Edwin M. Stanton, who was not loyal to President Johnson.

1868—On February 21, 1868, President Johnson finally removed Stanton and replaced him with General Grant. On February 25, President Johnson was impeached by the House of Representatives. Nine of 11 articles of impeachment were concerned with alleged violations of the Tenure of Office Act. President Johnson's trial went before Chief Justice Chase in the Senate on March 13; the President was acquitted.

The remainder of Johnson's term was a constant struggle with a hostile Congress. One of Johnson's last acts in office was an amnesty proclamation for all who had taken part in the secession.

The pardon was proclaimed on Christmas Day, 1868. Johnson's term ended on March 4, 1869.

1875—Johnson remained active in political life and was returned to the U.S. Senate in March 1875.

President Johnson died on July 31, 1875, of paralysis while on a visit to his daughter. He lies buried at Greenville, Tenn.

Reconstruction Acts—March 2, 1867, 14 Stat. 428; March 23, 1867, 15 Stat. 2; March 30, 1867, 15 Stat. 29; July 19, 1867, 15 Stat. 14, 30; March 11, 1868, 15 Stat. 41.
Alaska Purchase Treaty—March 30, 1867, 15 Stat. 539.
Civil Rights Act—April 9, 1866, 14 Stat. 27.
Fourteenth Amendment—June 16, 1866, 14 Stat. 358.
Tenure of Office Act—March 2, 1867, 14 Stat. 430.
Fifteenth Amendment—February 27, 1869, 15 Stat. 346.
Habeas Corpus Act—February 5, 1867, 14 Stat. 385.

ULYSSES S. GRANT

Eighteenth President of the United States
March 4, 1869 to March 3, 1877
(No. 118)

OBV. Ulysses S. Grant. Bust of the President.

REV. PRESIDENT OF THE UNITED STATES. Within a laurel wreath: Inaugurated First Term March 4, 1869. Second term March 4, 1873.

By William and Charles Barber.

ULYSSES SIMPSON GRANT

1822—Born at Point Pleasant, Clermont County, Ohio, the son of Jesse Root and Hannah (Simpson) Grant.

1843—Graduated from the U.S. Military Academy; commissioned brevet lieutenant in the 4th Infantry.

1845—Promoted to second lieutenant, Grant joined Gen. Zachary Taylor's army in Texas in 1845 and distinguished himself at Monterey.

1847—Served under Gen. Winfield Scott in the battles leading to the surrender of Mexico City; promoted to first lieutenant, for bravery. Was breveted captain at Chapultepec.

1848—Married Julia Dent of St. Louis, Mo.

1852—Assigned garrison duty in New York and Michigan. His previous service in the Mexican campaigns gave him an opportunity to know many of the men who, later, held commands in the Confederate Army.

1854–60—Resigned his commission, after service on the west coast. Farmed in Missouri and went into real estate in St. Louis.

1861—With the outbreak of the Civil War, Grant re-entered service, with the Union forces, as a colonel of the 21st Illinois Volunteers.

Promoted to brigadier general, with headquarters at Cairo, Ill., he occupied Paducah, Ky., a strategic point at the junction of the Tennessee and Ohio Rivers.

Fought at Belmont, Mo., where the Confederates forced him to retreat.

1862—Was ordered to take Confederate positions in northwestern Tennessee: Fort Henry on the east side of the Tennessee River and, 12 miles away, Fort Donelson on the west side of the Cumberland River. These two forts were constructed by the Confederates in 1861 to defend the Mississippi valley; they were manned by garrisons which totaled about 2,500 men.

On February 6, 1862, a fleet of Union gunboats attacked Fort Henry. Realizing the vulnerability of his forces, the Confederate commander ordered a retreat. Retaining a small force to man the guns, he covered the withdrawal of his men to Fort Donelson and then surrendered the fort. Confederate losses were 16 men; Union losses were 29 killed and wounded.

While Grant was moving his body of 16,000 troops overland to Fort Donelson, the Confederates moved 12,000 additional men into the garrison. They did this to protect their line of communications with Confederate forces north around Bowling Green, and to deny access to the Cumberland River which, if opened, would enable Union forces to reach Nashville.

The attack on Fort Donelson began on February 13. It was renewed the following day when an additional force of 11,000 Union troops arrived. By a surprise attack on the 15th, the Confederates succeeded in opening a road to Nashville, but failed to take advantage of it. During the night some of the Confederate troops escaped by steamer. On the 16th, realizing that he was greatly outnumbered, the Confederate commander asked for an armistice. Grant made the now famous reply:

"No terms except unconditional and immediate surrender can be accepted. I propose to move immediately upon your works."

The Confederate garrison, with its 11,500 men, 40 guns, and great quantities of ammunition, surrendered. Confederate losses at Donelson were 2,000 killed and wounded; Union losses, 2,700.

Soon after the capture of Fort Henry, Grant was made a major general of volunteers.

Grant's next major engagement was at Shiloh, in western Tennessee. After 2 days of bloody battle, and greatly outnumbered, the Confederates were forced to retreat. Confederate casualties were over 10,000; the Union more than 13,000.

On October 25, 1862, Grant was ordered to take Vicksburg, Miss., the principal Confederate stronghold on the Mississippi River.

1863—In January, Grant moved his troops down from Memphis and took a position at Young's Point, which is about 20 miles above Vicksburg, off the west bank of the Mississippi River. Situated on a steep bluff, 235 feet above the east bank of the river, Vicksburg held a strategic location and almost impregnable position. As early as 1791 it had been developed by the Spanish for use as a fortress.

After futile attempts to cross the river in the vicinity of Vicksburg, Grant moved his forces south to a point where Bruinsburg lay, across the river. Here he waited for the Union fleet which sailed downstream and withstood the fire of Vicksburg's guns on the night of April 16. Within 2 weeks, the Union forces were carried across the river and promptly moved northeast and dispersed a Confederate force at Fort Gibson.

Augmenting Grant's forces, Sherman arrived by crossing the river at Grand Gulf, above Bruinsburg, and proceeded to the east of Vicksburg, where they captured the main supply base at Jackson. The Confederates moved some forces out from Vicksburg and engaged Union troops at Champion's Hill, which lies midway between Jackson and Vicksburg; but they were driven back to Vicksburg. After two heavy, unsuccessful assaults on Vicksburg, Grant settled down to siege warfare. On July 4, unable to obtain reinforcements or supplies, Vicksburg finally surrendered. Confederate losses were 10,000 dead, 31,000 prisoners, including 15 generals; the Union losses were almost as staggering—9,400 dead.

The climax to Grant's achievements in the year 1863 took place when he moved on to Chattanooga in October, to relieve a beleaguered Union army which had been held in a state of siege by Confederate forces. As a major general and commanding the Army of the West (as the Vicksburg army was henceforth called), Grant was joined by the armies of his three generals, Sheridan, Sherman, and Thomas.

After a month of preparation, the Union forces engaged the Confederates in a battle. Union forces cleared the top of Lookout Mountain of Confederate troops on the 24th. On the 25th, Union troops were ordered to seize the Confederate rifle pits at the foot of Missionary Ridge. They seized the pits and then, without waiting for further orders, they stormed up the steep and crumbling sides of the mountain in the face of a deadly fire from 30 cannons trained on every path and drove the Confederate commander and his troops from the crest of the hill. After the latter action, the Confederate force of 35,000 men withdrew southward into Georgia.

On December 17, 1863, Congress awarded Grant a gold medal for Fort Donelson, Vicksburg, and Chattanooga.

1864—Appointed Commander in Chief of the U.S. Army, March 17, with the rank of lieutenant general.

1864–65—Heading the Army of the Potomac, he fought the Battles of the Wilderness and besieged Richmond.

1865—Suffered great losses at Battles of Spotsylvania and Cold Harbor. Received Lee's surrender at Appomatox Court House, April 9.

1866—Grant was given the rank of full General, the first since George Washington to hold that rank.

1867—Served as Secretary of War ad interim, but resigned when the Senate refused to replace E. M. Stanton, and the office was turned back to him.

1868–77—At the National Convention of the Republican Party which met at Chicago on May 20, 1868, Grant was unanimously nominated for President. His letter of acceptance was brief and contained the phrase: "Let us have peace."

Elected President of the United States in November 1868; reelected in 1872.

During Grant's administration occurred the ratification of the 15th amendment, the funding of the national debt, and the beginning of Civil Service reforms. The Treaty of Washington was negotiated with Great Britain, and specie payment was resumed in 1875.

Grant's administration as President was not wholly successful, some of his advisors proving most unworthy. He possessed an unassuming manner, yet was self-reliant and prompt in his decisions, calm and patient in all circumstances, and won considerable admiration by his moral and physical courage.

1877–79—After leaving the Presidency, Grant and his family traveled in Europe.

1880—Renominated for the Presidency, Grant lost the election to James A. Garfield.

Though afflicted with cancer, Grant spent the last years of his life writing his memoirs, to raise money to repay his debts.

1885—The President died on July 23, at Mount McGregor, N.Y., and is now buried in a great mausoleum on Riverside Drive in New York City.

Ku Klux Klan Act—February 28, 1871, 16 Stat. 433.
Civil Rights Act—May 31, 1870, 16 Stat. 140; April 20, 1871, 17 Stat. 13; March 1, 1875, 18 Stat. 335.
Reconstruction Act (Currency)—January 14, 1875, 18 Stat. 296.
Reorganization of D.C. Government—June 20, 1874, 18 Stat. 116.

RUTHERFORD BIRCHARD HAYES

Nineteenth President of the United States
March 4, 1877 to March 3, 1881
(No. 119)

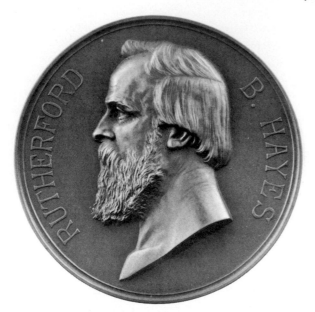 

OBV. Rutherford B. Hayes. Bust of the President.

REV. President of the United States. Within a laurel wreath: Inaugurated March 5, 1877.

By George T. Morgan.

RUTHERFORD BIRCHARD HAYES

1822—Born in Delaware, Ohio, on October 4, the son of Rutherford and Sophia (Birchard) Hayes. His father died 10 weeks before he was born. He was one of five children, but only he and his sister, Fanny, lived to maturity.

Attended a Methodist seminary at Norwalk, Ohio, and Isaac Webb's private school (later absorbed into Wesleyan University at Middleton, Connecticut).

1842–45—Graduated from Kenyon College in Gambier, Ohio; read law under Thomas Sparrow at Columbus, Ohio. He then attended Harvard Law School where he studied under Judge Joseph Story and Prof. Simon Greenleaf, finishing in 1845.

1845–49—Admitted to the bar on March 10, 1845, and practiced law in Lower Sandusky (later Fremont), Ohio.

1849—In December, Hayes established himself at Cincinnati, where considerable prominence came to him from several criminal cases. As volunteer counsel for the "underground railroad," he aided fugitive slaves to win their freedom, notably in the *cause celebre* of the slave girl, Rosetta.

1852—Married Lucy Ware Webb, formerly of Chillicothe, Ohio, on December 30.

1856—He helped found the Ohio Republican Party.

1858—Became city solicitor of Cincinnati.

1861—Volunteered for military service when the Civil War began. He served for 4 years, mainly with the 23d Ohio Volunteers, starting out as a major. He conducted himself courageously, was wounded five times, and won the rank of major general. He was wounded at the battle of South Mountain, and distinguished himself in the Shenandoah campaign of 1864 at Winchester, Fisher's Hill, and Cedar Creek.

1864—While still in the service and despite his refusal to conduct a campaign, Hayes was elected to Congress.

1866—Reelected to Congress, he had scarcely started his second term when he was elected Governor of Ohio in 1867.

1869—Respected, even by opposing partisans, he was reelected to the governorship, on the "honest money" issue.

While Governor, he obtained reforms in the treatment of the insane. He also helped create the Ohio Geological Survey.

After his service as Governor, Hayes retired from politics to take up life as a farmer at Fremont, Ohio, having inherited his uncle's large estate there.

1876—Won the Republican nomination for the Presidency in June. The 1876 election found Samuel J. Tilden, the Democratic candidate, with 184 electoral votes and Hayes with 185 only if he won four contested States: South Carolina, Louisiana, Florida, and Oregon. Tilden had won the popular vote. The voting in the South had been marked by many conflicts and irregularities related to the black vote. When the House of Representatives could reach no decision, an electoral commission was created consisting of five Representatives, five Senators, and five Supreme Court judges to settle the contest. This group included eight Republicans and seven Democrats. Hayes won the Presidency by a margin of one vote.

1877—In his inaugural address on March 4, Hayes stated: "He serves his party best who serves his country best." This was to be his theme in initiating civil service reforms, making meritorious appointments without regard to patronage. He established presidential independence which enraged "Old Guard" party leaders, but which enhanced the Presidency.

1877–81—Hayes supported "sound money" policies, Federal aid to education, and the building of the Isthmian Canal as an American enterprise, but these policies were obscured by the disputed election and by his pacification policy in the South.

1879—Hayes opposed free and unlimited coinage of silver. A bill providing for the resumption of specie payments became effective on January 1. Prior to this time Hayes had vetoed the Bland-Allison bill which provided that a silver dollar should be coined of the weight of 412½ grains to become full legal tender for all debts and dues, public and private, except where otherwise expressly stipulated in contracts. This bill had passed over Hayes' veto.

The withdrawal of the troops from the South during his administration hastened the recovery of the South from the effects of the war, and was highly beneficial to the Nation. This marked the end of the so-called "Reconstruction."

Adhering to a statement made before his election that he intended to serve only one term, Hayes did not seek reelection.

1881—After leaving the White House, Hayes served as president of the National Prison Association, and was on the board of trustees chosen to administer the John F. Slater Fund for the promotion of industrial education of the Negroes of the South. He was also a member of the board of trustees of the Peabody Education Fund for the promotion of education in the South. Various universities and colleges conferred honorary degrees on him. As Governor he had, in a sense, founded Ohio State University, and near the end of his life he suffered from exposure while attending a trustee meeting for Ohio State University. This quickened the end. After a heart attack in Cleveland, his death occurred at his estate, Spiegel Grove, in Fremont, on January 17, 1893. President Hayes was buried on his estate.

Bland-Allison Silver Act—February 28, 1878, 20 Stat. 25.

335-478 O - 69 - 4

JAMES ABRAM GARFIELD

Twentieth President of the United States
March 4, 1881 to September 19, 1881
(No. 120)

OBV. James A. Garfield. Bust of the President.

REV. Within a laurel and oak wreath with crossed ribbons: Inaugurated President of the United States March 4, 1881. Assassinated July 2, 1881. Died September 19, 1881.

By C. E. Barber.

JAMES ABRAM GARFIELD

1831—Born November 19, 1831, in Orange, Cuyahoga County, Ohio, the son of Abraham and Mary (Ballou) Garfield.

Fatherless at the age of two, Garfield grew up in a rural atmosphere; he attended school in a log hut; was an avid reader, a habit which carried through his entire life. At the age of 16 he worked on a canal towpath, taught school, worked on a farm, and did carpentry.

1849—While working, Garfield studied at Geauga Seminary at Chester, Ohio, and at Western Reserve Eclectic Institute (later, Hiram College), in Hiram, Ohio.

1856—After graduating from Williams College in Massachusetts, Garfield returned to Hiram College where he became a professor of the classics. While teaching, Garfield studied law and was later admitted to the bar.

1857—Became president of Hiram College, at the age of 26.

1858—Married Lucretia Rudolph, from which union seven children were born.

1859—Elected to the Ohio State Senate where he became known as an effective speaker and an antislavery man.

1861—Helped assemble the 42d Ohio Volunteer Infantry and was commissioned lieutenant colonel of the unit; later, was given command of a brigade and was assigned the task of driving the Confederate Gen. Humphrey Marshall from eastern Kentucky. This he accomplished, at Middle Creek, Ky., on January 10, 1862. President Lincoln promoted him to the rank of brigadier general. Later, Garfield participated in the Battle of Shiloh.

1863—Was appointed Chief of Staff to Gen. William S. Rosecrans; for his performance at the Battle of Chicamauga he was promoted to the rank of major general.

In December 1863, at the suggestion of President Lincoln, Garfield resigned his commission in the Army and took his seat in the U.S. House of Representatives, to which he had been elected. He became one of the leading debaters and orators on the Republican side.

Garfield served as a member of important committees, such as Military Affairs and Ways and Means, and was chairman of the committees on Banking and Currency and Appropriations.

44

1876—Chosen for the eighth time as a Congressman from his district, Garfield also became a member of the electoral commission which decided the 1876 election dispute involving Hayes. The following year Garfield became a Republican leader in the House of Representatives.

1880—On January 13, 1880, Garfield was elected U.S. Senator. He went to the Republican Convention as a campaign manager for Senator John Sherman. A deadlock developed between the presidential candidates Sherman, Grant, and Blaine. On the 36th ballot, Garfield emerged as the unanimous choice of the convention, as their candidate for the Presidency.

In November, Garfield and his running mate, Chester A. Arthur, defeated the Democratic candidates for the two highest offices of the Nation.

1881—Inaugurated on March 4, 1881, Garfield chose James G. Blaine for the State Department, Windom for the Treasury, and T. R. Lincoln for War. The first months of Garfield's administration were disturbed by the opposition of the New York Senators, Roscoe Conkling and Thomas C. Platt. Members of the "Stalwarts," these men claimed the right to control the Presidential appointments in their State. When the President refused to yield, they resigned their seats in the Senate and appealed to the State legislature to vindicate their attitude by reelection. They were not returned to office. On July 2, 1881, as Garfield was preparing to leave the Baltimore and Potomac Railroad Station in Washington, D.C., to deliver a commencement address, he was shot by a disappointed office seeker who proclaimed himself one of the "Stalwarts." Garfield lingered through the summer but passed away, September 19, 1881. He was buried in Cleveland, Ohio.

(No acts listed; administration less than 7 months in length; Congress was not in session during any of the time.)

CHESTER ALAN ARTHUR

Twenty-first President of the United States
September 20, 1881 to March 3, 1885
(No. 121)

OBV. Chester A. Arthur. Bust of the President.

REV. President of the United States. Within a laurel wreath: Inaugurated September 20, 1881.

By C. E. Barber

CHESTER ALAN ARTHUR

1830—Born on October 5, 1830, in North Fairfield, Franklin County, Vt. His father, Rev. William Arthur, had emigrated from Ireland; his mother was Malvina Stone of English descent.

1845—Entered Union College; was graduated in 1848; studied law at home and taught school. Later, was principal of an academy at Cohoes, Vt.

1853—Received final training for law in New York at the offices of Culver and Parker. Arthur was admitted to the bar in 1854. While practicing law, he obtained a local reputation as a champion of civil rights; he associated himself with the new Republican Party in New York and took part in the first Republican State Convention at Saratoga.

1859—On October 25, married Ellen Lewis Herndon, of which union three children were born.

1860—Campaigned for the 1860 Republican candidate for Governor of New York; when his candidate won, he was given the post of State Engineer-in-Chief, with the rank of brigadier general. He had previously taken part in the organization of the State militia and had been judge advocate of the 2d Brigade.

1861—At the outbreak of the war, Arthur became New York's assistant quartermaster general. As such, he began the work of preparing and forwarding New York's quota of troops. Was called to Albany in December for consultation concerning the defenses of New York Harbor. Summoned a board of engineers on December 24, of which he became a member, and on January 18, 1862, submitted an elaborate report on the condition of the national forts, both on the seacoast and on the inland border of the State.

1862–78—Arthur returned to and continued in his law practice, but remained active in party affairs. In 1871 he was appointed by President Grant as Collector of the Port of New York, a post which he held until 1878.

1880—After the bitter contest for the Republican nomination in 1880 had ended in the choice of Garfield, Arthur was selected for the second place on the ticket as a representative of the "Stalwart" faction of the Republican party. Becoming Vice-President in 1881, he was suddenly called to the Presidency by the assassination of Garfield, and took the oath of office on September 20, 1881.

The apprehensions caused by his active interference in New York politics during his short term as Vice President were happily allayed by his administration. Among his acts were the strengthening of naval defense, vetoes of a Chinese exclusion bill, and a disturbingly large river and harbor bill. To the surprise of many, Arthur consistently backed civil service reform; on January 16, 1883, he signed the Pendleton Civil Service Act. He also urged a reduction of the Treasury's large surplus.

1885—Arthur left office in 1885 as a respected and well-liked President who had done much for the internal reforms of his country.

1886—After returning to his New York law practice, President Arthur died of Bright's disease on November 18, 1886. He was 56. He is buried in Rural Cemetery, Albany, N.Y.

Civil Service Act (Pendleton)—January 16, 1883, 22 Stat. 403.
Chinese Exclusion Act—May 6, 1882, 22 Stat. 28.
Regulation of Immigration Act—August 3, 1882, 22 Stat. 214.

(STEPHEN) GROVER CLEVELAND

Twenty-second President of the United States
March 4, 1885 to March 4, 1889

Twenty-fourth President of the United States
March 4, 1893 to March 4, 1897

(No. 122)

OBV. Grover Cleveland. Bust of the President.

REV. Within an oak wreath: Inaugurated President of the United States March 4, 1885. Second Term March 4, 1893.

By C. E. Barber.

(STEPHEN) GROVER CLEVELAND

1837—Born March 18, at Caldwell, N.J., the son of Richard F. and Anna (Neal) Cleveland.

Self-educated, Cleveland's youth was spent in Fayetteville and Clinton, N.Y., where his father served as a Presbyterian minister.

1854—Became a clerk and an assistant teacher in the Institution for the Blind, in New York City.

1855–59—Became a clerk with the law firm of Rogers, Bowen & Rogers, in Buffalo; studied law and was admitted to the bar.

1863—Entered politics; was appointed assistant district attorney for Erie County, N.Y. Held this office for 3 years.

1865—Ran for district attorney, but was defeated; became a law partner of the firm, Lanning, Cleveland & Folsom.

1869—Elected sheriff for Erie County. Politically, this did not add to his popularity; he had to hang two murderers.

1873—Formed the law partnership of Bass, Cleveland & Bissell.

1881–82—Elected mayor of Buffalo on the Democratic ticket. He instituted vigorous reforms in the city and achieved a reputation for integrity. This led to his election as Governor of New York in 1882.

1884—Nominated by the Democratic National Convention, Cleveland ran for and was elected to the Presidency, defeating James G. Blaine.

The new President became known as a supporter of civil service reform, "hard money" and, especially, lower tariffs which he advocated in his celebrated message to Congress in December 1887.

1886—Married in the White House to Frances Folsom, daughter of his former law partner. Five children were born of this marriage.

1888—Was defeated by Benjamin Harrison in the presidential election, following a campaign in which the tariff was the leading issue.

1889—Retiring from office, Cleveland resumed the practice of law and settled in New York City.

1892—As the 1892 election approached, Cleveland's candidacy was again suggested, and he received the Democratic nomination for the third time. His former competitor was in the field, but this time was decisively beaten.

1893—President Cleveland commenced his second term in March 1893. He took office at a time when the country was faced with a financial crisis occasioned by a lowering of the gold reserve and other factors. He obtained repeal of silver purchases required under the Sherman Act which had expanded the currency in circulation, through issuance of certificates which at the time were redundant to the monetary system. He achieved a reduction in tariffs and passage of an income tax law (which the Supreme Court declared unconstitutional in 1895). He was also credited for limiting Civil War pension log-rolling.

Notwithstanding labor trouble and a severe depression, Cleveland refused to interfere in business matters and rejected demands for heavy work relief expenditures. In 1894, to move the mails,

Cleveland sent Federal troops to break the Pullman strike.

In foreign affairs, Cleveland refused to permit American aid to rebel movements in Hawaii and Cuba. Through friendly arbitration, he settled a border dispute between Great Britain and Venezuela, thereby strengthening the Monroe Doctrine.

1896—Supported the gold faction of the Democratic Party; lost renomination to the silverite, William Jennings Bryan after the latter's "Cross of Gold" speech stampeded the Chicago Democratic Convention.

1897—Cleveland returned to private life, where he served as an elder, respected statesman.

1908—Died in Princeton, N.J.

President Succession Act—January 19, 1886, 24 Stat. 1.
Interstate Commerce Act—Feb. 4, 1887, 24 Stat. 379.
Wilson-Gorman Tariff Act—August 27, 1894, 28 Stat. 509.

BENJAMIN HARRISON

Twenty-third President of the United States
March 4, 1889 to March 3, 1893
(No. 123)

OBV. Benjamin Harrison. Bust of the President.

REV. Within a laurel wreath: Inaugurated President of the United States, March 4, 1889.

By C. E. Barber

BENJAMIN HARRISON

1833—Harrison was born at North Bend, Ohio (near Cincinnati), on August 20, the son of John Scott

and Elizabeth (Irwin) Harrison, and grandson of William Henry Harrison, ninth President of the United States.

1847—Attended a school known as "College Hill," a few miles from Cincinnati.

1852—Graduated from Miami University at Oxford, Ohio.

1852–54—Read law in the offices of Storer and Gwynne, prominent attorneys in Cincinnati.

1853—Admitted to the bar; married Caroline Lavinia Scott, October 20.

1854—Moved to Indianapolis, Ind., and commenced the practice of law.

1857—Elected city attorney.

1860—Elected and reelected (1864) reporter of the Supreme Court of Indiana on the Republican ticket, Harrison's first active appearance in the political field.

1862–64—Commissioned as second lieutenant; recruited Company A of the 70th Indiana Regiment; became its colonel. Participated with his regiment in various engagements during Gen. Don Carlos Buell's campaigns in Kentucky and Tennessee in 1862 and 1863; took part in Gen. W. T. Sherman's march on Atlanta in 1864, and in the Nashville campaign of the same year; was transferred early in 1865 to Sherman's army in its march through the Carolinas. As the commander of a brigade, he served with distinction in the Battles of Kenesaw Mountain, Peach Tree Creek, and Nashville in 1864.

1865—Was duly mustered out of the service June 8, 1865, not however, until he had been breveted a brigadier general of volunteers for "ability and gallantry in command of brigade."

1867–80—Engaged in the practice of law; continued his interest in public affairs and local philanthropics, and became active in the Republican Party activities.

1876—Declined a nomination for Governor of Indiana on the Republican ticket, consenting to run only after the regular nominee had withdrawn; lost the election, by a small majority.

1879—Appointed a member of the Mississippi River Commission by President Rutherford B. Hayes.

1880—As Chairman of the Indiana delegation to the Republican National Convention Harrison played a key role in securing the presidential nomination for Garfield.

1880—Elected to the U.S. Senate, he served from 1881 to 1887.

1881—While a Senator, Harrison was chairman of the Committee on Territories and took an active part in urging the admission as States, North Dakota, South Dakota, Washington, Idaho, and Montana, which finally came into the Union during his Presidency. He served also on the Committee on Military and Indian Affairs, the Committee on Foreign Relations, and others. He advocated the tariff views of his party, the enlargement of the U.S. Navy, the reform of the Civil Service, regulation of the railroads, and labor legislation. Harrison opposed the pension veto messages of President Cleveland.

1884—Delegate to the Republican Convention.

1888—Harrison was nominated for the Presidency at the Republican National Convention and was elected over President Cleveland in a campaign in which tariff was the principal issue.

Harrison's administration was distinguished by the following:

The first Pan American Conference to promote trade, held in Washington, D.C., 1889.

The Tariff Act of 1890 which raised tariff duties, with the attendant feature of reciprocity.

The Sherman Act of 1890 which provided for the issuance of legal tender notes, the purchase of silver bullion and the coinage of silver dollars.

Denied the Louisiana Lottery Co., first capitalized at $1,000,000 and chartered by the Louisiana State Legislature, the use of the mails.

Enlargement of the U.S. Navy and the construction of steel ships; advancement in Civil Service reform.

An international monetary conference and establishment of commercial reciprocity with countries of the Americas and Europe.

Settlement of the Chile affair, concerned with an attack on American sailors; settlement of difficulties with Germany concerning the Samoan Islands, and arbitration between the United States and Great Britain of the Bering Sea seal fisheries issue.

1892—Renominated for the Presidency but was defeated by Grover Cleveland, for a variety of reasons, including reaction to the McKinley Tariff.

1885—Harrison returned to what developed into a highly successful law practice.

1893–94—Delivered a course of lectures on constitutional law at Leland Stanford Jr. University.

1896—Married Mrs. Mary Scott (Lord) Dimmick, a niece of his first wife, who died in 1892.

1899—Appeared as leading counsel for Venezuela in the arbitration of its boundary dispute with Great Britain, before an international arbitration tribunal in Paris.

1899—Appointed a member of the peace conference held at The Hague and became a member of the International Board of Arbitration.

1901—Died of pneumonia on March 13, and was buried in Crown Hill Cemetery, Indianapolis, Ind.

Sherman Silver Purchase Act—July 14, 1890, 26 Stat. 289.
Sherman Anti-Trust Act—July 2, 1890, 26 Stat. 209.
McKinley Tariff Act—October 1, 1890, 26 Stat. 567.
Eight Hour Day (Public Works)—August 1, 1892, 27 Stat. 340.
Railroad Safety Appliance Act—March 2, 1893, 27 Stat. 531.

WILLIAM McKINLEY

Twenty-fifth President of the United States
March 4, 1897 to September 14, 1901
(No. 124)

OBV. William McKinley. Bust of the President.

REV. Inaugurated President of the United States March 4, 1897. Second term March 4, 1901. Assassinated September 6, 1901. Died September 14, 1901. To left, Columbia standing, mourning, her right hand resting on a shield bearing Presidential eagle; below, palm branch and wreath with crossed ribbons.

By C. E. Barber.

WILLIAM McKINLEY

1843—McKinley was born on January 29, in Niles, Trumbull County, Ohio, son of William McKinley, owner of charcoal furnaces, and Nancy Allison McKinley.

1860—McKinley was educated at Union Seminary, Poland, Ohio, and at the age of 17 entered Allegheny College in Meadville, Pa.

1861—Forced by illness to discontinue his college education, he began to teach in public schools while a clerk in a Poland Post Office.

On June 11 he enlisted in Company E of the 23d Ohio Volunteer Infantry as a private and served under Rutherford B. Hayes.

1862—On April 15, while in camp at Fayetteville in western Virginia, he was promoted to commissary sergeant. On September 17, for his performances at Antietam, he was appointed second lieutenant of Company D.

1864—He was promoted to first lieutenant and later, for his services at Winchester, he was promoted to captain. While on the staff of Gen. George Crook, he participated in the Battles of Opequan, Fisher's Hill, and Cedar Creek.

1865—For McKinley's bravery and his valuable services, he was breveted major. At the finish of the war McKinley began the study of law at Youngstown, Ohio, and completed his studies at the Albany, N.Y., law school.

1867—Admitted to the bar, McKinley began practice at Canton, Ohio.

1870—Became the prosecuting attorney of Stark County; spoke against the "Greenback" craze.

1871—Married Ida Saxton.

1877–91—Elected to Congress as the Republican representative from the 17th Ohio District and served from March 4, 1877 to March 3, 1883, and again from March 4, 1887, to March 3, 1891.

1878—Took part in the debates over the protective tariff (Wood Tariff bill). Voted for the Bland-Allison silver bill.

1888—Chairman of the Committee on Resolutions at the Republican National Convention; a strong supporter of John Sherman for the Presidency.

1889—Appointed chairman of the Ways and Means Committee. Supported civil service laws. Became the Republican leader in the House of Representatives.

50

1890—October 1, the McKinley bill was approved by the President, which bill obtained for McKinley an international reputation as a foremost champion of the protective tariff.

1891—McKinley was elected Governor of Ohio. Controlled the labor riots and personally directed the relief work for the starving miners of the Hocking Valley district.

1892—Was appointed the permanent president of the National Republican Convention which met in Minneapolis.

1893—McKinley was reelected Governor of Ohio.

1896–97—In the National Republican Convention held in St. Louis, he was nominated for the Presidency on the first ballot. Defeated the Democratic candidate, William Jennings Bryan, to become President.

1898—April 25, upon McKinley's recommendation, Congress declared war on Spain. Earlier, in response to an aroused public sentiment and, finally on instruction from Congress, he intervened in the Cuban Civil War, which led to the sinking of the MAINE (February 15, 1898).

1899—Selected a delegation to represent the United States in the Hague Peace Conference. Peace treaty with Spain signed at Paris on December 10 and ratified by the United States on February 6.

Annexed the Hawaiian Islands and formed the Territory of Hawaii in April, 1900.

Puerto Rico, the Philippine Archipelago and Guam were transferred by Spain to the United States. Cuba came under American jurisdiction pending the establishment of an independent government there.

The Tripartite Goverment (German, British, and French) of the Samoan Islands was discontinued. The United States annexed these Islands east of 171°, including the harbor of Pago-Pago.

1900—Elected President, defeating William Jennings Bryan, for a second term.

Received the largest popular majority ever given a candidate for President up to that time.

1901—September 5, delivered an address at the Pan American Exposition in Buffalo, N.Y., suggesting lower tariffs.

September 6, while holding a reception in the Music Hall of the Exposition, McKinley was shot twice by an anarchist. He died on September 14, and 4 days afterward a day of mourning and prayer was called throughout the country by his successor, President Theodore Roosevelt.

He was buried in Canton, Ohio.

Hawaii Annexation Res.—July 7, 1898, 30 Stat. 750.
Dingley Tariff Act—July 24, 1897, 30 Stat. 151.
Recognition of Cuban Independence (Res.)—April 20, 1898, 30 Stat. 738.
Gold Standard Act—March 14, 1900, 31 Stat. 45.
Platt Amendment (Cuban-American relations)—March 2, 1901, 31 Stat. 897.

THEODORE ROOSEVELT

Twenty-sixth President of the United States
September 14, 1901 to March 3, 1909
(No. 125)

OBV. Theodore Roosevelt. Bust of the President.

By C. E. Barber.

REV. Inaugurated President of the United States September 14, 1901. Second term March 4, 1905. To left, Columbia, her right hand resting upon a column bearing a cinerary urn and devices symbolizing the authority of the United States; the U.S. Capitol in the background.

By George T. Morgan.

THEODORE ROOSEVELT

1858—Born on October 27, 1858, to Theodore and Martha (Bulloch) Roosevelt, at New York City, the second of four children. The Roosevelt background was that of wealthy merchants dating back to the Dutch founders of New York City.

Young Roosevelt's early education was private. He was handicapped with asthma and poor eyesight as a child and was forced to restrain his activity. He read widely and developed an intense interest in natural history.

1876—He entered Harvard College. While there, he started writing his first book, *The Naval War of 1812,* published in 1882. This narrative was based on original research and was recognized by the British Government as being an authentic account.

1880—Graduated from Harvard and on October 27 he married Alice Hathaway Lee of Chestnut Hill,

Mass. She was to die 4 years later after giving birth to their daughter, Alice, on February 14, 1884.

1882—Roosevelt served as a member of the State Assembly of New York, where he gained popularity for espousing the cause of the working man.

1883—September, Roosevelt bought a ranch in the Bad Lands of Western Dakota. Staying at his ranch on and off for 3 years, his health was much improved, and there he became familiar with the problems and customs of the West.

1884—Roosevelt was elected a delegate to the National Republican Convention.

1886—Ran for mayor of New York; went abroad after he was defeated.

On December 2, 1886, he married Edith Kermit Carow in London, whom he had known since childhood. She bore him five children: Theodore, Jr., Kermit, Archibald, Quentin, and Ethel.

1889—President Harrison appointed Roosevelt to serve as a U.S. Civil Service Commissioner. In this post he did much to strengthen the Commission.

1895—Became president of the Board of Police Commissioners of New York City.

1897—Appointed Assistant Secretary of the Navy under President McKinley; he prepared the Navy for war with Spain, which he felt was imminent.

1898—Took to the field as executive officer of the 1st U.S. Volunteer Cavalry under Col. Leonard Wood, who commanded the "Rough Riders." When Wood was promoted, Roosevelt was given command. The action at San Juan Hill and Roosevelt's defiance of the War Department orders to quarter his troops in fever infested areas, made him a popular hero. (Roosevelt was later to publish his book, *The Rough Riders*.)

Was nominated for Governorship of New York; he won the election and was inaugurated in January 1899.

1900—Roosevelt won election as Vice President of the United States and was inaugurated on March 4, 1901.

1901—On September 6, 1901, President McKinley was shot by an assassin. Upon his death, 8 days later, Theodore Roosevelt was inaugurated President of the United States.

1902—Roosevelt took a strong stand against trusts and demanded that, in the public interest, they be subjected to Federal control.

The Newlands Act, passed in 1902, established a Reclamation Service. Roosevelt increased the forest reserves from 43 million to 194 million acres. He was also responsible for the construction of the Roosevelt Dam.

1903—On February 11, 1903, the Expedition Act was passed, giving the Government power to hasten to trial its prosecutions under the Interstate Commerce and Anti-Trust Acts.

On February 19, 1903, the Elkins Law was passed, regulating rebates of freight rates.

Roosevelt settled the Alaskan Boundary dispute, approved pure food and drug legislation and negotiated the peace that ended the Russian-Japanese War.

1904–8—Roosevelt was nominated for the Presidency and won election easily.

Roosevelt attacked the Northern Securities Co. as a conspiracy in restraint of trade; on March 14, 1904, the Supreme Court dissolved the company.

Roosevelt solved a dangerous coal strike and established a precedent for future government intervention in industrial matters, when the public interest and welfare are affected.

Roosevelt also created the Departments of Labor and Commerce.

In the area of foreign policy, Roosevelt was generally prudent. He refused to take possession of Cuba or the Dominican Republic even though popular feeling was for expansion; he was given the Nobel Peace Prize for ending the Japanese-Russian War. Responding to a plea from Kaiser Wilhelm, Roosevelt took part in the Algeciras Conference which possibly postponed the outbreak of a world war.

Roosevelt recognized Panama when it revolted from Colombia. A treaty was soon signed with Panama, and the Canal was placed under construction.

As a step to preserve peace, Roosevelt unofficially committed the United States to support British-Japanese policy in the Orient.

1908—Roosevelt did not seek reelection in 1908. As soon as he left office, he departed for Africa, travelling on an extensive hunting and scientific expedition for the Smithsonian Institution.

Roosevelt's presence in Africa centered the world's attention there. Mrs. Roosevelt joined him in Kartoum on March 14, 1910, returning to the United States via Europe. Their trip was highlighted by speeches at Oxford, the Sorbonne, Christiania, and the University of Berlin.

Returning to New York, Roosevelt took up the duties of contributing Editor of *The Outlook* magazine.

1912—On February 25, 1912, Roosevelt announced that he was available as a presidential candidate. However, at the Chicago Republican National Convention, Taft won the nomination; Roosevelt formed his own Progressive ("Bull Moose") Party. The election was won by the Democratic candidate, Woodrow Wilson.

1913—During the winter of 1913–14, Roosevelt went on his last colorful expedition, to Central Brazil.

1914—With the outbreak of World War I, Roosevelt supported the neutrality policy of President Wilson and he later offered to raise a volunteer division.

1918—In July 1918, Roosevelt's youngest son was killed while flying over German lines.

1919—President Theodore Roosevelt died peacefully in his sleep on January 6, 1919, at Oyster Bay, N.Y.

Permanent Census Act—March 6, 1902, 32 Stat. 51.
Spooner Isthmian Canal Act—June 28, 1902, 32 Stat. 388.
Hepburn Railroad Rate Act—June 29, 1906, 34 Stat. 584.
Naturalization Act—June 30, 1906, 34 Stat. 596.
Pure Food and Drug Act—June 30, 1906, 34 Stat. 768.
Citizenship and Expatriation Act—March 2, 1907, 34 Stat. 1228.
Aldrich-Vreeland Emergency Currency Act—May 30, 1908, 35 Stat. 546.

WILLIAM HOWARD TAFT

Twenty-seventh President of the United States
March 4, 1909 to March 3, 1913
(No. 126)

OBV. William H. Taft. Bust of the President.

REV. Inaugurated President of the United States March 4, 1909. Columbia, seated, bearing in her left hand a scroll; in the background, the Capitol of the United States. Below, a laurel branch with ribbon inscribed: E. PLURIBUS UNUM.

By C. E. Barber

WILLIAM HOWARD TAFT

1857—Born on September 15, 1857, in Cincinnati, Ohio, the son of Alphonso and Louise Maria (Tarry) Taft, of New England. Alphonso Taft was a judge in the Cincinnati Superior Court of Ohio for two terms.

1870—Attended Woodward High School in Cincinnati, Ohio.

1874—Entered Yale and graduated in 1878, with honors.

1880—Graduated in a tie for first place from Cincinnati Law School; he was admitted to the bar in Ohio.

1881—Appointed assistant prosecuting attorney of Hamilton County, Ohio. Resigned in 1882 to become the U.S. Collector of Internal Revenue for Cincinnati, but resigned in a few months rather than to submit to pressure to dismiss certain employees for purely political reasons. This personal integrity characterized his whole life.

1883–87—Practiced law; was appointed assistant county solicitor.

1886—Married Helen Herron of Cincinnati; they had three children.

1887—Appointed as judge to an unfinished term on the Ohio Superior Court.

1888—Elected for a 5-year term on the Ohio bench; was the author of many exhaustive and scholarly opinions of law affecting labor and management.

1890—Appointed Solicitor General of the United States by President Benjamin Harrison.

1892—Appointed as U.S. Circuit Court Judge for the Sixth District in Ohio. Again, attracted national attention for his rulings in the Pullman car strike, and in other railroad cases. Other rulings he made served to strengthen the Sherman Anti-Trust Act.

1896–1900—Professor of law at the University of Cincinnati.

1900–1904—President McKinley appointed Taft as President of the Philippines Commission, where his ability as an administrator and conciliator became evident.

Taft successfully negotiated an agreement by which the United States purchased for resale to the residents the huge landholdings of the Catholic Church, thus adjusting ancient grievances of the Philippine people. Later, Taft was made Civil Governor in a reorganization of the government of those islands. His devotion to duty was illustrated by his previous refusal of two offers of appoint-

54

ment to the U.S. Supreme Court, an honor to which he had long aspired, because he felt his work in the Philippines was not completed. His interest in the islands continued throughout his life.

1908—When President Roosevelt declined renomination, Taft was the obvious choice as successor. He won over William Jennings Bryan, the latter making his third attempt at the Presidency. Taft's Vice President was John Sherman of New York.

1909–13—Taft's accomplishments as President are many. He recommended establishment of a Federal budget, urged postal service reform and "trust busting" amendments to interstate commerce laws, conservation of natural resources, and he advocated publication of campaign contributions.

In foreign affairs, Taft negotiated treaties for arbitration with France and Great Britain; he also negotiated reciprocal trade agreements with many countries.

During Taft's administration, Arizona and New Mexico were admitted to statehood in the Union.

Tackling the highly controversial subject of tariff revisions, Taft signed the Payne-Aldrich Tariff Bill, which did not add to his popularity in many quarters.

Taft's dismissal of Gifford Pinchot, the renowned forester, touched off a controversy over the conservation issue.

1912—Taft and his old friend, Theodore Roosevelt, battled bitterly for the Republican nomination for the Presidency. Though Taft won the nomination of his party, he was defeated in the election by Woodrow Wilson.

1913—Retired to Yale as a Kent Professor of Constitutional Law. Elected president of the American Bar Association.

1918—Appointed by President Wilson as head of the National War Labor Board.

1921—President Harding appointed William Howard Taft as Chief Justice of the U.S. Supreme Court. Taft served as an outstanding administrator, relieving a great deal of the Court's heavy workload by coordinating Federal judicial procedures and lessening dissensions within the Court. He is primarily responsible for congressional authorization to construct a new U.S. Supreme Court building.

Taft was conservative in his views, and many of his earlier rulings were not prolabor. However, dissenting opinion in the case of Adkins v. Children's Hospital (261 U.S., 525) formed a constitutional basis, later, for minimum wage laws, on the theory that sweatshop wages did as much to impair health and morale as did long hours. To the extent that he favored control of commerce, Taft's decisions favored Federal, rather than State control.

1930—Poor health forced Taft to retire from the Bench in February 1930. He died a month later, on March 5, 1930.

William Howard Taft and John Fitzgerald Kennedy are the only Presidents buried in Arlington National Cemetery.

Sixteenth Amendment—July 12, 1909, 36 Stat. 184.
Payne-Aldrich Tariff Act—August 5, 1909, 36 Stat. 184.
Seventeenth Amendment—May 13, 1912, 37 Stat. 646.
Webb-Kenyon Act (Interstate commerce of liquor)—March 1, 1913, 37 Stat. 699.

WOODROW WILSON

Twenty-eighth President of the United States
March 4, 1913 to March 4, 1921
(No. 127)

OBV. Woodrow Wilson. Bust of the President.

REV. Eagle, with spread wings, holding in its talons crossed branches of olive and oak. In the background, the Capitol of the United States. Inaugurated President of the United States March 4, 1913. Second Term March 5, 1917.

By George T. Morgan

WOODROW WILSON

1856—Born in Staunton, Va., on December 28, the son of Janet (Woodrow) and Rev. Joseph Ruggles Wilson, a Presbyterian minister.

1858—Moved to Augusta, Ga., and, in 1870, to Columbia, S.C., where his father became a professor in a theological seminary. The atmosphere of piety and intellectuality in which Wilson grew up, and his hatred of war acquired in childhood were strong influences in his life.

1873–74—Attended Davidson College in North Carolina.

1875—Entered the College of New Jersey (Princeton University), graduating in 1879. Here he developed great interest in political history and government, and became skilled in debate and public speaking.

1879–80—Attended the Law School of the University of Virginia.

1882—Was admitted to the bar, and opened a law office in Atlanta, Ga.

1883—Entered the graduate school of Johns Hopkins University in Baltimore to prepare himself for a teaching career.

1885—Married Ellen Louise Axson in Rome, Ga.; accepted an associate professorship of history at Bryn Mawr College, near Philadelphia.

1886—Awarded a Ph. D. by Johns Hopkins University for his published thesis on *Congressional Government*, which was a brilliant analysis of American legislative practice.

1888—Accepted a professorship of history and political economy at Wesleyan University in Connecticut.

1889—Published a major work in comparative government, *The State*. Coached one of the most successful football teams in Wesleyan's history.

1890—Accepted a professorship from Princeton, in jurisprudence and political economy.

1902—Inaugurated President of Princeton University, the first layman to serve in that capacity.

While at Princeton, Wilson achieved a reform in the academic life of the college by emphasizing scholarly achievement and minimizing social and athletic activities. He endeavored to bring the student and the instructor together in a form of personalized study, whereby discussion conferences with preceptors supplemented course lectures.

1911—Inaugurated as Governor of New Jersey, January 17.

By keeping pressure on the State legislature, Wilson was able to secure most of his legislative program, which included direct primaries, effective State regulation of public utilities, workmen's compensation, municipal reform, reorganization of the school system, and antitrust legislation to drive industrial monopolies from New Jersey.

The vigor with which Wilson carried out his campaign promises drew the attention of national political leaders, among whom was Col. Edward M. House of Texas, who was impressed with the strength and purposefulness of Wilson's ideals. The two became friends soon after they met in 1911. Colonel House led the drive which gave Wilson the Democratic nomination and elected him President of the United States on November 5, 1912.

The campaign waged by Wilson was on a "New Freedom" platform, a program liberating American economic energies by drastic tariff reductions, strengthening of antitrust laws, and reorganization of the banking and credit system.

1913—Wilson was inaugurated President of the United States on March 4, 1913.

Wilson built a new administration from the ground up, the Democrats having been out of office for 20 years. The chief Cabinet post, Secretary of State, was given to William Jennings Bryan. The appointment of other party regulars signified that Wilson would work through established machinery instead of bipartisan coalition.

On April 8, 1913, Wilson broke a century-old precedent and addressed a joint session of the Congress, to emphasize his determination to assume legislative leadership. The legislation which he requested and obtained was primarily to strengthen democratic government through protection of the individual.

The Underwood Tariff Act, approved on October 3, was the first tariff legislation uninfluenced by special interests since the Civil War. It also imposed the first income tax under the 16th amendment, to counterbalance the loss of revenue resulting from the lowering of tariffs.

Wilson was successful in achieving congressional approval of the Federal Reserve bill. This legislation established 12 Federal Reserve banks to perform central banking functions, with branch banks, under the coordination and control by a Federal Reserve Board of Presidential appointees in Washington, D.C. The measure also created a new currency: Federal Reserve notes issued by Federal Reserve banks against gold and commercial credits.

1914—The Clayton Anti-Trust Act was passed as a means of preventing interlocking directorates and exempted trade associations from the antitrust laws.

The Federal Trade Commission bill was enacted, outlawing unfair trade practices in sweeping terms,

and creating a Commission with authority to prevent unfair competition.

Both Wilson and Bryan inaugurated a new foreign policy of cooperation. Treaties with 30 nations were signed, providing for the investigation of disputes that might lead to conflict.

Argentina, Brazil, and Chile mediated a potential conflict in a border dispute between the United States and Mexico.

World War I started on August 6, 1914, causing the President to turn his attention more and more to international affairs. Under his leadership the United States maintained neutrality during the first 2 years of the conflict.

1915—On December 18, Wilson married Edith Bolling Galt of Washington, D.C., his first wife having died the previous year.

The Germans sank the British ship SUSSEX on March 24. When Wilson threatened to break relations with Germany, the German Government gave a sweeping pledge to follow conventional rules in attacking merchantmen.

On May 7, a German submarine torpedoed and sank the British liner, LUSITANIA, without warning. A lengthy exchange of notes followed between Wilson and representatives of the German Government. Secretary of State Bryan resigned, believing Wilson's protest warnings were too strong.

On August 19, the Germans sank the British liner, ARABIC.

1916—Wilson sent a small force under Gen. John J. Pershing into Mexico to pursue Pancho Villa, who had been conducting guerrilla raids into New Mexico.

Wilson was renominated by the Democrats under the slogan "He kept us out of war."

Running against Charles Evans Hughes, Associate Justice of the Supreme Court, Wilson won sufficient Progressive votes to transform a Democratic minority into a majority on November 7, although the change of some 1,500 votes in California would have given Hughes a majority in the electoral college.

1917—On January 31, 1917, the German Government retracted its pledge and announced the use of unlimited submarine warfare against all maritime commerce, neutral as well as belligerent. Wilson broke diplomatic relations on February 3.

The sinking of American ships and loss of American lives, added to the publication of the Zimmerman note outlining a plan for drawing Mexico into the war on the side of Germany and against the

United States, so inflamed public opinion that Wilson felt compelled to recommend to Congress a declaration of war, which was voted on April 6, 1917.

When the United States entered the war, Wilson demanded absolute defeat of the German Government, but he made a distinction between the Government and the German people, and continued to plead for peace founded on justice without vindictiveness.

Gen. John J. Pershing was appointed Commander of the United States Expeditionary Forces. In May, 1917, the Selective Service Act was passed.

When industrial mobilization lagged, Wilson took control of industry and established an economic agency under Bernard M. Baruch, who headed the War Industries Board.

1918—Wilson succeeded in reaching Allied agreement to his famous Fourteen Points Address of January 8, 1918, which called for a League of Nations, open diplomacy, freedom of the seas, removal of trade barriers, reduction of armaments, the independence of each nation to follow its own policies without outside interference, and a peace without victory, but with reconciliation.

In May, Congress passed the Overman Act which enabled Wilson to delegate emergency powers to the various boards he had created.

President Wilson transmitted to the German Government the basic conditions of peace, after which the armistice of November 11, 1918, was signed.

In the fall of 1918 Wilson had aroused political opposition at home by appealing for the return of a Democratic majority in the congressional elections, and the Republican Party had gained control of the Senate. Political opposition was further increased by the President's insistence on attending the European peace conference himself.

On December 4, 1918, Wilson and a large body of advisers sailed from New York aboard the GEORGE WASHINGTON to take part in the Paris Peace Conference. In Europe, Wilson was hailed as a savior of mankind and the hope of the future.

1919—The Peace Conference opened on January 18, and continued until the Versailles Treaty with Germany was signed on June 28. Wilson was a member of the Big Four, together with Prime Minister David Lloyd George of Great Britain, Premier Georges Clemenceau of France, and Prime Minister Vittorio Orlando of Italy. These four made the major decisions relating to the surrender of Germany.

Wilson's primary objective was the establishment of a League of Nations, and in spite of warnings from the opposition he felt that approval by the Senate would be more probable if the covenant were a part of the treaty of peace.

Wilson was forced to accept many compromises, but he succeeded in his efforts to make the covenant of the League of Nations an integral part of the Treaty of Versailles. He pinned his hopes on the League to rectify eventually many parts of the treaty which he regarded as unjust.

In the meantime the opposition at home had been gathering strength, some of it sincere, and some political. The reservations proposed by the Senate to the treaty, including the convenant, were unacceptable to President Wilson.

In September 1919, Wilson determined to take the issue to the people in a tour of the country. He made some 30 speeches between September 3 and September 25, but was forced to cancel the rest of the tour under the threat of a nervous collapse. He returned to Washington where, on October 2, he suffered an attack of paralysis, from which he never fully recovered.

1920—Wilson appealed once more to the people to make the 1920 presidential election a referendum on the question of membership in the League of Nations. When the Republican candidate won, many regarded it as a sign of repudiation of Wilson's internationalism, in spite of the fact that leading Republicans had expressed themselves in favor of some sort of a league. After his inauguration in March 1921, Harding expressed the view that the "League was dead."

1921—Disappointed and ill, Wilson retired from the public eye almost completely, at his home on "S" Street NW., in Washington, D.C.

1924—President Wilson died on February 3, 1924, of heart disease. His body was entombed in the Bethlehem Chapel of the Episcopal Cathedral of Saint Peter and Saint Paul in Washington.

Underwood Tariff Act—October 3, 1913, 38 Stat. 114.
Federal Reserve Act—December 23, 1913, 38 Stat. 251.
Establishment of Federal Trade Commission—September 26, 1914, 38 Stat. 71.
Clayton Anti-Trust Act—October 15, 1914, 38 Stat. 730.
Establishment of Coast Guard—January 28, 1915, 38 Stat. 800. September 1, 1916, 39 Stat. 675.
Adamson Eight Hour Law—September 3, 5, 1916, 39 Stat. 721.
Immigration Act—February 5, 1917, 39 Stat. 874.
Selective Service Act—May 18, 1917, 40 Stat. 217.
Espionage Act—June 15, 1917, 40 Stat. 76.
Trading with the Enemy Act—October 6, 1917, 40 Stat. 411.
Eighteenth Amendment—January 29, 1919, 40 Stat. 1050.
Nineteenth Amendment—June 4, 1919, 41 Stat. 362.
Volstead Prohibition Act—October 28, 1919, 41 Stat. 614.
Civil Service Retirement Act—May 22, 1920, 41 Stat. 614.
Merchant Marine Act (Jones)—June 5, 1920, 41 Stat. 988.

WARREN GAMALIEL HARDING

Twenty-ninth President of the United States
March 4, 1921 to August 2, 1923
(No. 128)

OBV. Warren G. Harding. Bust of the President.

REV. Standing beside a column symbolizing strength, a mourning female figure, holding laurel branch; adaptation of the Presidential Seal; Inaugurated President of the United States Mar. 4, 1921. Died Aug. 2, 1923. Palm branch entwined with wreath.

By George T. Morgan.

WARREN GAMALIEL HARDING

1865—Born on November 2, at Corsica, Morrow County, Ohio, the son of Dr. George Tryon Harding and Phoebe Dickerson Harding, who moved from the farm to Marion, Ohio, during Harding's childhood.

1879—Entered Ohio Central College.

1882—Taught school, studied law, and worked as an insurance canvasser. Printer, pressman and a reporter on the Marion Democratic Mirror.

1844—Bought the failing four-page Marion, Ohio Star with a circulation of less than 500; became its editor and made the paper a great success, a process that was facilitated by the growth of Marion.

1891—Married Mrs. Florence Kling De Wolfe, daughter of a Marion banker.

1898–1902—Served on the Ohio State Senate, having established himself as a powerful voice in Ohio.

1903—Elected Lieutenant Governor of Ohio and served until 1906; was defeated for the Governorship in

1910. His service in the State offices gave him the reputation of a party "regular".

1914—Elected to the U.S. Senate, by a plurality of more than 100,000, a vote which caused him to be mentioned as a presidential "dark horse." He served on the Senate committees on Foreign Relations and Commerce. He voted conservatively, along his party line.

1916—Chosen temporary chairman of the Republican National Convention; made the "keynote" speech.

1917—Voted for the bill to arm merchant ships and the resolution for declaration of war against Germany; favored the prohibition amendment, voted for equal suffrage for women.

1920—On June 12, on the 10th ballot at the National Convention in Chicago, Harding was nominated as the Republican candidate for the Presidency.

He conducted his campaign in support of high tariffs, immigration restrictions and a public welfare department. He appealed for a return to normalcy. Vague on the League issue, he secured partisan votes from both sides. In November, Harding and his running mate, Calvin Coolidge, were given a large majority at the polls, defeating James Cox and Franklin D. Roosevelt.

1921—In his inaugural address on March 4, Harding called for a prompt and thorough revision of the tax system; he called for the creation of a federal

335- 478 O - 69 - 5

budget system, an emergency tariff act, the readjustment of war taxes and the establishment of a merchant marine. He took a strong stand against U.S. participation in the then existing League of Nations. He recommended the passage of a resolution declaring peace with the Central Powers, which was approved by the Congress and signed on July 2, 1921.

Notable Cabinet appointments were Charles Evans Hughes as Secretary of State, Herbert Hoover as Secretary of Commerce, and Andrew J. Mellon as Secretary of the Treasury.

In August 1921, Harding signed the Knox Resolution of Peace with Germany.

Earlier, on June 10, Harding signed the Budget and Accounting Act which provided for a Budget Bureau in the Treasury Department. (This bureau was later transferred to the Executive Office of the President.) Charles G. Dawes was appointed the first Director of the Budget.

The Budget and Accounting Act also established the General Accounting Office, headed by the Comptroller General of the United States, with responsibilities for making independent audit of Government expenditures and reporting the results directly to Congress.

The most notable achievement of President Harding's administration was the Conference on the Limitation of Armaments which convened in Washington in November 1921. The purpose of the conference was to seek solutions of Pacific Ocean and East Asian problems by reaching agreement on a limitation of naval armaments. Peaceful solutions of most of the major problems were reached by the countries which participated: the United States, Great Britain, and the Dominions, Japan, France, Italy, the Netherlands, Portugal, Belgium, and China. The Nine Power Agreement which evolved from this conference provided for an open door policy in China, with all countries agreeing not to take advantage of conditions in China to obtain special concessions. A naval treaty resulted in decreasing the navies of the great powers with provisions for scrapping many ships already built or then in the process of construction.

In June 1921, President Harding named former President William Howard Taft as Chief Justice of the U.S. Supreme Court.

1922—Harding approved the Co-Operative Marketing Bill which provided for a system of orderly marketing of farm products, by legalizing cooperative marketing associations for farmers. Further protection was given the farmers through enactment of higher tariffs provided by the Fordney-McCumber Act of 1922, raising rates to the highest in American history.

Harding opposed the leading bankers by demanding Government supervision of foreign loans placed in the American market, as a means of protecting U.S. domestic economic stability; he stood up against the steel industry when he backed the abolition of the 12-hour work day and the 84-hour work week; and he vetoed the so-called McNary-Haugen bill which provided for regimentation of farmers and governmental price fixing of farm products.

1923—Scandal was brewing within the administration when in June 1923, the President and Mrs. Harding, with a large entourage, set forth on an extensive trip to the west coast, including British Columbia and Alaska. On the night of July 28, while returning to San Francisco from Alaska, Harding developed bronchial pneumonia and on August 2, 1923, he died, apparently due to an embolism. Best known for his amiable characteristics, President Harding was mourned as the funeral train brought his body across the country to Washington, for a state funeral which took place on August 8, 1923. Burial took place at Marion, Ohio.

Three Percent Immigration Act—May 19, 1921, 42 Stat. 5.
Establishment of Veteran's Bureau—August 9, 1921, 42 Stat. 147.
Fordney-McCumber Tariff Act—September 21, 1922, 42 Stat. 858.

CALVIN COOLIDGE

Thirtieth President of the United States
August 3, 1923 to March 3, 1929
(No. 129)

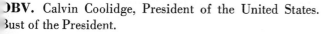

OBV. Calvin Coolidge, President of the United States. Bust of the President.

REV. Inside a stylized wreath of laurel: Inaugurated Aug. 3, 1923 and Mar. 4, 1925. Seated female figure holding fasces, symbol of authority. An heraldic eagle atop the shield of the United States; a cornucopia. 1928.

By John Ray Sinnock

CALVIN COOLIDGE

1872—Coolidge was born on July 4, 1872, in Plymouth, Vt., the son of John C. Coolidge and Victoria T. (Moor) Coolidge, an old New England farming family.

1891—After attendance at Black River and St. Johnsbury Academies, Coolidge entered Amherst; he graduated in 1895, cum laude.

1895—Studied law at the firm of Hammond & Field of Northampton, Mass., and began practicing in 1898.

1899—Elected councilman of Northampton.

1900—Elected city solicitor of Northampton.

1904—Appointed to the county office of clerk of courts. Married Grace Anna Goodhue. They had two sons, the younger dying at the age of 16 from blood poisoning.

1907–08—Served two terms in the General Court of Massachusetts, the legislative body of that State.

1910–11—Served two terms as the mayor of Northampton, becoming known for his coolly efficient, capable, and frugal administration.

1912–15—State senator, and in 1914 and 1915 was elected president of the Massachusetts State Senate.

1916–18—Served three terms as Lieutenant Governor of the State of Massachusetts.

1919–20—Elected Governor of Massachusetts. Again, his administration was marked by efficiency, economy, and determination. When Boston police threatened to strike, Coolidge drew national attention by refusing to yield to them and calling out the State Guard with the statement: "There is no right to strike against the public safety by anybody, anywhere, anytime."

1920—A split in his own Massachusetts delegation to the Republican National Convention denied Coolidge the nomination of the party for President in the deadlocked convention. When Warren G. Harding was nominated, Coolidge became the vice-presidential nominee on the first ballot.

1923—Upon the death of President Harding, Coolidge was sworn into office by his father, a justice of the peace, at the latter's Vermont home early on the morning of August 3, 1923.

After some months in office, Coolidge published a statement of his political views; the simplicity, honesty, and straight-forwardness of the document received wide domestic acclaim. The statement came out against further downward tariff revisions; it advocated a reduction in taxes; it opposed the soldiers' bonus and direct governmental aid to farmers; and it opposed the entrance of the United States into the League of Nations, although it supported the participation of the United States in the World Court.

1924—Coolidge stood firm against the accusations aroused by the Teapot Dome Scandal; he refused to hastily dismiss indicted officials and relied upon personal integrity to weather the storm.

Coolidge was renominated for the Presidency and won the election by a large margin. His Vice President was Charles G. Dawes of Illinois. During the campaign, Coolidge made few speeches, remaining in Washington. He became known for his non-loquaciousness and his conciseness of speech.

1925—On March 4 was inaugurated as President at a time when prosperity began to sweep the country. In all of his administration-sponsored legislation Coolidge fought to reduce waste. He also reduced income taxes and the national debt.

1924–28—At home, Coolidge was unshakeable in his belief that the Government should not interfere with private enterprise. In foreign affairs he stressed American ideals of nonintervention and protection of the Western Hemisphere. A conference between Great Britain, Japan, and the United States was called to limit naval armaments, but it ended in deadlock. However, a plan for repayment of war debts to the United States by foreign powers was agreed upon.

1927—With characteristic brevity and conciseness, President Coolidge announced that he did not plan to run for renomination.

1929—Coolidge retired to Northampton and wrote his *Autobiography*.

1933—President Coolidge died of a sudden heart attack in Northampton, Mass., on January 5, 1933. He lies buried beside his father, wife, and son at Plymouth, Vt.

Reorganization of the Foreign Service—May 24, 1924, 43 Stat. 140.
Immigration Act of 1924—May 26, 1924, 43 Stat. 153.
World War Veterans Act—June 7, 1924, 43 Stat. 607.
Railway Labor Act—May 20, 1926, 44 Stat. 577.

HERBERT CLARK HOOVER

Thirty-first President of the United States
March 4, 1929 to March 3, 1933
(No. 130)

OBV. Herbert Hoover, President of the United States, MCMXXIX. Bust of the President.

REV. Female figure, eagle decoration on bodice, standing between fasces bearing devices symbolic of war and peace. Engineer. Scholar. Statesman. Humanist. Inaugurated March 4, 1929.

By John Ray Sinnock

HERBERT CLARK HOOVER

1874—Born August 10, 1874, a son of the village blacksmith, Jesse Clark and Hildah (Minthorn) Hoover both of long American Quaker ancestry.

His father died when he was 6 years old; his mother died a few years later. Hoover lived with his Uncle

62

Alban on an Iowa farm, and his Uncle Leban in Osage Indian Territory.

1884—Hoover moved to Newberg, Oreg., to attend a Quaker academy and lived with his uncle John Minthorn, a country doctor and a man of wide academic attainments.

1891–95—Entered Leland Stanford University, when this school first opened its doors. Earned his way by working on the Arkansas and U.S. Geological Surveys and as a professor's secretary. Graduated in 1895 with a degree in geology and engineering.

1895–97—Employed as a mining engineer in Colorado and New Mexico. In October 1897, he became associated with the British firm of Bewick, Moreing & Co., handling its gold mining operations in western Australia.

1899–1902—Accepted a position offered by the Chinese Government, as chief engineer of the Chinese Engineering & Mining Co., a large coal mining and cement manufacturing business.

In February 1899, married Lou Henry, daughter of a country banker at Waterloo, Iowa. They were to have two sons, Herbert, Jr., and Allen.

Hoover and his bride reached Peking early in 1899. The following year, during the Boxer Rebellion, they lived through the siege of Tientsin by anti-foreign Chinese. It was here that Hoover first witnessed the tragedy of war, famine and refugees.

After the war, Hoover served as general manager of the Chinese Engineering & Mining Co., until Belgian interests acquired majority control.

1902–8—Hoover was made a junior partner in the London-based mining firm of Bewick, Moreing & Co. Remaining with this firm for some time, and working in the field, Hoover's travels took him around the globe five times.

1908—Hoover returned to America where he hoped to be of service in public life. He organized his own consulting engineering firm which again took him on extensive world travel. He joined the National Republican Club in 1909. During that year he delivered a series of engineering lectures at Columbia and Stanford Universities which were later published under the title, *Principles of Mining*. Three years later he became a trustee of Stanford University.

1914—Hoover was in London when World War I broke out. He was persuaded by the American Ambassador to England, to organize and direct the American Committee in London. Its purpose was to help thousands of stranded Americans, who had come in from all over Europe, to return to the United States.

1914–20—Hoover's career as an engineer having ended, he had now entered what he later called "the slippery road of public life." His next service was as head of the American Commission for Relief in Belgium and Northern France. This commission disbursed over $1.5 billions in feeding and clothing 10 million civilians.

1917–19—When the United States entered the war on April 6, 1917, President Wilson recalled Hoover and appointed him U.S. Food Administrator, a member of the War Trade Council and chairman of the Inter-Allied Food Council. In the meantime, Hoover continued in his unsalaried post of Belgian Relief Administrator.

1918—Following the armistice on November 11, 1918, Hoover combined his duties of U.S. Food Administrator with the new assignment of heading the American Relief Administration. This agency had responsibility for the economic rehabilitation of Europe—a program which fed and clothed over 200 million people. This agency also helped the Russians survive the famine which swept through the Russian Ukraine in 1921–23.

1921–28—Hoover was appointed Secretary of Commerce, serving ably and with distinction under Presidents Harding and Coolidge. Reorganizing the Department of Commerce, Hoover brought new life and importance to this agency in the postwar development of foreign and domestic commerce.

Hoover established an agency, now known as the Business Advisory Council, with leaders of business, labor, and agriculture, to counsel him on board policy matters.

As Secretary of Commerce, and later as President, Hoover spearheaded a program to eliminate waste in many areas of our national economy. Other programs undertaken were better utilization of our water resources for cheaper transportation of commodities; conservation of fuel and labor by an enlarged electrification system; improvement of railway transportation; smoothing of the peaks and valleys of business cycles which caused periodic unemployment and bankruptcy; establishing standards for commercial products; development of pure and scientific research as the foundation of genuine labor-saving devices; and development of agricultural cooperatives, to reduce waste in agricultural distribution.

In 1922, Hoover published his political philosophy in his book, *American Individualism*.

1928—At the Kansas City Republican National Convention, Hoover was nominated for the Presidency on the first ballot. He conducted a dignified campaign, making only seven speeches, in which he declared his dedication to traditional doctrines, equality of opportunity, individual enterprise without governmental interference, and faith in the American economic system. A few weeks after winning an overwhelming victory at the polls, Hoover began a goodwill tour of Central and South America.

1929—A few months after his inauguration as President, Hoover secured authority from the Congress to create the Federal Farm Board. This agency, with a large capital, undertook the task of aiding agriculture by purchasing surpluses, and strengthening cooperatives so as to decrease destructive competition between farmers. The work of this Board was hardly underway when the stock market crash of October 1929 struck the country. This was followed by the European financial panic of 1931. To solve these difficulties, Hoover turned the Board into a depression remedy.

Following the pledge made in his inaugural address, Hoover undertook and achieved substantial success in law enforcement reforms. He improved the quality of judicial appointments, reformed judicial procedures in criminal cases, and bankruptcy proceedings, and he strengthened the Federal Bureau of Investigation headed by his friend, J. Edgar Hoover. He was not so successful in enforcing prohibition. He later stated: "I should have been glad to have humanity forget all about strong alcoholic drinks. They are moral, physical, and economic curses to the race. But in the present stage of human progress, this vehicle of joy could not be generally suppressed by Federal law."

1930—Enacted into law during the Hoover administration was highly controversial legislation known as the Hawley-Smoot Tariff Bill. Hoover held out against fixed tariff rates (the highest in history) and obtained language in the legislation which permitted the administration to apply flexible rates, thus removing tariffs from politics.

Upon the recommendation of the President, the Congress authorized the creation of the Federal Power Commission as an agency "with real teeth," to control water-generated power. The Interstate Commerce Commission was given additional authority to control railroads and their reorganization. Putting them on a sound financial basis was one of the great tasks later undertaken by the Hoover-recommended Reconstruction Finance Corporation.

In 1930, the Congress approved the administration's request for a public works program, one of the largest undertaken up to that time, to condition the blows occasioned by the stock market crash. At the same time, Hoover sought to stimulate private business initiative, and he encouraged humanitarian efforts of local governments and private charities.

Hoover obtained Senate ratification on July 22, 1930, of the London Naval Treaty, limiting armament by world powers.

1931–32—Hoover insisted that foreign countries repay war debts due the United States. However, when the depression hit Europe, he supported a moratorium suspending payments.

A serious foreign crisis developed in September 1931, when Japan invaded Manchuria. On January 7, 1932, Hoover promulgated the "Stimson Doctrine," serving notice to the world that the United States would not recognize territorial conquest.

As for Latin American policy, Hoover reversed the interventionist policies of his predecessors and laid the foundation for the "Good Neighbor Policy."

In 1932, with a deepening depression, Herbert Hoover lost the presidential election to Franklin D. Roosevelt.

1933—Hoover retired to California where he founded the Hoover Library on War, Revolution, and Peace, at Stanford University.

1942—Published two books: *America's First Crusade*, and with Hugh Gibson, *The Problems of Lasting Peace*.

1946—At the request of President Truman, Hoover undertook the mission of making on-the-spot surveys throughout the world, to deal with the postwar famine problem.

1947—On September 29, 1947, Truman appointed Hoover as Chairman of the Commission on Organization of the Executive Branch of the Government, better known as the "Hoover Commission." His task was to recommend ways of simplifying and achieving economies in the executive branch of Government. Two years later, the Commission issued its reports; most of the recommendations made were enacted into law or were otherwise put into effect through presidential administrative action.

1953—President Eisenhower created a second Hoover Commission which also worked on policy matters. Appointed its chairman on July 30, 1953, Hoover stated this would be his last public service. The Commission finished its work in 1955.

1955—Now over 80 years old, Hoover continued to write and occasionally undertake speaking engagements, presenting his views on national and international affairs.

1958—At the age of 83, Hoover published what many regard as his greatest work, *The Ordeal of Woodrow Wilson.*

1961—Hoover's last published work was, *An American Epic.*

1964—President Hoover died in New York City on October 20, 1964.

Agricultural Marketing Act—June 15, 1929, 46 Stat. 11.
Hawley-Smoot Tariff Act—June 17, 1930, 46 Stat. 590.
Reconstruction Finance Corporation Act—January 22, 1932, 47 Stat. 5.
Twentieth Amendment—February 6, 1933, 47 Stat. 745.

FRANKLIN DELANO ROOSEVELT

Thirty-second President of the United States
March 4, 1933 to April 12, 1945
(No. 131)

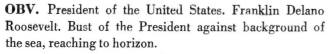

OBV. President of the United States. Franklin Delano Roosevelt. Bust of the President against background of the sea, reaching to horizon.

REV. Seated figure representing a sorrowing Nation, dropping a wreath upon the waters. A ship, symbolizing the spirit of the late President, sails into the distant mist. The palm branch of mourning. The inscription, *For Country and Humanity*, indicates the President's labors for the benefit of all mankind. Dates of inauguration; the rows of crosses signifying that he, also, was a war casualty. Date of death. In lower left field, new leaves are sprouting, representing the dawn of a new era of peace; in exergue, *In Memoriam.*

By John Ray Sinnock.

FRANKLIN DELANO ROOSEVELT

1882—Franklin Delano Roosevelt was born January 30, at Hyde Park, N.Y., the son of James and Sara (Delano) Roosevelt.

James Roosevelt was a wealthy landowner and railroad vice president. He was a direct descendant of a Dutch immigrant who arrived in New Amsterdam about 1649, and a remote cousin of Theodore Roosevelt, 26th President of the United States.

1896—At the age of 14, he entered Groton School, already well spoken in the German and French languages due to private tutoring and wide travel experiences.

1900—He entered Harvard, where he studied literature, history, American politics, and government. He also wrote for "The Crimson" and became editor of the magazine in his senior year.

1904—Having completed his studies at Harvard, he enrolled in the Columbia University School of Law, which he attended until 1907.

1905—On March 17, Roosevelt married Anna Eleanor Roosevelt, his fifth cousin and niece of former President Theodore Roosevelt. They had five children.

1907—Admitted to the New York State bar, after which he began his practice in New York with the firm Carter, Ledyard & Milburn. Began to buy extensive acreage of his own at Hyde Park for farming and forestry experiments.

1910—Roosevelt was nominated to run for the Dutchess County State senatorship on the Democratic ticket. He was elected after a hard campaign.

1912—While in the State Senate, Roosevelt organized support in New York State for Woodrow Wilson's nomination and campaign for the Presidency. Roosevelt's friend, Louis McHenry Howe, an Albany newspaperman, took charge of Roosevelt's own successful campaign for reelection to the State Senate.

1913—Roosevelt accepted the post of Assistant Secretary of the Navy under President Wilson, whereupon he resigned as State Senator. He held this Navy post until 1920.

Began to modernize and expand the Nation's fleet by converting useless Navy yards into industrial plants for making naval supplies. Along with Josephus Daniels, broke up an alleged combination of armor plate manufacturers.

1918—Roosevelt was placed in charge of inspecting the American Naval Forces in European waters and was largely responsible for the North Sea mine barrage which helped break the German submarine menace and shortened World War I.

1918–24—Overseer of Harvard University.

1919—Gained valuable experience handling naval affairs when he attended the Versailles Peace Conference. Returning to the United States with President Wilson, on the *George Washington*, Roosevelt became a convert to peace organization.

1920—Nominated as vice presidential candidate, at the Democratic Convention, to run with John M. Cox. After losing election, he left politics to become the vice president of the Fidelity and Deposit Co. of Maryland and became a member of the Emmet & Marvin law firm.

1921—While staying at Campobello he suffered an attack of poliomyelitis. He was 39 at the time. The attack paralyzed his legs and lower abdomen.

1922–24—Worked at convalescence. Established quarters at Warm Springs, where he became president of the Georgia Warm Springs Foundation.

1924—Formed the law firm of Roosevelt & D. B. O'Conner, with which he was associated until 1933.

Managed Alfred E. Smith's campaign for the Democratic nomination for President. He nominated Smith at the convention, giving the famous "Happy Warrior" speech. Smith lost the nomination.

1928—Now able to walk with the aid of braces and a cane, Roosevelt attended the Democratic National Convention to give, again, the main nominating speech for Alfred E. Smith. This time Smith won the nomination, but lost the election to Herbert Hoover. Roosevelt ran for the Governorship of New York and was elected. While holding this post he started the public development of the St. Lawrence water power and developed an old-age pension system. Reelected Governor in 1930.

1932—Holding their National Convention in Chicago, the Democrats nominated Franklin D. Roosevelt for the Presidency. Roosevelt began a campaign that took him all over the country, building his platform upon the misfortunes of the time, appealing to the "Forgotten Man" in "The Great Depression." He offered a "New Deal" as the only hope of recovery from the depression.

The election was a landslide with Roosevelt carrying all but six States and winning with a plurality of over 7 million.

1933—Roosevelt was inaugurated on March 4, 1933, as President of the United States. Soon after taking office, he delivered his famous "fireside chat" in which he stated: "We have nothing to fear but fear itself."

Roosevelt called a special session of Congress to meet on March 9, 1933. Using authority of the Trading with the Enemy Act of 1917, he declared a national emergency, closing the banks for a "holiday." The new Congress quickly approved the proposed Emergency Banking Act, giving the President broad economic powers—authority to prohibit transactions in gold, to reopen solvent banks, and to appoint "conservators" for others.

The first 100 days of Roosevelt's administration saw enactment of an amazing amount of legislation. Young men were given an opportunity to work on reclamation and National Park projects. (the Civilian Conservation Corps). Matching State and local grants, unemployment relief was provided by the Federal Emergency and Relief Adiminstration and refinancing of mortgages was made possible through the Home Owners Loan Corporation. Recovery measures enacted for the farmer, industry, and labor, were the Agricultural Adjustment Act (AAA) and the National Industrial Recovery Act (NIRA). With the object of raising farm prices, a subsidy was provided to curtail crop production and funds were made available to buy surplusage, until such time as demand could catch up with supplies. As a further means of increasing commodity prices, an amendment to the Agricultural Adjustment Act (the Thomas amendment) gave the President authority to change the content of the gold dollar—the standard unit of value. Under the National Industrial Recovery Act, codes of fair competition were established in each industry; minimum wages and hours were agreed upon, and machinery was provided for collective bargaining.

The Tennessee Valley Authority was organized to provide electrical power to a large area embracing seven States. For the protection of the public investor, the Securities Act of May 27 required that new issues of securities be registered. For the protection of depositors' money, the Glass-Steagall Act separated commercial and investment banking. The Federal Reserve Board was given authority to control interest rates, and insurance of bank deposits, up to $5,000 (later increased) was provided by the Federal Deposit Insurance Corporation.

Additional employment was made possible through an extension of the public works program inaugurated by the Hoover administration.

Prohibition was repealed when ratification of the 21st amendment to the Constitution was completed on December 5, 1933.

1934—President Roosevelt stabilized the content of the gold dollar at 59.06 percent of its former value. To stimulate foreign trade, he obtained authority to negotiate reciprocal trade agreements which were ably handled by Secretary of State, Cordell Hull. These treaties served to further the "Good Neighbor" policy of removing the United States from interference in Latin-American internal affairs.

1935—Following President Roosevelt's message on March 4, 1935, the Congress enacted the administration-proposed Social Security Act providing for unemployment and old-age pension insurance. Employment projects were organized under the Works Project and the National Youth Administrations. Tax revisions were enacted to achieve a wider distribution of wealth. Public utility companies were brought under closer regulation. After the National Industrial Recovery Act was declared unconstitutional (as were many other measures, this year) the National Labor Relations Board was established to handle collective bargaining and to conduct elections of labor representatives.

The threat of war in Europe caused President Roosevelt to strengthen his neutrality policy by seeking legislation, which was enacted in 1935, 1936, and 1937, prohibiting Americans from furnishing money or munitions to foreign belligerents and refused protection to Americans sailing on belligerent's ships. This legislation was superseded by the Neutrality Act of 1939.

1936—Roosevelt was reelected to the Presidency.

1937—In accordance with the 20th amendment to the Constitution, Roosevelt was inaugurated on January 20, instead of March 4.

To speed decisions on constitutional issues, the President proposed that the cases involved be referred directly to the Supreme Court, without consideration in the lower courts, and that the Supreme Court be enlarged to provide "new blood." The Judiciary Procedure Reform Bill, which was enacted, did not make any provision for a change in the number of judges to sit on the bench of the Supreme Court. (By the end of 1942, Roosevelt had replaced every member on the Supreme Court, except two.)

When Japan invaded North China, Roosevelt warned of international lawlessness, urged that positive efforts be made to preserve peace, and asked for a "quarantine of aggressor nations."

1938—A second Agricultural Adjustment Act was passed, the first such act having been declared unconstitutional, as a means of controlling surplus crops. This permitted farmers to place surpluses in graineries, under Government seal, and to receive loans on them until sold at parity prices determined upon by the Government.

The Fair Labor Standards Act was passed, seeking an ultimate 40 hour workweek and a minimum work rate of 40 cents an hour.

1939—In his annual message to the Congress in January 1939, President Roosevelt urged repeal of the arms embargo. Enacted later that year, after the outbreak of war between Germany on the one hand and Poland, France and Great Britain on the other, the Neutrality Act of 1939 made it possible for the United States to supply arms to its friends on a "cash and carry" basis.

Ordering a study of American war capacity, Roosevelt moved ahead to build U.S. strength and make this country "an arsenal for democracy."

1940—Roosevelt took major executive action to aid the British, then undergoing a blitz from the Germans, and the French, whose country had fallen to the Germans. Partly in return for 50 World War I destroyers, the British granted naval and air bases to the United States in British possessions stretching from Newfoundland to South America. Military aircraft built for the United States were leased back to the manufacturers so they could be sold to the British.

At home, to achieve bipartisan support, Roosevelt appointed two Republicans—Henry L. Stimson to serve as Secretary of War and Frank Knox to serve as Secretary of the Navy. A National Defense Commission was established; the Selective Service Act was passed and the Office of Production Management was established.

Breaking tradition, Roosevelt ran for a third term. Though encountering strong opposition from the Republicans candidate, Wendell Wilkie, Roosevelt won the election.

1941—Inaugurated as President, Roosevelt's third (and his fourth) administration is the story of the United States as a nation at war. In his inaugural address he asked for additional aid to our allies, their cash and credit having been exhausted. In March 1941, the Lend Lease Act started the flow of war materials and services to our allies which eventually totaled $50 billion.

German advances on the European continent enabled Roosevelt to gain legislative authority to freeze enemy assets in the United States and to install U.S. Armed Forces in Greenland and Iceland. American destroyers patrolled North Atlantic waters and merchant ships were armed with orders from the President to "shoot on sight" any threatening craft.

In August 1941, Roosevelt met Churchill in Argentia Bay off Newfoundland and drafted the Atlantic Charter (a document which grew in importance after 26 nations later signed it as part of the United Nations Declaration) pledging economic equality to all nations, victors and vanquished, in the postwar period, together with abandonment of the use of force as a matter of national policy.

On December 6, 1941, President Roosevelt sent a personal peace message to Emperor Hirohito. The following day, "a day that will live in infamy," the Japanese attack on Pearl Harbor, plunged the United States into the war. Four days later, Germany and Italy declared war on the United States, followed by U.S. declarations the same day, December 11.

Two weeks after the Japanese attack on Pearl Harbor, Roosevelt and Churchill met in Washington to organize and combine Anglo-American economies and military planning and the joint administration of many war activities.

1942—At home, Roosevelt placed the Nation on a war-time basis, seeking and obtaining legislation to create the War Production Board, the National War Labor Board, the War Shipping Board, the War Manpower Commission, the Pacific War Council and the Office of War Information. Early in 1942 the Price Control Act became law.

Roosevelt's "Good Neighbor" policy, of many years standing, led to all the Central and South American States (except Argentina) breaking diplomatic relations with the Axis powers and their offer of manpower and material to the Allied cause.

Of immense psychological value was Roosevelt's declaration, in October 1942, that there would be a tribunal to investigate war crimes and criminals. This led to the postwar Nuremberg trials and the prosecution of the Japanese warlords.

1943—A series of joint conferences between Roosevelt and Churchill, together with other allied heads of state took place this year.

Meetings with Henri H. Giraud and Charles de Gaulle at Casablanca, French Morocco, on January 14–24, resulted in a declaration that World War II would end only with the unconditional surrender of the Axis States.

The Quebec Conference in August 1943, with Foreign Minister T. V. Soong of China, resulted in establishment of a unified Allied Command under Lord Louis Mountbatten in the China-Burma-India Theater of Operations. Limited recognition was given to Charles de Gaulle's French Committee of National Liberation and approval was given to Allied military plans for a landing in Normandy, France.

The Cairo Conference with Generalissimo Chiang Kai-shek of China resulted in a joint declaration foreswearing territorial ambitions and pledging continuation of the war in the Pacific until the Japanese gave an unconditional surrender. The agreement also provided that Korea was to receive its independence "in due course."

The conference held at Teheran, November 28–December 1, 1943, was the first three-power conference attended by Stalin. Agreement was reached on military strategy and tactics to be directed against Germany, including plans for the Allied invasion of France. Soviet forces were pledged for the fight against Germany, after the defeat of Japan. The conference released a statement expressing the need for meeting the problems of peace through a proposed new world body, the United Nations.

1944—In June, the Allies invaded Germany occupied Normandy and by the end of August most of France was occupied by Allied Forces.

In August 1944, at Dumbarton Oaks in Washington, D.C., the United States, the U.S.S.R., China, and Great Britain met and agreed upon a charter for a permanent international organization and for the maintenance of world peace and security—the United Nations.

At the Second Quebec Conference held in September, Roosevelt and Churchill agreed upon broad issues of war strategy and discussed plans for the future of Germany.

Roosevelt was reelected for a fourth term, along with Harry S. Truman as Vice President, after a campaign opposing Thomas E. Dewey, Governor of New York and John Bricker, Governor of Ohio.

1945—From February 4 to 11, at Yalta in the Crimea, Roosevelt, Churchill, and Stalin agreed upon demands for the unconditional surrender of Germany and dividing it into four zones of occupation (American, British, French, and Russian) under the unified Central Commission in Berlin. The conferees also agreed upon inviting China and France to join them in sponsoring the founding conference of the United Nations at San Francisco on April 25, 1945.

President Roosevelt died suddenly on April 12, 1945 at Warm Springs, Ga., not quite a month before Germany surrendered to the Allies. He was buried on the family estate at Hyde Park, most of which he donated to the Nation.

Emergency Bank Acts—March 9, 1933, 48 Stat. 1; June 15, 1933, 48 Stat. 147.

Agricultural Adjustment Act—May 12, 1933, 48 Stat. 51.
Tennessee Valley Authority (TVA)—May 18, 1933, 48 Stat. 58.
Gold Repeal Joint Resolution—June 5, 1933, 48 Stat. 112.
Employment Service Act—June 6, 1933, 48 Stat. 113.
Home Owners Loan Act—June 13, 1933, 48 Stat. 128.
Glass-Steagall (Federal Deposit Insurance) Act—June 16, 1933, 48 Stat. 56.
National Industrial Recovery Act—June 16, 1933, 48 Stat. 195.
Twenty-first Amendment—December 5, 1933, 47 Stat. 1625.
Philippine Independence Act—March 24, 1934, 48 Stat. 456.
Securities and Exchange Act—June 6, 1934, 48 Stat. 881.
Reciprocal Trade Agreement Act—June 12, 1934, 48 Stat. 943.
National Housing Act—June 27, 1934, 48 Stat. 1246.
National Labor Relations Act—July 5, 1935, 49 Stat. 449.
Social Security Act—August 14, 1935, 49 Stat. 620.
Neutrality Resolution—August 31, 1935, 49 Stat. 1081.
Soil Conservation Act—February 29, 1936, 49 Stat. 1148.
"Pump Priming Act"—June 21, 1938, 52 Stat. 809.
Fair Labor Standards Act—June 25, 1938, 52 Stat. 1060.
Neutrality Revision Act—November 4, 1939, 54 Stat. 7.
Selective Service Act—September 16, 1940, 54 Stat. 885.
Lend Lease Act—March 11, 1941, 55 Stat. 31.
Selective Service Extension Act—August 18, 1941, 55 Stat. 626.
Repeal of Neutrality Act of 1939—November 17, 1941, 55 Stat. 764.
Declaration of a State of War with Japan—December 8, 1941, 55 Stat. 795.
Declaration of a State of War with Germany—December 11, 1941, 55 Stat. 796-7.
Emergency Price Control Act—January 30, 1942, 56 Stat. 23.
Second War Powers Act—March 27, 1942, 56 Stat. 176.
"GI Bill of Rights" Act—June 22, 1944, 58 Stat. 284.
War Mobilization and Reconversion Act—October 3, 1944, 58 Stat. 785.

HARRY S. TRUMAN

Thirty-third President of the United States
April 12, 1945 to January 20, 1953
(No. 132)

OBV. President of the United States. Harry S. Truman. Bust of the President.

By John Ray Sinnock.

REV. View of the south portico of the White House, after reconstruction, showing balcony; Presidential Seal. Inaugurated April 12, 1945. January 20, 1949.

By Gilroy Roberts.

HARRY S. TRUMAN

1884—Born at Lamar, Barton County, Mo., on May 8, 1884, the son of John Anderson and Martha Ellen (Young) Truman.

1888—The Truman family moved to Grandview, and later to Independence, Mo., where Truman attended public schools; worked for the *Kansas City Star* (1901).

1906–17—After working for a railroad and two banks, Truman returned to a rural life, operating the family farm at Grandview.

1911—Honorably discharged as a corporal in the National Guard, with which he had been associated since 1905.

1917–19—Attended the Field Artillery School at Fort Sill, Okla.; commissioned a first lieutenant in the Missouri National Guard, serving in Battery F and, later, as a captain in Battery D of the 129th Field Artillery, 35th Division, American Expedi-

tionary Force in France. He took part in the Vosges, St. Mihiel, and Meuse-Argonne offensives August 18 to November 11, 1918. Was discharged with the rank of major, U.S.A.R.C. May 6, 1919; in 1927 was commissioned a colonel, Field Artillery Reserve.

Married Elizabeth (Bess) Wallace, a schoolteacher. They had one child, Mary Margaret.

Established a clothing store in downtown Kansas City and participated in civic politics.

1922–34—Was elected judge of the Jackson County Court; attended the Kansas City School of Law; reelected to the court; elected presiding judge in 1926 and reelected in 1930. This court, an administrative, rather than a judicial body, enabled Truman to accomplish a great deal, especially in the construction of public roads and buildings.

1934—Elected to the U.S. Senate from Missouri and reelected in 1940. While in the Senate, Truman served on a number of committees: Appropriations, Enrolled Bills, Military Affairs, Printing, Interstate Commerce, and Public Buildings and Grounds. He was one of the authors of the Civil Aeronautics Act of 1938 and the Railroad Transportation Act of 1940.

National attention was directed to Truman for his efficiency and inflexible honesty when he served as chairman of the Special Committee to Investigate the National Defense Program. The economies he promoted are estimated at over $15 billion. At all times he sought to protect the interests of the small businessman and the wage earner.

1944-45—Truman was elected Vice President of the United States on November 4, and took office January 20, 1945. He acceded to the Presidency on the death of Franklin D. Roosevelt on April 12, 1945.

1945—The founding United Nations Conference at San Francisco was opened with a speech which Truman delivered by telephone on April 25.

At 9 a.m. on the morning of May 8, 1945, President Truman spoke from the White House, proclaiming the unconditional surrender of Germany and the end of the war in Europe.

Meeting with Churchill and Stalin at Potsdam from July 17 to August 2, 1945, Truman undertook joint discussions on political and diplomatic problems related to Europe and Asia. While en route to the conference the President was informed of the successful testing of the atom bomb. On July 26 Truman released a joint communique, now known as the Potsdam Declaration, calling for the unconditional surrender of Japan and announcing that "the only alternative for Japan is prompt and utter destruction."

Failure of the Japanese to surrender and to minimize further combat losses of American lives, President Truman made the historic decision to use the atom bomb. The first bomb was dropped on Hiroshima August 5, 1945, followed by the second bomb on Nagasaki on August 9. A day later, by radio, the Japanese broadcast their intention to surrender on the basis of terms set forth in the Potsdam Declaration. The Acts of Surrender were formally signed on September 2, 1945.

The postwar famine which developed in Europe prompted Truman to secure funds to finance a food supply program, undertaken by the Relief and Rehabilitation Commission of the United Nations.

Truman announced in 1945 the intention of the United States to prevent the use of atomic energy for destructive purposes but expressed this country's willingness to promote the use of this vast new source of energy "for peaceful and humanitarian ends" under proper safeguards.

On September 6, 1945, 4 days after V-J Day, President Truman sent to the Congress a 21-point program on domestic legislation which constituted the platform of his administration and marked the beginning of the "Fair Deal." Much of the legisla-

tion requested was not enacted until Truman's second administration of the Presidency.

1946—Early in 1946, Truman advocated statehood for Hawaii and Alaska, self determination for Puerto Rico, and more self-government for the Virgin Islands. On July 4, he proclaimed the independence of the Philippines.

Under Truman's leadership, the United States began to abandon its policy of friendly conciliation with the Soviets and to take a strong stand against Communist expansion in France, Italy, Turkey, and Iran.

On December 31, 1946, an act signed by the President placed the top management of atomic research and development in the United States in the hands of a civilian agency, the Atomic Energy Commission.

1947—The tragedy of Pearl Harbor, as well as purposes of efficiencies which could be obtained by a single department of the Armed Forces led Truman to achieve legislation which he had previously requested. The National Security Act of 1947 placed the Army, Navy, and Air Force under the new U.S. Department of Defense, charged with full responsibility for armed national security.

Early in 1947, Truman blocked Soviet expansion by providing military assistance to Turkey and Greece and offering to help any other country threatened by Communist aggression. Known as the "Truman Doctrine," this became American policy—a radical departure from traditional isolationism.

Truman obtained a change in the presidential succession law to provide for contingencies if the President or Vice President should die or become incapacitated.

Recalled by Truman from private life, Herbert Hoover performed another of his great public services by heading a commission to study and make recommendations for reorganization of the executive branch of Government. Most of its recommendations were enacted into law or were carried out by executive action.

The President secured legislation from the Congress which authorized the United States to participate in the International Refugee Organization. Making a "good neighbor" trip in August 1947, Truman met with heads of 20 Western Hemisphere countries in Rio de Janeiro, Brazil, which resulted in a pact for mutual assistance, should any aggression be made on an American nation, whether by an outside power or by signatories to the treaty.

1948—With bipartisan support of the Congress, the President obtained legislation to help the European nations rebuild their war-torn economies. In April 1948, the first of several appropriations was made, eventually totaling $13 billion, to place the mutual aid program into effect. Known as the Marshall Plan, after its author, Gen. George C. Marshall, this program is responsible for a postwar reconstruction of European economies which raised their gross national product well above prewar levels. The Soviets refused to participate in the program. In his *Memoirs*, Truman stated: "The Marshall Plan will go down in history as one of America's greatest contributions to the peace of the world. I think the world now realizes that without the Marshall Plan it would have been difficult for Western Europe to remain free from the tyranny of Communism."

On February 2, 1948, Truman sent a 10-point civil rights message to Congress which, in general, received a less than enthusiastic reception.

When the Russians closed the Berlin borders, Truman made the decision to maintain U.S. rights to the Allied portions of that city by assigning all planes of the American European Command to a continuing airlift.

After a vigorous whistle stop campaign throughout the country in the fall of 1948, Truman was re-elected to the Presidency, to the surprise of many who had predicted a victory for his opponent, Thomas E. Dewey, Governor of New York.

1949—In his inaugural address President Truman announced his famous "Point Four" foreign policy program: Technical aid to underdeveloped countries, unfaltering support of the United Nations, continuation of the Marshall Plan, and a strengthened military basis for non-Communist countries to withstand Soviet aggression.

In his State of the Union Message to the Congress, the President advanced 24 proposals for a broad domestic program called the "Fair Deal."

In the spring of 1949, Truman put into effect a program (the Brannan Plan) whereby farm commodities were left to find their own price level on the market, the consumer paying less for his food, while the Government subsidized the producer by making up the difference through parity support prices.

The Congress approved an administration-sponsored low cost public housing bill, enacted as the National Housing Act of 1949. Under this law, Federal grants were made to redevelop slum centers in urban areas throughout the country.

On June 11, 1948, the Senate approved a resolution proposed by the President, as a further deterrent to the spread of communism, to participate in a program providing for the military security of Europe. An alliance was signed in Washington on April 4, 1949, whereupon the North Atlantic Treaty Organization came into existence. The funding for the U.S. share of costs of this new body was provided by the Mutual Defense Assistance Act. A single NATO defense force was established with Gen. Dwight D. Eisenhower as Supreme Commander, and American troops were committed to Europe as part of the NATO Forces.

1950—In June 1950, the Congress gave the President authority to help underdeveloped countries. Industrial and scientific technicians were sent to 27 countries to work on food supply problems, prevent disease, provide basic and vocational education, improve transportation, build dams, and work on a variety of other projects.

Failure to achieve international agreement on the control of nuclear fission and an atomic explosion accomplished by Russia in 1949 led Truman to maintain superiority in the armament race by ordering construction of an H bomb—a bomb many times more powerful than an atomic bomb.

President Truman's last few years in the White House were absorbed by the problems of the civil war in China and the establishment of a provisional Chinese Government on Formosa under the leadership of Chiang Kai-shek. His last great stand against Communist aggression led to the deployment of U.S. troops in Korea, which were later joined with United Nations Forces. (The Korean armistice, signed July 27, 1953, preserved the independence of South Korea at the 38th parallel.)

The rebuilding of the White House began in 1950, after President Truman observed threats to the safety of the occupants. During the reconstruction the President and his family moved to the Blair House until March 1952, when the work was completed.

1952—On March 29, 1952, at the Jefferson-Jackson Day dinner in Washington, D.C., the President advised the Nation he would leave public office.

1953—The President and Mrs. Truman retired to their home in Independence, Mo.

Bretton Woods Agreement Act—July 31, 1945, 59 Stat. 512.
United Nations Participation Act of 1945—December 20, 1945, 59 Stat. 619.
Full Employment Act of 1946—February 20, 1946, 60 Stat. 23.
Authorization of the British Loan Act—July 15, 1946, 60 Stat. 535.
Provision for membership of the United States in UNESCO—July 30, 1946, 60 Stat. 712.

Atomic Energy Control Act—August 1, 1946, 60 Stat. 755.

Legislative Reorganization Act of 1946—August 2, 1946, 60 Stat. 812.

Veterans' Emergency Housing Act of 1946—May 22, 1946, 60 Stat. 207.

Greek-Turkish Aid Act—May 22, 1947, 61 Stat. 103.

Foreign Relief Act—May 31, 1947, 61 Stat. 125–128.

The Taft-Hartley Labor Management Relations Act of 1947—June 23, 1947, 61 Stat. 136–162.

The Presidential Succession Act—July 18, 1947, 61 Stat. 380.

National Security Act of 1947 (Armed Services Unification), 61 Stat. 495–610.

Presidential Tenure Constitutional Amendment—Signed by Speaker of House and President pro tem of Senate, March 24, 1947, 80th Congress, 1st Session. Went into effect February 26, 1951, with Nevada's ratification.

Foreign Aid Act (aid to Austria, China, France, and Italy)—December 17, 1947, 61 Stat. 934–939.

Civil Service Retirement Amendments of 1948—February 28, 1948, 62 Stat. 48.

Displaced Persons Act—June 25, 1948, 62 Stat. 1009.

Reorganization Act—June 25, 1949, 63 Stat. 203.

Fair Labor Standards Amendments of 1949—October 26, 1949, 63 Stat. 90.

National Science Foundation Act—May 10, 1950, 64 Stat. 149.

Foreign Economic Assistance Act (including Point Four program)—June 5, 1950, 64 Stat. 198.

Social Security Act Amendments of 1950—August 28, 1950, 64 Stat. 477.

Defense Production Act of 1950—September 8, 1950, 64 Stat. 798.

Internal Security Act of 1950—September 23, 1950, 64 Stat. 987.

Revision of the Immigration and Naturalization Law—June 27, 1952 (Public Law 414) (McCarran Act).

DWIGHT DAVID EISENHOWER

Thirty-fourth President of the United States
January 20, 1953 to January 20, 1961
(No. 134)

OBV. Dwight D. Eisenhower. Bust of the President. By Gilroy Roberts.

REV. The figure of Freedom, atop the U.S. Capitol. Four allegorical figures representing Plenty, Industry, Chemistry, and Commerce. Atoms for Peace. The Shield of the United States. Inaugurated President of the United States. Second Term January 20, 1957.

By E. von Hebel.

DWIGHT DAVID EISENHOWER

1890—Born October 14, in Denison, Tex., the son of David Jacob and Ida Elizabeth (Stover) Eisen-hower. He was of German Mennonite stock. His forebears left the Rhineland in the 1780's because of religious persecution, to settle in Pennsylvania. His grandfather, Jacob Eisenhower, a leader of the River Brethren Sect of Mennonites, migrated to Kansas in 1878.

When Dwight Eisenhower was a year old, his father took the family to Abilene, Kans., where he grew to manhood. The father, a deeply religious man, worked as a mechanic; his mother was a person of strong pacifist convictions.

1910—After graduation from Abilene High School, Eisenhower received a senatorial appointment to West Point in 1910. He was an outstanding football player for Army until injured in the Carlisle-Tufts game in 1912. He ended his Military Academy studies 61st in the 1915 class of 164 and 95th in deportment.

Commissioned a second lieutenant of infantry, Eisenhower was assigned to the 19th U.S. Infantry Regiment at Fort Sam Houston, San Antonio, Tex.

1916—Married Mamie Geneva Doud, in Denver, Colo. They had two sons; the first child, Dwight Doud, dying of scarlet fever in infancy; the other son, John Sheldon Doud Eisenhower, now serving as U.S. Ambassador to Belgium.

1918—At the age of 27, he was placed in command of Camp Colt, Gettysburg, Pa., a tank training center, where he developed a strong interest in the potentialities of tank warfare. He held the permanent rank of captain and was soon advanced to the temporary rank of lieutenant colonel. Received orders for overseas duty, which were canceled due to the Armistice. Was later awarded a distinguished service medal in recognition of his Camp Colt service, one of the few young officers awarded the medal for service within the United States.

After World War I, Eisenhower reverted to the permanent rank of captain, but was later promoted to major and held that rank for 16 years.

1919–22—Assigned to Camp Meade, Md.; graduated from Infantry Tank School. Assigned to the Panama Canal Zone.

1925–26—Assigned to the Command and General Staff School at Fort Leavenworth, Kans., the key command school of the U.S. Army, where he graduated first in his class of 275.

1928–29—Assigned to the American Battle Monuments Commission. During this time he studied the battlefields of World War I, and mastered the terrain, road net, and towns from the Bay of Biscay to the Rhine. He prepared a guidebook to American battlefields in France which was to remain an excellent reference work on World War I. In 1944, when planning the invasion of Europe, he was thus uniquely prepared for the solution of tactical and strategic problems.

Was graduated from the Army War College in Washington, D.C.

In July 1928 he sailed for France and revised the guidebook, becoming more familiar with the European terrain.

1929–33—On November 8, Eisenhower served as assistant executive officer in the Office of the Assistant Secretary of War in Washington, D.C., where he was concerned with military supply procurement. He worked directly with industry, surveying sources of raw materials, analyzing labor and transport problems, and helped to establish the Army Industrial College, which he himself attended.

1933–35—Assigned to Office of Chief of Staff, U.S. Army, Washington, D.C.

1935—In September 1935, Eisenhower sailed for the Philippines, to serve under General MacArthur, as assistant military advisor to the Commonwealth, which was then preparing for independence.

While in the Philippines, he helped to develop a defense plan, to found a military academy and organize, train, and equip the first Philippine Army and reserve force.

On December 12, 1939, the President of the Philippines, Manuel L. Quezon, awarded Eisenhower the Distinguished Service Star of the Philippines.

1940–41—Eisenhower returned to troop duty, first as executive officer of the 15th Infantry Regiment at Fort Ord, Calif., and Fort Lewis, Wash.; then as Chief of Staff of the 3d Division and, later, IX Corps.

1941—As Chief of Staff, 3d Army, Eisenhower was one of the organizers of Army maneuvers in a 30,000 square mile area of Louisiana. Here a half million troops staged the greatest peacetime "war" in Army history. The overwhelming victory of the 3d Army was attributed to the strategy conceived and directed by Eisenhower. Having been promoted to Colonel on March 11, 1941, he became a brigadier General on September 29.

1941–42—A week after the attack on Pearl Harbor, Eisenhower reported to Washington. During the next 2 months, the chief responsibility, assigned to him by Chief of Staff, Gen. George C. Marshall, was to develop plans to limit Japanese conquests in the Pacific. Additionally, he was to prepare for recovery of overrun areas, while strengthening the Pacific, Caribbean, and Atlantic defenses of the United States.

On February 16, 1942, Eisenhower became head of the War Plans Division, War Department General Staff, and on March 9, he headed the Operations Division, a new agency designed to develop strategic information and to execute command decisions of the chief of staff.

In May 1942, Eisenhower was sent to England to study possibilities of opening a second front in Europe. Following his personal report to authorities, he was appointed Commanding General of all American Forces allocated to the European areas. He left in June to assume command.

Appointed lieutenant general, Eisenhower commanded allied forces, landing in North Africa, November 8, 1942.

1943—Eisenhower was promoted to the rank of full general. By May 13, 1943, all resistance in North Africa had ceased; 240,000 enemy troops had been captured.

Opened an amphibious assault on Sicily on July 10, 1943, which was concluded on August 17, with the fall of Messina and the escape of the German garrison across the Strait of Messina under cover of darkness. Plans for an immediate attack on Italy were delayed by negotiations for surrender by the Italian Government.

On September 3, Gen. Bernard Montgomery shipped two British divisions across the Strait of Messina. On September 9, American troops, in an amphibious assault, landed at Salerno. By December the southern areas had been completely cleared. Eisenhower's headquarters were then established at Naples.

On December 24, 1943, President Roosevelt announced that General Eisenhower had been promoted to Supreme Commander of the Allied Expeditionary Forces. He was given the responsibility of directing the final assault to liberate France and to compel the unconditional surrender of Germany.

1944—Eisenhower planned and coordinated land, sea, and air invasion of the cross-channel invasion of Europe, which took place on June 6, 1944, with landings on Normandy. The enemy was caught by surprise as American and British troops, after sea and air bombardment of German fortifications, poured ashore from the east coast of the Contentin Peninsula to the mouth of the Orne River, while two American divisions of paratroopers and one British division landed behind German lines.

The breaking through of the American forces at St. Lô on July 25, and the encirclement of the counterattacking Germans in early August brought rapid liberation to France.

On August 25, the German force in Paris surrendered.

Eisenhower was appointed General of the Army (temporary), December 20, 1944.

1944–45—Hitler threw his last offensive at the Allies in December, 1944, in the Ardennes. The attack was beaten back and crushed. After this, the Allied forces crossed the Rhine River in March 1945, and overran Germany beyond the Elbe.

Eisenhower accepted the unconditional surrender of Germany at Rheims on May 8, 1945.

Following brief visits to the United Kingdom, the United States, and Russia, Eisenhower served as Commander of the U.S. occupation forces in Germany. He was called home to become Chief of Staff of the U.S. Army on November 19, 1945. He held this post until February 1948, during which time he was given the permanent rank of General of the Army.

Eisenhower's own account of the Allied defeat of Germany appears in his book, *Crusade in Europe.*

1948—In May 1948, Eisenhower moved to New York City where he was installed as president of Columbia University. He began the university's first new building project since 1933 and organized a study group on human resources. He instituted a forum for the examination of public issues free from partisan pressures, the Education Citizenship program, and the Institute for War and Peace studies, devoted to the examination of the causes of war and means for their correction.

1950—On December 18, President Truman appointed General Eisenhower as Supreme Allied Commander, Europe, to integrate the defenses of the North Atlantic Treaty nations. Eisenhower took temporary leave from Columbia and opened NATO headquarters in France.

1952—In 1948, both the Republicans and the Democrats had sought to persuade Eisenhower to run for the Presidency, but he declined and his name was not placed in nomination by either party. In 1952, he let it be known that he was a Republican, and yielded to demands that his name be entered as a candidate for the Presidency.

In June 1952, Eisenhower returned to the United States, retired from the Army and conducted an active campaign. In a bitter convention fight Eisenhower was nominated over Senator Robert A. Taft of Ohio. On November 4, 1952, Eisenhower was elected President, and took the oath of office on January 20, 1953.

1953—The new administration found the country prosperous, but anxious about its foreign policy. Eisenhower's principal foreign difficulties, like those of his predecessor, concerned relations with Communist Russia and China. After almost 2 years of discussion between American and North Korean negotiators, a truce in Korea was signed late in July 1953.

In December 1953, President Eisenhower proposed his "Atoms-for-Peace" program, inviting the Soviets to join the United States in contributing part

335-478 O - 69 - 6

of its atomic stockpile to an international pool for peaceful purposes. This led to the establishment of the United Nations Atomic Energy Agency.

In the field of domestic affairs Eisenhower's first year was spent largely in studying the difficult problems before him relating to labor, agriculture, taxation, conservation, and defense. In 1953, the new Department of Health, Education, and Welfare was created.

1954—When French Indochina was threatened by communism in 1954, Eisenhower played a leading role in establishing the Southeast Asia Treaty Organization (SEATO). Established on September 8, 1954, by Australia, France, New Zealand, Pakistan, the Philippines, Thailand, the United Kingdom, and the United States, SEATO's mission provides for collective defense and economic cooperation in Southeast Asia.

At the President's request, the Congress approved an overall revision in the tax structure, eliminating the excess profits tax, reducing the income tax, and removing other inequalities in the treatment of taxpayers.

Following a partnership agreement reached by the Canadian and U.S. heads of state, construction on the St. Lawrence Seaway started in the summer of 1954.

In the fall elections of 1954, a Democratic House and Senate were elected. Although defeated on some measures in Congress, Eisenhower obtained action on a portion of his legislative program.

1955—When the Federal Republic of West Germany became a sovereign state on May 5, 1955, President Eisenhower signed an order ending its occupation by U.S. troops, and was one of the sponsors for inclusion of the new republic, as a strengthening force, in the North Atlantic Treaty Organization.

As top negotiator for the United States, Eisenhower offered his "open skies" proposal at a summit meeting with France, Great Britain, and the U.S.S.R. at Geneva. However, the Soviets rejected the proposal of an international aerial inspection system, which would serve as a basis for world disarmament.

1956—On July 22, President Eisenhower and heads of 18 other Western Hemisphere states, signed the Principles of Organization of the American States, outlined in the Declaration of Panama City.

The President balanced the Federal budget, and the gross national product rose from a rate of $345 to $413 billion.

On August 22, Eisenhower was unanimously renominated by the Republican National Convention in San Francisco, as their presidential standard bearer. Running against Adlai E. Stevenson, again, he defeated him by an even greater margin than in 1952. However, the Democrats captured the Congress, as they did again in 1958.

In October 1956, the Soviets violently squelched an uprising in Hungary. Eisenhower strongly protested against their intervention and he led the United States in the decisive role of securing United Nations condemnation of that action.

The Middle East crisis in 1956 prompted Eisenhower to take a stand both against Egypt's unilateral nationalization of the Suez Canal, and against the invasion of Egypt by Israel, France, and Great Britain later that year.

1957—President Eisenhower appeared before a joint session of the Congress on January 5, to urge adoption of a program (the Eisenhower Doctrine) to provide increased economic aid to Middle East countries and authority to use military forces, if necessary, to prevent communist aggression in that area.

The President established a Commission on Civil Rights, under newly enacted authority, to investigate any denial of equal rights, especially of the right to vote, regardless of color, race, religion, or national origin.

On September 24, 1957, Eisenhower sent Federal troops to Little Rock, Ark., to enforce a Federal court-ordered school integration decision.

1958—Under the Eisenhower Doctrine, U.S. troops were sent to Lebanon in July 1958, to forestall a possible overthrow of the Lebanese Government, by outside forces. U.S. troops were withdrawn, the following month, after calm was restored. (In the course of his presidency, Eisenhower also prevented communistic efforts to dominate Iran, Guatemala, Formosa, and South Vietnam.)

1959—President Eisenhower was host to Soviet Premier Khrushchev who made a transcontinental tour of the United States.

Also, in 1959, Alaska and Hawaii achieved statehood.

1960—Plans of President Eisenhower to attend a summit conference at Paris were cancelled because of the U-2 reconnaissance plane incident.

1961—On January 3, 1961, President Eisenhower broke diplomatic relations with Cuba.

Eisenhower relinquished the Presidency on January 20, 1961.

With the aid of his own party and that of the "loyal opposition" in the Congress, Eisenhower has a record of other important achievements not otherwise noted above:

Initiation, and the greatest progress of any nation in an ambitious road program.

Slowing up and practically eliminating inflation.

Initiation of space program with successful orbits in less than 3 years, starting from scratch.

Initiating a strong ballistic missile program.

Conceiving and building the Polaris program.

Starting Federal medical care for the aged (Kerr-Mills Act).

Desegregation in Washington, D.C., and the Armed Forces.

Fighting for responsible fiscal and financial policies throughout 8 years.

Extension of old age survivors insurance to over 10 million persons.

Intelligent application of Federal aid to education (defense educational bill).

Preservation, for the first time in American history, of adequate military establishment after cessation of war.

Goodwill journeys to more than a score of nations in Europe, Asia, Africa, South Africa, and in the Pacific.

Initiation of plan for social progress in Latin America, after obtaining necessary authorization from Congress for $500 million (later called, Alliance for Progress).

Shortly after leaving the presidency, and while taking up residence at Gettysburg, Pa., Eisenhower was restored to the rank he held as a "five star" general.

1969—Gen. Dwight David Eisenhower died on March 28, 1969, in Washington, D.C., after a long and heroic battle against overwhelming illness. Following a simple, solemn state funeral, and mourned by the world, the President's body was taken to Abilene, Kans., for interment in a chapel located on the site of his boyhood farm.

Submerged Lands Act—May 22, 1953, 67 Stat. 29.
Small Business Administration Act—July 30, 1953, 67 Stat. 230.
Farm Credit Act of 1953—August 6, 1953, 67 Stat. 390.
Refugee Relief Act of 1953—August 7, 1953, 67 Stat. 400.
Outer Continental Shelf Lands Act—August 7, 1953, 67 Stat. 462.

United States participation with Canada in development of St. Lawrence Seaway—May 13, 1954, 68 Stat. 92.
Housing Act of 1954—August 2, 1954, 68 Stat. 590.
Internal Revenue Act of 1954—August 16, 1954, 68A Stat. 3.
Communist Control Act of 1954—August 24, 1954, 68 Stat. 775.
Mutual Security Act of 1954—August 26, 1954, 68 Stat. 832.
Atomic Energy Act—August 30, 1954, 68 Stat. 919.
Social Security Amendments of 1954—September 1, 1954, 68 Stat. 1052.
Customs Simplification Act of 1954—September 1, 1954, 68 Stat. 1136.
President authorized to use Armed Forces in defense of Formosa and Pescadores—January 29, 1955, 69 Stat. 7.
Fair Labor Standards Amendments of 1955—August 12, 1955, 69 Stat. 711.
Mutual Security Act of 1956—July 18, 1956, 70 Stat. 555.
Authorized $33.4 billion for 13-year highway construction program—June 29, 1956, 70 Stat. 374.
Agricultural Act of 1956—May 28, 1956, 70 Stat. 188.
Colorado River storage project—April 11, 1956, 70 Stat. 105.
Servicemen's and Veterans' Survivor Benefits Act—August 1, 1956, 70 Stat. 857.
Civil Service Retirement Act Amendments of 1956—July 31, 1956, 70 Stat. 743.
Social Security Amendments of 1956—August 1, 1956, 70 Stat. 807.
Authorizing Economic and Military Cooperation with Nations of Middle East—March 9, 1957, 71 Stat. 5.
Mutual Security Act of 1957—August 14, 1957, 71 Stat. 355.
International Atomic Energy Participation Act—August 28, 1957, 71 Stat. 453.
Civil Rights Act—September 9, 1957, 71 Stat. 634.
To Amend the Immigration and Nationality Act by Revising Quota system—September 11, 1957, 71 Stat. 639.
Federal-Aid Highway Act of 1958—April 16, 1958, 72 Stat. 89.
Mutual Security Authorization Act of 1958—June 30, 1958, 72 Stat. 261.
Admission of the State of Alaska into the Union—July 7, 1958, 72 Stat. 339.
National Aeronautics and Space Act of 1958—July 29, 1958, 72 Stat. 426.
National Defense Education Act of 1958—September 2, 1958, 72 Stat. 1580.
Admission of the State of Hawaii into the Union—March 18, 1959, 73 Stat. 4.
Labor-Management Reporting and Disclosure Act of 1959—September 14, 1959, 73 Stat. 519.
Housing Act of 1959—September 23, 1959, 73 Stat. 654.
Federal Employees Health Benefits Act of 1959—September 28, 1959, 73 Stat. 708.
Civil Rights Act of 1960—May 6, 1960, 74 Stat. 86.
Federal Highway Act of 1960—July 14, 1960, 74 Stat. 522.
Social Security Amendment of 1960—September 13, 1960, 74 Stat. 924.

JOHN FITZGERALD KENNEDY

OBV. John F. Kennedy. Bust of the President.

By Gilroy Roberts.

REV. Inaugurated President January 20, 1961. The Presidential Seal. Burning torches of liberty flank the following excerpt from the President's Inaugural Address:

We shall pay any price, bear any burden, meet any hardship, support any friend, oppose any foe to assure the survival of liberty. John F. Kennedy. January 20, 1961.

By Frank Gasparro.

JOHN FITZGERALD KENNEDY

1917—Born in Brookline, Mass., on May 29, 1917, the son of Joseph P. and Rose (Fitzgerald) Kennedy, of Irish American background.

Attended public schools in Brookline, Mass., and the Choate School at Wallingford, Conn.

1935–40—Studied at the London School of Economics and entered Princeton University in the fall of 1935, but illness forced him to withdraw. Entered Harvard University in the fall of 1936 and graduated in 1940, *cum laude.*

1940–41—Graduate work at Stanford University. Published *Why England Slept*, an extension of his Harvard honors thesis, pointing to the failure of leaders to arouse their countries to the dangers of mounting European tensions.

1941–45—Commissioned as a lieutenant in the U.S. Navy. Served as a PT commander in the South Pacific where he boat was rammed by a Japanese destroyer in August 1943. Was instrumental in guiding 10 of his crew of 12 to safety at a nearby island where they were eventually rescued. Decorated for heroic conduct in saving three lives, Kennedy also received the Purple Heart. In April 1945, he was retired from the service due to disability, with the rank of lieutenant.

1945—As a newspaper correspondent, Kennedy covered the San Francisco United Nations Conference, the Potsdam Conference, and the British elections.

1946–52—At the age of 29, Kennedy was elected in 1946 to the U.S. House of Representatives from the 11th District of Massachusetts, which included densely populated East Boston. As Massachusetts' youngest Congressman in half a century, he broke the record held by his grandfather, John Francis Fitzgerald, who was elected to the Congress at the age of 31. Kennedy was reelected in 1948 and 1950. As a Congressman, Kennedy was especially active in the field of housing, health and labor legislation.

During his 6 years in the House of Representatives, Kennedy served on the Education and Labor Committee, the Subcommittee on Education, the Joint Committee on Labor-Management Relations, and the District of Columbia Committee.

1952–60—Kennedy opposed Henry Cabot Lodge for election in 1952 to the U.S. Senate. Some 70,000 votes as a plurality marked his victory for the term which expired January 3, 1959. He was reelected November 4, 1958, to a 6-year term in the Senate. His committee assignments included: Labor and Public Welfare Committee, Select Committee on Small Business, Select Committee on Improper Activities in the Labor or Management Field, Foreign Relations Committee, and the Joint Economic Committee.

In 1953 John F. Kennedy married Jacqueline Lee Bouvier. They had four children, two of whom died.

1954–55—While recuperating from illness, Kennedy wrote *Profiles in Courage*, which won a Pulitzer Prize.

1956—At the 1956 Democratic National Convention, Mr. Kennedy was an active contender for the nomination to the Vice-Presidency. He lost by a slim margin when the choice was thrown open to the convention.

1959—Kennedy's service on labor committees resulted in his selection as floor manager in the Senate to handle major labor reform bills. He was instrumental in securing passage of the Landrum-Griffin Act of 1959 which insured free and democratic union elections and protection of union members from unreasonable union leader actions.

1960—Prior to the 1960 Democratic National Convention, Kennedy had begun an active bid for the Presidency. On January 2, 1960, he announced his candidacy and stated in part:

> "In the past 40 months I have toured every state in the Union and I have talked to Democrats in all walks of life. My candidacy is therefore based on the conviction that I can win both the nomination and the election. I believe that any Democratic aspirant to this important nomination should be willing to submit to the voters his views, record and competence in a series of primary contests."

Subsequent, Kennedy won presidential primary victories in New Hampshire, Wisconsin, Massachusetts, Pennsylvania, Indiana, West Virginia, Nebraska, and Illinois.

John Kennedy was nominated for the Presidency on the first ballot on July 13, 1960, at the Democratic Convention, and overcame the opposition of some of the most powerful men in the party. The Kennedy organization moved the delegates into what was called "remarkable attainments."

In one of the most intensive and vigorous political campaigns in the history of the Nation, Mr. Kennedy and his Republican opponent, Mr. Richard M. Nixon, took their political philosophies to every corner of the United States.

In his acceptance speech at the convention, Kennedy referred to "The New Frontier" and it was readily accepted as the slogan for his administration. In Kennedy's own words—"It sums up not what I intend to *offer* the American people, but what I intend to *ask* of them."

Mr. Kennedy was elected President on November 8, 1960, and took the oath of office on January 20, 1961. He was the youngest President elected in the Nation's history.

1961—Kennedy devoted his inaugural address to the world crisis, calling for a worldwide struggle against tyranny, poverty, disease, and war. In his first state of the Union message, and in later messages, he proposed to revitalize the economy and to use the Government to combat a host of current problems. His news conferences and public addresses showed a command of information and quick wit.

In April 1961, an invasion of Cuba from the American mainland by Cuban exiles attempting to overthrow the regime of Fidel Castro was crushed. For this, Kennedy assumed personal responsibility.

Kennedy gave the full support of the United States to the United Nations, to prevent a Communist takeover in the Congo; he warned the Soviets against moving into Laos. With a show of force he defied Soviet attempts to force the Allies out of Berlin, and he sent additional aid to South Vietnam.

Through his Treasury Secretary, Douglas Dillon, Kennedy offered U.S. aid for the economic development of Latin America under his Alliance for Progress Program.

Because of the Berlin crisis, and the possibility of deployment of U.S. troops in Southeast Asia, Kennedy strengthened the U.S. military establishment.

In 1961 and 1962, Kennedy traveled to Austria, Bermuda, Britain, Canada, Colombia, France, Mexico, Venezuela, and Brazil to confer with world leaders concerning the international tensions that had arisen since World War II. These years were also eventful because of the emphasis placed by the President on the space program and the successes achieved in that field.

On September 4, 1961, Kennedy signed the Foreign Assistance Act, making substantial changes in the foreign aid program, and establishing the Peace Corps, an organization of volunteers dedicated in their work of providing technical assistance to foreign countries.

1962—In March 1962, President Kennedy reluctantly authorized further nuclear tests in the atmosphere after negotiations on a nuclear test-ban treaty with the Soviets failed.

In October 1962, Kennedy reported to the Nation that air reconnaissance photos revealed Soviet missile sites in Cuba capable of destroying all major American cities. He ordered a naval and air quarantine on shipment of offensive military equipment to the island. Reaching an agreement with Soviet Premier Kruschev on October 28, the Soviet missile bases in Cuba were dismantled.

The Trade Expansion Act of 1962 gave President Kennedy unprecedented authority to work out tariff reductions, on a basis of reciprocity with each of the countries involved, thus setting in motion the mechanism for expanding markets for U.S. goods. Bringing moral suasion to bear on the large steel corporations, Kennedy caused them to rescind increases in steel prices.

1963—In June 1963, President Kennedy proposed a "strategy of peace" to lead the United States and the Soviet Union out of the "vicious and dangerous cycle" of the cold war. The result was a treaty banning nuclear weapons tests in space, in the atmosphere, and under water. The accord was reached in the Soviet Union by representatives of the United States, Great Britain, and Russia.

From the beginning of his term of office, President Kennedy was deeply involved in the problems of civil rights. Sit-in demonstrations, rioting, and unrest caused him to send a special message to Congress in June 1963, asking it to help end "rancor, violence, disunity, and national shame" by passing what was described as the most sweeping civil rights bill since Reconstruction days. Another Kennedy "must" bill before the 88th Congress was a broad tax-reduction program to spur the economy.

Accompanied by Mrs. Kennedy, the President journeyed to Texas in November 1963 to fulfill a speaking tour. While greeting a tremendous crowd lined along the path of his motorcade route, he was shot and killed by an assassin in downtown Dallas on November 22. Profound grief extended out from the Capital of the United States and around the world. Dignitaries of 92 countries joined in the requiem for the 35th President, as he was buried on November 25, 1963, in Arlington National Cemetery.

On the day of his death, John F. Kennedy delivered an unintentional prophecy, in his last spoken address at Fort Worth, Tex.: "This is not an easy effort. This requires sacrifice by the people of the United States. This is a very dangerous and uncertain world."

President Kennedy did not achieve 100 percent success in obtaining his full legislative program. However, compromises were utilized and a large percentage of his recommendations were enacted.

Federal-Aid Highway Act of 1961—June 29, 1961, 75 Stat. 122.

Social Security Amendments of 1961—June 30, 1961, 75 Stat. 131.

Housing Act of 1961—June 30, 1961, 75 Stat. 149.

Peace Corps Act—September 22, 1961, 75 Stat. 612.

Manpower Development and Training Act of 1962—March 15, 1962, 76 Stat. 23.

Public Welfare Amendments of 1962—July 25, 1962, 76 Stat. 172.

Foreign Assistance Act of 1962—August 1, 1962, 76 Stat. 255.

Communication Satellite Act of 1962—August 31, 1962, 76 Stat. 419.

Public Works Acceleration Act—September 14, 1962, 76 Stat. 541.

Authorizing $100,000,000 for Purchase of U.N. Bonds—October 2, 1962, 76 Stat. 695.

Drug Amendments of 1962—October 10, 1962, 76 Stat. 780.

Trade Expansion Act of 1962—October 11, 1962, 76 Stat. 872.

Revenue Act of 1962—October 16, 1962, 76 Stat. 960.

Federal-Aid Highway Act of 1962—October 23, 1962, 76 Stat. 1145.

LYNDON BAINES JOHNSON

Thirty-sixth President of the United States
November 22, 1963 to January 20, 1969
(No. 137)

OBV. LYNDON B. JOHNSON. Portrait of the President.

REV. A quotation from the President's January 20, 1965 Inaugural Address:

> On this occasion the oath I have taken before you and before God—is not mine alone but ours together. We are one Nation and one people . . . Lyndon B. Johnson.

A reproduction of the Seal of the President of the United States, and the inaugural date.

By Frank Gasparro.

LYNDON BAINES JOHNSON

1908—Born on August 27, 1908, near Stonewall, Tex., the son of Sam Ealy and Rebekah (Baines) Johnson.

At the age of 5, Johnson moved with his parents to Johnson, Tex., which had been founded by his grandfather. Both his father and grandfather had been members of the Texas Legislature.

Lyndon Johnson was graduated from high school at 15. After pursuing a number of "odd jobs" enroute to California and return, he entered Southwest Texas State Teachers College. He worked his way through college and graduated in 1930 with a B.S. degree. He then taught school in Houston, Tex.

1932–35—Served as secretary to the late Representative Richard U. Kleberg.

Married Claudia Alta (Lady Bird) Taylor on November 17, 1934. They had two daughters, Lynda Bird and Luci Baines. Johnson attended Georgetown University Law School.

1935—Appointed by President Roosevelt to serve as Texas administrator of the National Youth Administration.

1937—At a special election held April 10, 1937, Johnson was elected to the U.S. Congress from the 10th Congressional District of Texas. He was reelected to the 76th through the 80th Congresses. On June 28, 1941, though endorsed by President Franklin D. Roosevelt, Johnson was narrowly defeated in a special Senatorial election by W. Lee O'Daniel, former Governor of Texas.

1941–42—Three days after the Japanese attack on Pearl Harbor, Johnson became a member of the U.S. Navy. He was commissioned a lieutenant commander and for 7 months served as President Roosevelt's special emissary to Australia and New Zealand. He was awarded the Silver Star for gallantry under fire. In July 1942, he was recalled by a Presidential order requiring that all Congressmen on active military duty return to Washington to resume their responsibilities in the Congress.

1948—Elected to the U.S. Senate November 2, 1948, and was reelected November 2, 1954. Elected as Democratic Whip in 1951; elected Democratic Leader

January 3, 1953, and reelected to this post at each succeeding Congress.

Throughout his service in the Congress, Johnson devoted his energies to building a record for the Democratic Party and built his own reputation as a masterful legislative craftsman. He was especially active in the areas of military preparedness, outer space exploration, and civil rights.

1961—Elected Vice President of the United States, Johnson took the oath of office January 20, 1961. The duties of that office having been expanded by President Kennedy, Johnson served as Chairman of the National Space Council, as Chairman of the President's Committee on Equal Opportunity, as Chairman of the Advisory Council of the Peace Corps and as member of the Executive Committee of the National Security Council.

1963—On the afternoon of November 22, 1963, Lyndon B. Johnson took the oath of office of the President of the United States on the Presidential plane at Love Air Field, Tex., after the assassination of President John F. Kennedy. President Johnson pledged his deep desire to "maintain the fabric of your nation" and honor the commitments already established at home and abroad.

1964—Speaking before a Joint Session of the Congress on January 8, 1964, President Johnson stated:

"Let this session of Congress be known as the session which did more for civil rights than the last hundred sessions combined; as the session which enacted the most far-reaching tax cut of our time; as the session which declared an all out war on human poverty and unemployment in these United States; as the session which finally recognized the health needs of our older citizens; as the session which reformed our tangled transportation and transit policies; as the session which achieved the most effective, efficient foreign aid program ever; and as the session which helped to build more homes, and more schools, and more libraries, and more hospitals than any single session of Congress in the history of our Republic. All this and more can and must be done."

The President, in later special messages to the Congress, outlined the specifics of a housing program to meet the needs of the poor for shelter and for encouraging community development in the suburbs, a proposal to increase job opportunities, a program for providing medical and hospital care for the aged, to be financed through social security, his proposals for a war on domestic poverty, and plans for the economic rehabilitation in the 10-State Appalachian region.

As the proposed legislation emerged from the Congress in 1964, the President promptly enacted it into law. Increased Federal aid to libraries was made available on February 11; Federal income taxes were ordered reduced on February 26, and a revised farm subsidy bill was enacted on April 11. In a televised ceremony at the White House on July 1, the President signed the Civil Rights Act of 1964. On July 9 he signed the Urban Mass Transportation bill providing Federal grants of $375 million to rehabilitate bus, train, and subway systems for urban commuters. Federal assistance to State food programs for needy families was provided by legislation enacted August 31. Two days later, $1.1 billion was made available for Federal housing and urban renewal programs. On September 3, 9.1 million acres in the United States were set aside as a permanent national wilderness system.

In the field of outer space exploration, Johnson obtained funds to lay the groundwork for outer space flights, including the Apollo project to land men on the moon and return them to earth.

In foreign affairs, Johnson met with foreign leaders of Great Britain, Mexico, the Philippines, and Germany. He strengthened the Alliance for Progress programs of the Latin American countries and restated the rights of the Western powers in Germany and Berlin; and he reaffirmed the U.S. commitment to the defense of Southeast Asia under the SEATO treaty. The Congress approved $3.4 billion for continuance of the foreign aid program.

The President ordered retaliatory attacks against North Vietnam by reason of torpedo assaults on U.S. ships in the Gulf of Tonkin and the Congress authorized $125 million in economic and military aid to South Vietnam.

In November 1964, President Johnson was reelected to the U.S. Presidency, along with Hubert H. Humphrey as the Vice President.

1965—Lyndon Baines Johnson and Hubert Horatio Humphrey took the oath of office of President and Vice President of the United States on January 20, 1965.

In his second annual message to the Congress, on January 4, 1965, the President spoke of Vietnam:

"We are there, first, because a friendly nation has asked us for help against Communist aggression. Ten years ago we pledged our help. Three Presidents have supported that pledge. We will not break it.

"Second, our own security is tied to the peace of Asia. Twice in one generation we have had to fight against aggression in the Far East. To ignore aggression would only increase the danger of a larger war.

"Our goal is peace in southeast Asia. That will come only when aggressors leave their neighbors in peace.

"What is at stake is the cause of freedom. In that cause we shall never be found wanting."

The year 1965 witnessed an increasingly larger buildup of U.S. military strength in Vietnam. At the same time, President Johnson announced the willingness of the United States to open diplomatic discussions to end the conflict, and he solicited the support of the United Nations in pressing efforts to bring about a peace in Vietnam.

To the free republics of Latin America, Johnson pledged his support of continuing aid for the Alliance for Progress "as the instrument of our war against poverty and injustice in this hemisphere." On September 24, he announced that agreement had been reached with Panama to bring it into partnership in connection with the United States operation of the canal.

In his state of the Union message, the President voiced the goals of his domestic legislative program which he termed "The Great Society."

As a means of giving farmers "the opportunity to earn a fair reward", a 4-year omnibus farm program was enacted (Food and Agricultural Act of 1965) lowering support prices but providing for cash subsidies for certain basic commodities.

Congress approved the President's proposal for funds to study high-speed rail transportation between urban centers, beginning with test projects between Boston and Washington. Ninety million dollars were provided for a 3-year study program on this subject.

At Independence, Mo., President Johnson signed into law the Social Security Amendments of 1965. Popularly known as "Medicare" this act provides health insurance to persons over 65. By other legislation, the Older Americans Act of 1965, training programs for the aged were established.

By the Voting Rights Act of 1965, literacy tests were suspended and Federal registration of voters was authorized in all States and localities where less than 50 percent of the voting age population was registered or had voted in November 1964. (On July 2, 1965, a provision of the Civil Rights Law of 1964 came into effect, prohibiting discrimination against minority groups in employment practices. The poll tax was abolished on Febru-

ary 4, 1964, when the 24th amendment became a part of the U.S. Constitution.)

Standing before the Statue of Liberty on October 3, 1965, President Johnson abolished the U.S. immigration quota system, which had been in effect since 1924. New criteria were established for admission to the United States, with priorities given to close relatives of residents of the United States, artists, scientists, and other professional and skilled workers.

Aid was authorized for primary and secondary public schools serving low income families (Elementary and Secondary Education Act of 1965), and scholarships and Federal-guaranteed loans were provided for needy college students (Higher Education Act of 1965).

"Greatness requires not only an educated people but a healthy people." Following the President's recommendations, Federal grants were authorized to aid development and operation of regional programs related to heart disease, cancer, stroke, and other major diseases. Also authorized was mental health research.

The President proposed, and the Congress approved, the creation of a Department of Housing and Urban Development to give particular attention to the housing needs of the Nation. The Omnibus Housing Act of 1965, among other things, provided for Federal rent subsidies for low income tenants of new housing projects operated by nonprofit organizations and provided grants to rehabilitate residences of low income owners.

Toward a "more beautiful America", legislation was enacted outlawing advertising in interstate and primary highway systems. Programs for the study of water resources and for effective methods of preventing pollution were also instituted.

To promote and honor creative achievements there was established the National Foundation on the Arts and Humanities.

Also during the year, the President obtained legislation for the first major change in coinage alloys since 1792. Research grants were authorized to the extent of $7 million for crime prevention and it was made a Federal offense to assassinate, kidnap, or assault the President of the United States or the officer next in line for the Presidency. On July 9, 1965, a constitutional amendment was transmitted to the States for ratification providing for succession in the event of Presidential disability.

As the year 1965 closed, the country witnessed great progress in the space program, including outer space probes sending back to earth photographs of Mars, the Gemini spacecraft flights, and the live television broadcast by President Johnson over the Early Bird, the world's first communication satellite.

1966—In his third annual message to the Congress, the President announced that the United States will stay in Vietnam "until aggression has stopped." Further, the President stated: "We have also made it clear from Hanoi to New York that there are no arbitrary limits to our search for peace. We stand by the Geneva Agreements of 1954 and 1962. We will meet at any conference table. We will discuss any proposals * * * and we will consider the views of any group. We will work for a cease fire now, or once discussions have begun. We will respond if others reduce their use of force and we will withdraw our soldiers once South Vietnam is securely guaranteed the right to shape its own future."

By the end of the year, over 1.1 million men, representing seven nations, were committed to the defense of South Vietnam, approximately 381,000 from the United States.

The President expressed his belief that "we can continue the Great Society while we fight in Vietnam." Much of the legislation he requested for his domestic programs was approved by the Congress.

Taking steps towards the goal of "a decent home for every American family" $1.3 billion in pilot projects were authorized for 60 or more U.S. cities to clear slums and later carry out urban renewal.

For the purpose of efficiency and to better serve the needs of the Nation, the President obtained legislation on October 15, to bring together 35 transportation agencies of the Federal Government which deal with air, rail, and road travel. This resulted in a Cabinet-level post headed by the the Secretary of the new Department of Transportation.

Following the President's recommendation to "attack the wasteful and degrading poisoning of our rivers, and as the cornerstone of this effort clean completely entire large river basins", the Congress approved the expenditure of $3.6 billion for this program. In addition, the Congress also approved the Clean Air bill which provided for the establishment of standards for vehicle emission of air pollutants and prohibition of sale of vehicles not meeting standards.

The Elementary and Secondary School Act of 1965 was extended another 2 years, with an increased appropriation of $6.2 billion; and additional large grants were authorized for needy small colleges and the student loan program.

In line with the President's recommendation that "we prosecute with vigor and determination our war on poverty", the Congress approved $1.75 billion for antipoverty programs. As one of the antipoverty measures, the administration initiated Project Head Start, a program for giving preschool children in "culturally deprived homes" some of the advantages shared by children in middle class families.

The President called for authority "to prevent the deception of the American consumer, requiring all packages to state clearly and truthfully their contents; all interest and credit charges to be fully revealed; and keeping harmful drugs and cosmetics away from our stores." This was followed by enactment of the Fair Practice and Labeling Act on November 3, 1966.

Attacking the problem of hunger in foreign lands, the President was given funds to finance a $5.6 billion, 2-year "Food for Peace" program.

1967—The war in Vietnam continued to absorb a large part of the Nation's effort and attention. Early in the year, the President reiterated in strong terms his refusal to stop the bombing of North Vietnam without some reciprocal reduction of military action by the North Vietnamese. The President traveled to Guam for high-level talks with South Vietnamese leaders; he visited the troops in South Vietnam; he stepped up troop strength in that country from 380,000 to approximately 500,000 and he made additional efforts to negotiate with the North Vietnamese.

At Punta del Este, Uruguay, the President and all the other member heads of the Organization of American States (with the exception of Ecuador) signed the Declaration of the Presidents of America, containing plans for a Latin American common market. In the course of the year he also met with other foreign leaders, including Premier Kosygin at Glassboro, N.J.

President Johnson secured enactment of major legislation raising social security benefits by 13 percent and he secured substantial funding for major programs related to foreign aid, education, and the war on poverty.

A wide range of other legislation was also signed into law.

Funds were provided for a start on the air pollution program, for a peacetime atomic energy program, extension of the Civil Rights Commission (a research study group); a reorganization plan to make the District of Columbia Government more representative went into effect; a program to desalt sea water was started; and measures were passed to enlarge the activities of community mental health centers and to attack the problems of mental retardation.

Funds were provided to start the President's "Model Cities" program and for rent subsidies to low income families; the Peace Corps was extended and a railroad strike was ended by reason of a special law which required compulsory arbitration.

The Nation's space program was given substantial financial aid, particularly the Apollo project of landing men on the moon. As part of this project, on November 7, 1967, a successful launching was made of the Saturn V rocket, carrying the unmanned Apollo 4 spacecraft, the heaviest and most powerful weapon ever fired.

Prototypes for two supersonic transport planes were placed under construction; the Selective Service Act was extended for another 4 years, and a corporation was established to help finance educational TV and radio programs.

On February 10, 1967, the 25th amendment to the Constitution went into effect, providing for a clear line of presidential succession, should the President become disabled.

1968—In the last year of President Johnson's term of office, much of his long-range domestic legislative program was completed.

On April 11, 1968, the President signed into law the first open housing legislation enacted since Reconstruction days. Becoming fully effective in 1970, this act prohibits discrimination in the sale or rental of about 80 percent of all housing.

On June 19, 1968, the President signed the broadest anticrime legislation ever enacted, providing grants to law enforcement agencies for police training and research. An additional measure was enacted later in the year placing the same restrictions on long guns and ammunition that were placed on the handguns by the June 19, 1968, act.

A far-reaching national housing and urban development program for new and rehabilitated housing to replace substandard housing of low income families was enacted on August 1.

Regional medical programs for heart disease, cancer and stroke were authorized for continuance for another 2 years. Also extended were Federal Vocational education programs.

For the purpose of promoting the efficiency and effectiveness of Federal grants-in-aid for State administered programs, the Congress completed action on the Intergovernmental Cooperation bill which was enacted into law in October, 1968.

1969—On January 14, 1969, President Johnson delivered a farewell address to the Congress and to the Nation, in which he stated:

> "I hope it may be said, a hundred years from now, that by working together we helped to make our country more just, more just for all of its people—as well as to insure and guarantee the blessings of liberty for all of our posterity. That is what I hope, but I believe that it will be said that we tried."

Tax Cut and Reform—February 26, 1964, 78 Stat. 19.

Civil Rights—July 2, 1964, 78 Stat. 241.

Mass Transportation—July 9, 1964, 78 Stat. 302.

Poverty Program—August 20, 1964, 78 Stat. 508.

Wilderness System—September 3, 1964, 78 Stat. 890.

Education (NDEA, Impacted Areas)—October 16, 1964, 78 Stat. 1100.

Appalachian Regional Development Act of 1965—March 9, 1965, 79 Stat. 5.

Elementary and Secondary Education—April 11, 1965, 79 Stat. 27.

Presidential Disability and Succession. (A constitutional amendment transmitted to the States for ratification July 9, 1965)

Older Americans Act—July 14, 1965, 79 Stat. 218.

Drug Controls—July 15, 1965, 79 Stat. 226.

Medicare—July 30, 1965, 79 Stat. 286.

Voting Rights—August 6, 1965, 79 Stat. 437.

Mental Health Research and Facilities—August 9, 1965, 79 Stat. 448.

Omnibus Housing Act (Including rent supplements, and low and moderate income housing)—August 10, 1965, 79 Stat. 451.

Presidential Assassination—August 28, 1965, 79 Stat. 580.

Department of Housing and Urban Development—September 9, 1965, 79 Stat. 667.

Law Enforcement Assistance Act of 1965—September 21, 1965, 79 Stat. 827.

Arts and Humanities Foundation—September 29, 1965, 79 Stat. 845.

High Speed Ground Transportation—September 30, 1965, 79 Stat. 893.

Water Pollution Control—October 2, 1965, 79 Stat. 903.

Heart Disease, Cancer and Stroke Research and Facilities—October 6, 1965, 79 Stat. 926.

Highway Beautification—October 22, 1965, 79 Stat. 1028.

Higher Education—November 8, 1965, 79 Stat. 1219.

Urban Mass Transit—September 8, 1966, 80 Stat. 715.

Highway Safety—September 9, 1966, 80 Stat. 731.

Minimum Wage Increase—September 23, 1966, 80 Stat. 830.

Department of Transportation—October 15, 1966, 80 Stat. 931.

Protection for Savers (Increase in Federal insurance for savings accounts)—October 16, 1966, 80 Stat. 1028.

Water Pollution Control—November 3, 1966, 80 Stat. 1246.

Demonstration Cities—November 3, 1966, 80 Stat. 1255.

Fair Packaging and Labeling Act—November 3, 1966, 80 Stat. 1296.

Narcotics Rehabilitation—November 8, 1966, 80 Stat. 1438.

Higher Education Act of 1965, Amendment to—June 29, 1967, 81 Stat. 81.

Air Quality Act of 1967—November 21, 1967, 81 Stat. 485.

Fair Housing Act—April 11, 1968, 82 Stat. 73.

Consumer Credit Protection (Truth in Lending) Act—May 9, 1968, 82 Stat. 146.

Omnibus Crime Control and Safe Streets Act of 1968—June 19, 1968, 82 Stat. 197.

Housing and Urban Development Act of 1968—August 1, 1968, 82 Stat. 876.

Amendment to the Public Health Service Act—October 15, 1968, 82 Stat. 1005.

Intergovernmental Cooperation Act—October 16, 1968, 82 Stat. 1098.

Higher Education Amendments of 1968—October 16, 1968, 82 Stat. 1014.

Vocational Education Amendments of 1968—October 16, 1968, 82 Stat. 1064.

Gun Control Act of 1968—October 22, 1968, 82 Stat. 1213.

RICHARD MILHOUS NIXON

Thirty-seventh President of the United States
January 20, 1969 to —
(No. 138)

OBV. Richard Milhous Nixon, President of the United States. Bust of the President.

REV. Within a wreath of 50 stars, the Presidential Seal. Inaugurated January 20, 1969. Excerpt from the speech accepting the presidential nomination in August 1968:

A NEW DAY FOR AMERICA
A NEW DAWN FOR PEACE AND
FREEDOM IN THE WORLD
Richard M. Nixon

By Frank Gasparro.

RICHARD M. NIXON

1913—Born January 9, 1913, in Yorba Linda, Calif., the son of Francis A. and Hannah (Milhous) Nixon. Of pioneer American ancestry who had migrated to New England from Ireland before the American Revolution, and went on to the west coast by way of Indiana and Ohio.

1919—Attended public schools, Whittier, Calif.; graduated in 1934 with an A.B. degree from Whittier College where he majored in history.

1934—With the aid of a scholarship to the newly formed Duke University Law School, Durham, N.C., Nixon was granted the LL.B. degree with honors.

1937—Admitted to the California State bar, Nixon practiced law in Whittier, Calif., with a part-time position of city attorney.

Married in 1940 to Patricia Ryan, daughter of a Nevada miner, who had worked her way through the University of Southern California and was a schoolteacher in Whittier. They have two children, Patricia (Tricia) and Julie (Mrs. Dwight David Eisenhower II).

From January to August, 1942, served as an attorney with the Office of Price Administration.

1942—Volunteered for military service and was commissioned a lieutenant (junior grade) in the U.S. Naval Reserve on August 17, 1942. Following his appointment, Nixon had aviation indoctrination training at the Naval Air Station, Quonset Point, R.I., and duty at the Naval Reserve Aviation Base, Ottuma, Iowa. He then reported to Commander, Air Force, U.S. Pacific Fleet and was assigned as Officer-in-Charge of the South Pacific Combat Air Transport Command at Guadalcanal and later at Green Island. For his services he was awarded two commendations and earned two engagement stars for supporting air action in Treasury-Bougainville operations (October 27–December 15, 1943) and consolidation of the northern Solomons (Bougainville) (December 15, 1943–July 22, 1944).

1946—Became the Republican candidate for the U.S. House of Representatives from California's 12th Congressional District. Won election over a five-term opponent, by more than 15,000 votes.

1947—While serving in the U.S. House of Representatives, Nixon supported U.S. participation in the United Nations, the North Atlantic Treaty Organization, technical assistance for underdeveloped areas, and reciprocal trade agreements.

Nixon also supported civil rights, Alaska and Hawaii statehood, income tax reductions, increase in minimum wages, additional social security benefits and coverage, selective service, the McCarran-Walter immigration and displaced persons acts and the St. Lawrence Seaway legislation.

As a member of the House Committee on Education and Labor, Nixon participated in drafting the Taft-Hartley Act of 1947, which provides a cooling off period of 80 days for strikes that jeopardize the national interest.

It was as a member of the Committee on Un-American Activities of the U.S. House of Representatives that Nixon attracted national attention. Pursuing an investigation which at first looked hopeless and aroused much antagonism toward his committee, Nixon persisted in laying the groundwork by further investigation of the activities of a former State Department official accused of passing classified information to the Russians. The official was convicted and sent to prison in 1951 for lying under oath. This case became the keystone of the fiery political issue of "Communists in Government."

As a member of the Select Committee on Foreign Aid, Nixon visited Europe to study American economic aid programs. Upon his return, he became a staunch supporter of the Marshall Plan and of a bipartisan foreign policy.

1948—Nixon joined Congressman (later, Senator) Mundt in sponsoring a bill to control communist activity in the United States. Though the bill failed of passage, much of its substance was incorporated into the Internal Security Act of 1950.

Winning the endorsement of the Democratic Party as well as the Republican Party, under a unique cross-filing California law, Nixon ran for a second congressional term in 1948. He was reelected with 141,509 of the 162,807 votes cast.

1950—Again, with bipartisan support, Nixon was elected, this time to the U.S. Senate. Obtaining a margin of nearly 700,000 votes, the campaign was largely on the issue of communism—what the United States should do about it, at home and abroad.

1952—When Gen. Dwight D. Eisenhower was nominated by the Republican Party as its choice for the Presidency, the General asked the convention to make Richard Nixon his running mate. The decision came by acclamation.

1953—After winning election, Nixon became the second youngest Vice President in American history. In January 1953, he was sworn into office at the age of 39. (John C. Breckenridge, in 1856, was 4 years younger.) Nixon was reelected to the Vice-Presidency in 1956 and was again sworn into office in January 1957.

As presiding officer of the U.S. Senate, Nixon broke more tie votes than any other Vice President in history.

In the 8 years of his Vice-Presidency, Nixon became a leading spokesman for the Eisenhower administration. Much of his time was devoted to liaison work between the White House and the Congress, and in directing administration-sponsored legislation through the Congress. As time went on, he was given an increasingly more important role in policymaking decisions. Well informed as to administration policies, Nixon effectively assumed increased responsibilities during President Eisenhower's illnesses in 1955, 1956, and 1957, by presiding over Cabinet and National Security Council meetings.

Nixon headed the President's committee which monitored antidiscrimination clauses in Government contracts, to assure equality in employment, and he also served as chairman of the Cabinet Committee on Price Stability for Economic Growth. He is also credited with a major role in settling the steel strike in 1959.

In a speech delivered in December 1957, Nixon stated his views on foreign and domestic policies: "In the international field, I am an internationalist. I believe deeply in adequate programs of mutual security and foreign aid, a strong national defense, and reciprocal trade. On civil rights, I call myself a moderate in the true sense. I believe we must have steady, determined progress toward guaranteeing the rights and equal opportunities of citizens. On domestic policy I am basically conservative in the classical sense * * *: Can we meet the need without help or interference from the Federal Government? If not, then go to the Government—as a last resort. As to fiscal policy—I believe strongly in the concept of a balanced budget. But in times of national emergency it is obvious we must put national security above fiscal considerations."

During his term as Vice President, Nixon visited almost 60 countries and five continents, on good will missions as the personal emissary of President Eisenhower. In 1953, he went around the world; in 1955, he visited the Caribbean and Central America; in 1956, Brazil, the Philippines and the Orient. Also, in 1956, represented the President on a mission to Germany and Austria where he assisted those governments in resettling refugees who had fled from Hungary. In 1957, he went to Africa and Italy; in 1958, he was stoned by Communist incited mobs in Peru and Venezuela while touring nine South American countries. Later that year he went to London, England, and in 1959 he visited the Union of Soviet Socialist Republics and Poland—a visit which became historic because of the "kitchen debate" with Soviet Premier Nikita Khrushchev, which was televised around the world.

As Vice President Nixon's tenure of office was coming to a close, President Eisenhower spoke of him: "No man in history was ever better trained for the Presidency, if such duties should fall upon him."

1960—Nixon was the overwhelming choice of the Republican Party for the Presidency in 1960. His democratic opponent was Senator John F. Kennedy of Massachusetts. The campaign was close and hard-fought from the beginning. Nixon lost the closest national election in 76 years by a margin of 118,574 votes out of a total of 68,838,218; he carried 26 States to 22 for Kennedy. However, the crucial electoral vote was: Kennedy 303, Nixon 219, Byrd 15.

1961—Returning to California, Nixon resumed the practice of law and was later an unsuccessful candidate for the governorship. In 1963, he moved from Los Angeles to New York where he later became the senior partner of the law firm Nixon, Mudge, Rose, Guthrie, Alexander & Mitchell. He wrote *Six Crises*, a book which outlined the major crises of his political career.

From 1963 through 1968, Nixon campaigned intensively for Republican candidates all over the country, and in these years he undertook a program of foreign travel which equaled that of his vice-presidential years.

1968—Mr. Nixon was nominated for President of the United States on the first ballot at the Republican National Convention in Miami Beach, Fla., on August 7, 1968. He was elected to the Presidency in November 1968.

1969—Standing on the steps at the Capitol of the United States, Richard Milhous Nixon took the oath of office at high noon on January 20, 1969, becoming the 37th President of the United States.

In his inaugural address, Richard Nixon spoke of the future of the Nation and of the world:

"What kind of a nation we will be, what kind a world we will live in, whether we shape the future in the image of our hopes, is ours to determine by our actions and our choices.

"The greatest honor history can bestow is the title of peacemaker. This honor now beckons America—the chance to help lead the world at last out of the valley of turmoil and onto the high ground of peace that man has dreamed of since the dawn of civilization.

"If we succeed, generations to come will say of us now living that we mastered our moment, that we helped make the world safe for mankind.

"This is our summons to greatness."

Concluding his inaugural address, the President stated:

"Our destiny offers not the cup of despair, but the chalice of opportunity. So let us seize it not in fear, but in gladness—and, 'riders on the Earth together,' let us go forward, firm in our faith, steadfast in our purpose, cautious of the dangers; but sustained by our confidence in the will of God and the promise of man."

Secretaries of the Treasury

ALEXANDER HAMILTON

Secretary of the Treasury
September 11, 1789 to January 31, 1795
(No. 201)

OBV. Alexander Hamilton 1757–1804.

REV. Treasury Seal. The circular design of the seal is dominated by a shield upon which appear the scales of justice, a key (emblem of official authority), and thirteen stars for the original States. The Latin inscription Thesauri Americae Septentrionalis Sigillium means "The Seal of the Treasury of North America."

By George T. Morgan.

(Note: This Seal was modified on January 29, 1968, by Order of the Secretary of the Treasury dated the same date, and now appears as follows: A shield upon which appear a pair of balanced scales, a key and thirteen stars. Surrounding the shield is the inscription "Department of the Treasury;" at the base, the date, 1789. The central device of the Seal is essentially the same as that used by Treasury throughout its entire history.)

ALEXANDER HAMILTON

1757—Born on the Island of Nevis (West Indies), January 11th. Was sent to New York in 1772 for his formal education, commencing with enrollment in grammar school. He later attended King's College, now Columbia University.

1774—Young Hamilton took a firm stand on the side of the patriots resisting domination by the mother country, and became a leader in the movement advocating independence.

1776—Applied for and received a commission to command an artillery company, participating in battles on Long Island, at Harlem Heights, White Plains, Trenton, and Princeton. As aide-de-camp to Washington from 1777 until 1781, he interested himself in many problems, among which were the reorganization of the Army; the preparation of military regulations; and representative government. After leaving Washington, Hamilton headed an infantry regiment and took part in the siege of Yorktown.

1782—Served as a member of the Continental Congress in 1782 and 1783, but retired to open a law office in New York City, maintaining, however, his political interests and affiliations.

1786—Hamilton's public career continued with his attendance as a delegate, in 1786, to the Annapolis Convention to study commercial affairs in general; service in the New York State Legislature; the Philadelphia Convention in 1787, called to study and discuss the adequacies of the Constitution of the United States, which it subsequently adopted; and in 1788, another term in the Continental Congress, the last time this body met under the old Articles of Confederation.

1789—The Treasury Department was established by an act of the first Congress to function under the new Constitution, dated September 2, 1789. Hamilton was long an advocate of a stronger government, with a single man at the head of the departments, and his career was climaxed when President Washington appointed him on September 11th as Secretary of this important agency. In this post he contributed greatly until his resignation from the Cabinet in January of 1795, to resume his law practice.

On October 21, 1789, he approached the Collectors of Customs for their ideas on using boats to secure the revenue against contraband. By summer of the following year, Congress authorized a Revenue Marine of 10 cutters, creating thereby the first seagoing branch of the military service, which flourishes today as the U.S. Coast Guard.

He also played a crucial role in the creation of the U.S. Navy. He argued that seapower would form a kind of great barrier reef behind which our Nation could progress in peace and security. These arguments bore fruit with the passage of the Naval Act of 1794, which officially created a U.S. Navy. Five years later he recommended to the Secretary of War the creation of a Naval Academy—an idea that proved somewhat in advance of his time.

Hamilton concerned himself with every phase of public policy, and it has been said that more than those of any other single individual, it was his influence and ideas that gave shape and direction to the new nation in its first few decades. His was an extraordinarily perceptive and creative mind, and his ready grasp of problems, coupled with a driving ambition to set his ideas in motion and attain his goals, made him one of the leaders of his time, and an outstanding statesman for all time.

In his first report to the Congress, in 1790, an historic document, Hamilton presented such subjects as a plan for raising a revenue, including the levy of both import duties and excise taxes; suggestions on navigation laws and the regulation of trade, and more. His arguments resulted in the successful funding of the revolutionary debt, the charter by Congress of the first bank of the United States, and the placing of the revenues on a firm basis.

As a result of another report made January 28, 1791, the Congress, by Act of April 2, 1792, approved a national coinage and the establishment of a mint. Strangely enough, however, President Washington placed it under supervision of the Secretary of State, where it remained until 1799.

An important segment of a report on manufactures, made to the Congress during its 1791–92 session was the proposal that protection be given infant industries by either import duties or bounties.

Hamilton's plan presented to the House, for an excise tax on spirits, met with strong opposition. When the insurrection known as the "Whiskey Rebellion" broke out in western Pennsylvania and Virginia in 1794, over collection of this tax, it was he who insisted it be put down and he accompanied General Henry Lee and his troops part of the way in a supervisory capacity. He felt it should be established that the Government could maintain itself financially and had the right to levy such a tax.

1795—Hamilton's resignation as Treasury Secretary in January did not herald his retirement from public life. He resumed his law practice, but remained close to Washington, continuing to advise him. Hamilton's political ideas kept him always in the forefront and the calls upon him were many and diversified. In 1798, when war with France threatened to materialize, Washington commissioned Hamilton Inspector-General in the Army, and he immediately set out to organize a large force for active service in Florida and Louisiana, lands which, he argued, were important to this country. He was even called upon to draft a plan for the fortification of New York harbor, though this was not a part of his duties in the Army.

1804—Hamilton was instrumental in the defeat of Aaron Burr in his race for the governorship of New York State and Burr, angry in his loss, challenged Hamilton to a duel, which took place on July 11, 1804. Hamilton was fatally wounded and died in New York City the following day.

ALBERT GALLATIN

Secretary of the Treasury

May 14, 1801 to February 8, 1814

(No. 221)

OBV. Bust of Albert Gallatin, Secretary of the Treasury, 1801–1814. By Frank Gasparro.

REV. Treasury Seal.

By George T. Morgan.

ALBERT GALLATIN

1761—Born on January 29, 1761, in Geneva, Switzerland, the son of Jean and Sophie Albertine (Rolaz) Gallatin, of an old and noble family.

Graduated with honor from the Geneva Academy.

1780—Gave up fortune and social position because of "a love for independence in the freest country of the universe."

Offered a commission as lieutenant colonel by the Landgrave of Hesse, whose hated "Hessians" were mercenaries with the British forces, he refused by saying he "would never serve a tyrant." He escaped the resulting family indignation by secretly leaving home. With a friend, he took passage for America.

Gallatin's first business venture was launched in Boston, and he later taught French at Harvard, but soon went southward.

1785—Took the Oath of Allegiance in Virginia.

Settled finally in Pennsylvania and became a member of the State Legislature, after which he was sent to the United States Senate.

His citizenship being in debate, Gallatin was rejected by the Senate, but not before calling upon the Secretary of the Treasury for a statement of the debt as of January 1, 1794, distinguishing the moneys received under each branch of the revenue, and expended under each appropriation.

When Gallatin was again returned to the Congress, this time to the House, he immediately became a member of the new Standing Committee of Finance, the forerunner of the Ways and Means Committee.

1800—Prepared a report entitled, "Views of the Public Debt, Receipts and Expenditures of the United States." This report, analyzing the fiscal operations of the Government under the Constitution, is still regarded as a classic.

In Congress, Gallatin struggled successfully to keep down appropriations, particularly those for warlike purposes. The opposition party attacked him personally, as well as politically, because of his foreign birth, and Jefferson believed the Sedition Bill was framed to drive Gallatin from office.

1801—As soon as Jefferson was elected President, he tendered Gallatin the post of Secretary of the Treasury.

Gallatin took his oath on a "platform" of debt reduction, the necessity for specific appropriations, and strict and immediate accountability for disbursements. Eight years after assuming office, his estimates on revenues and debt reduction had been proven uncannily accurate. He had succeeded in reducing the public debt by $14 million, and had built up a surplus. At the same time, $15 million had gone for the purchase of the Louisiana Territory, an acquisition which established the United States as a great continental power.

A meticulous bookkeeper and originator of many accounting practices still in use in the Treasury, Gallatin also sponsored the establishment of marine hospitals, the forerunner of the U.S. Public Health Service; while in 1807 he submitted to Congress an extensive plan for internal improvements, particularly the construction of highways and canals. His greatest contribution, however, was that for the first time Congress received a detailed report of the country's fiscal situation. Earlier Secretaries had conscientiously reported disbursements, but Gallatin gave a breakdown of receipts, a concise statement of the public debt, and an estimate of expected revenue.

1814—Gallatin left the Treasury. Though he was offered the post again by President Madison in 1816, he declined because he thought its responsibilities demanded "an active young man." He felt this even more strongly in 1843, when President Tyler offered him the post, but must have recognized this as a striking tribute to his past achievements.

Gallatin's public service was by no means over when he left the Treasury. The Treaty of Ghent, ending the War of 1812, was considered largely Gallatin's personal triumph, for he was the most effective of the American Commissioners. Thereafter, he negotiated a commercial convention with England, by which discriminating duties were abolished. He served as Minister both to France and to England, concluding his years in the field of diplomacy in 1817, when he returned to take up his residence in New York.

1817—Became president of the National Bank of the City of New York, later the Gallatin National Bank of the City of New York, and now the Central Hanover Bank and Trust Company. Here, too, he participated in the community's cultural activities. He was a founder of New York University, and of the American Ethnological Society, making valuable contributions on languages of the Indian tribes. When, as president of the New York Historical Society, he presided at an anniversary celebration in 1844, John Quincy Adams, long his political opponent, paid high tribute to Gallatin as a patriot and citizen.

1849—Albert Gallatin died on Long Island, New York, on August 12, at the age of 88.

Always an enthusiast for American ideals on liberty, Gallatin was a firm believer in the essential soundness of the Government and its finances. "If I have not wholly misunderstood America," he wrote, "I am not wrong in the belief that its public funds are more secure than those of all the European powers." For the greater part of his long life, he devoted himself to making this ideal an actuality, and carried out his vision with honor to himself and for the lasting benefit of his country and fellow citizens.

WILLIAM WINDOM

Secretary of the Treasury
March 5, 1881 to November 14, 1881
March 5, 1889 to January 29, 1891
(No. 202)

OBV. Bust of William Windom.

REV. Representative in Congress, 1859–1869. Senator of the United States, Dec. 5, 1870–Mar. 4, 1881. Dec. 5, 1881–Mar. 4, 1883. Secretary of the Treasury, Mar. 5, 1881–Nov. 14, 1881.
By C. E. Barber.

WILLIAM WINDOM

1827—Born on May 10, 1827, in Belmont County, Ohio, the son of Hezekiah and Mary (Spencer) Windom.

1850—Admitted to the bar, after taking an academic course at Martinsburg Academy at Mount Vernon, Ohio, and having read law at Mount Vernon under Judge R. C. Hurd. Commenced the practice of law at Mount Vernon.

1852–1855—Elected on the Whig ticket, to serve as prosecuting attorney of Knox County.

1855—Moved to Winona, Minnesota Territory, continuing his law practice, as a member of the firm of Sargent, Wilson & Windom. Became interested in politics and joined the Republican party.

1856—Married Ellen Towne Hatch. They had three children.

1859–69—Elected as a Republican to the U.S. House of Representatives; reelected four times. Served on various committees, including public lands and public expenditures. For two terms he was chair-

man of the Committee on Indian Affairs and was head of a special committee which visited the western tribes in 1865. Also, was on a committee to investigate the conduct of an Indian Commissioner in 1867. Served on the Special Peace Committee of Thirty, after Lincoln's election to the Presidency.

1870–81—Appointed to the U.S. Senate to fill a vacancy for the term ending March 4, 1871. Elected for a full term in the Senate in 1871.

Served as chairman of a committee on transportation routes to seaboard, recommending Federal licensing of competitive routes, as well as Federal development of waterways. Was chairman of the Committee on Appropriations from 1876 to 1881; later, was chairman of the Foreign Relations Committee.

1880—Was a candidate for the Presidency; again in 1884 and 1888.

1881—Appointed Secretary of the Treasury by President Garfield on March 5, 1881, and served until November of that year.

In the short time that Windom was Secretary of the Treasury he became a financial authority. It was at a time when a financial crisis confronted the Government; the public debt was enormous and the annual interest charge very heavy. His predecessor had begun the work of refunding the public debt at a lower rate of interest and Windom pushed this matter with great energy. He invited the banks to exchange their higher interest bonds for new bonds bearing a much lower rate of interest. When they demurred, Windom informed them he would call in the higher bonds and redeem them, thus leaving the banks without bonds upon which to issue their currency. This brought the banks to accept his terms and the exchange was promptly made, the expense to the Government being only about $10,000, while the saving in the annual interest charge was in excess of $10 million.

1881—In November, Windom was again elected to the Senate and resigned his Treasury post to serve with that body. He remained until 1883, when he failed in his bid for reelection.

1883–89—Practiced law in New York City.

1889–91—Appointed Secretary of the Treasury by President Benjamin Harrison on March 5, 1889, and served until his death in New York City on January 29, 1891. In his second term as Treasury Secretary, Windom proposed a plan for Government purchases of domestic silver at open market prices and issuance of certificates redeemable in silver. This was enacted as the Sherman Silver Act. The administration's support of this silver measure gained sufficient backing in the Congress to obtain passage of the McKinley Tariff Law of 1890.

DANIEL MANNING

Secretary of the Treasury
March 8, 1885 to March 31, 1887
(No. 204)

OBV. Bust of Daniel Manning. Two keys in saltire.

REV. Within a laurel wreath: Secretary of the Treasury, 1885–1887.

By George T. Morgan.

DANIEL MANNING

1831—Born in Albany, N.Y., on May 16, 1831, the son of John and Eleanor (Oley) Manning.

Self-educated. At the age of 12 he went to work for the Albany "Atlas," which later became the "Argus." Was associated with this newspaper practically all his life, eventually becoming its president and owner. The "Argus" became one of the leading Democratic papers in the State and fought corruption, including "Tweedism" in the State legislature.

1853—Married Mary Little, who died in 1882, leaving four children. Married Mary Margarette Fryer in 1884.

1869–82—Trustee of the National Savings Bank of Albany.

1873—Was made a director of the National Commercial Bank of Albany; in 1881, its vice president and in 1882, its president.

1874–84—Member of the State Democratic Committee and of following State Democratic conventions. Aided in achieving reforms in the State operated prisons and canal system.

1876—Delegate to the Democratic National Convention; again in 1880, and in 1884. During the latter convention he worked for Cleveland's candidacy for the Presidency.

1885—Appointed Secretary of the Treasury by President Cleveland. He held this post at a time of unsettled economic conditions: Foreign capital was leaving the United States at a rapid rate; the Treasury's stock of gold was rapidly reaching the point where it would be too low to meet redemption pledges; and the balance of trade was unfavorable. Manning endeavored to conserve the Treasury's cash surplus, and to increase its gold reserve.

To lessen the drain on gold which was being paid out in redemptions of legal tender notes, Carlisle obtained authority to issue silver certificates in denominations of $1, $2, and $5 instead of $10 or higher. Eventually, all the small denomination greenbacks were replaced.

To the disappointment of many in the Congress and in his own party, Manning came out against bimetallism on the theory that it would work only if it were adopted internationally; otherwise, acting alone in the United States, all the Treasury's stock of gold would be drawn out and the country would be on a silver standard.

Manning succeeded in the retention of the cash surplus held in the Treasury and he urged that the time was appropriate for the country to reduce tariffs.

1887—Manning retired from his Treasury post, and later assumed the presidency of the Western National Bank of New York City. He died in that city on December 24, 1887.

JOHN G. CARLISLE

Secretary of the Treasury
March 7, 1893 to March 5, 1897
(No. 203)

OBV. Bust of John Griffin Carlisle.

REV. Representative in Congress, 1877–1890. Speaker of the House, Forty-eighth, Forty-ninth, and Fiftieth Congresses. Senator, 1890–1893. Secretary of the Treasury, March 6, 1893. Ribbon inscribed, Treasury, with crossed keys. Fasces and wreath.

By C. E. Barber.

JOHN G. CARLISLE

1835—Born in Campbell (now Kenton) County, Ky., September 5, 1835, the son of L. H. and Mary A. (Reynolds) Carlisle.

Self-educated; taught school at the age of 15.

1857—Married Mary Jane Goodson of Covington, Ky.; they had two children.

1858—Admitted to the State bar, having studied law under William B. Kinkhead and John W. Stevenson. Commenced practice in Covington, Ky.

1859–61—Member of the Kentucky House of Representatives, at a time when one of the main issues was secession. Taking a conservative position, Carlisle served on a committee which prepared a resolution supporting neutrality in the war between the States.

1864—Nominated for presidential elector on the Democratic ticket, but declined to run.

1866—Member of the Kentucky Senate; reelected in 1869 and resigned in 1871. Voted against a right-of-way

for the Cincinnati Southern Railway to transit Kentucky, though he later reversed his position and voted to support this project.

1868—Delegate-at-large to the Democratic National Convention in New York City.

1871–75—Lieutenant Governor of Kentucky, serving from August 1871, to September 1875. Also editor of the Louisville Daily Ledger in 1872.

1876—Alternate presidential elector-at-large.

1877—Elected as a Democrat to the U.S. House of Representatives and reelected to six more terms. Carlisle's knowledge of parliamentary law was exceeded by few in the Congress; he discharged his responsibilities as Speaker of the House for three terms with impartiality, for which he gained the respect of both political parties. He was especially interested in tariff legislation and supported the position that the main purpose of tariffs should be to raise revenue. As a member of the Ways and Means Committee of the House, he was active in securing Democratic sponsored tariff legislation directed towards free trade.

1890–93—Elected and took his seat May 26, 1890, in the U.S. Senate and served until February 4, 1893.

1893–97—Served as Secretary of the Treasury under President Cleveland. Carlisle familiarized himself with the intricacies of the money questions before the Treasury, centering around a financial panic which had drained the Treasury's gold supply. The public was demanding that the Treasury redeem its notes of 1890 in gold, whereas, the silver interests urged that the notes be redeemed in silver. Late in October 1893, the obligation of the Treasury to buy silver was withdrawn. With the approval of President Cleveland, Carlisle issued a series of bonds for gold, under authority of legislation enacted in 1875. Later, to prevent suspension of species payments in gold, which were running

heavy, Carlisle bought gold at a premium price at home and abroad. Through a number of additional measures, the Treasury weathered the run on gold and kept the country on the gold standard. By reason of his stand on gold, Carlisle became identified as a "sound money" man and lost his influence on many in the Democratic party who favored free silver coinage.

1897—Moved to New York City and resumed the practice of law.

1910—Died in New York City, July 31.

LYMAN J. GAGE

Secretary of the Treasury
March 6, 1897 to January 31, 1902

(No. 205)

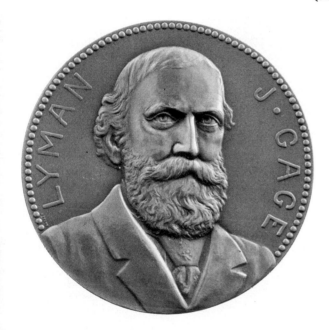 

OBV. Bust of Lyman J. Gage.

By C. E. Barber.

REV. Secretary of the Treasury, 1897. Oak and laurel branches.

By George T. Morgan.

LYMAN J. GAGE

1836—Born on June 28, 1836, in De Ruyter, Madison County, N.Y., the son of Eli A. and Mary (Judson) Gage.

Educated in an academy at Rome, N.Y.

1850–55—Clerk in the post office and at the Oneida Central Bank at Rome.

1858—Having moved to Chicago, Gage became a book-keeper for the Merchants' Loan and Trust Company, becoming its cashier in 1861.

1864—Married Sara Etheridge in 1864, who died in 1874. They had two children. Married Mrs. Cornelia Washburn and, after her death, Mrs. Frances Ada Ballou.

1868—Accepted position as cashier of the First National Bank of Chicago; became its president in 1891. Under his leadership this bank weathered the financial panic of 1893, and became one of the leading banks of the Nation.

Gage early identified himself with the "sound

99

money" issue and was one of the organizers of "The Honest Money League of the Northwest."

1870—Was one of the organizers of the Chicago Clearing House Association; thereafter was active, for many years, in its operations.

1892—Began his first of three terms as president of the American Bankers Association.

1893—Helped finance and served as president of the board of directors of the World's Columbian Exposition.

1894—Became president of the Civic Federation of Chicago; active in a program of municipal reform.

1897–1902—Served as Secretary of the Treasury under Presidents McKinley and Roosevelt. His major achievement in this post was to float a $200 million loan at an extremely low rate of interest (3 per-

cent), to finance the war with Spain. He was also instrumental in securing the Act of 1900, which established the gold dollar as the standard unit of value in the United States.

Gage was an early exponent of the principle that the money supply of the Nation should be elastic and governed by the needs of the time, though his ideas on this subject did not materialize until the Federal Reserve System was created in 1913.

1902–06—President of the United States Trust Company of New York.

1906—Retired to San Diego, Calif., travelled to the Orient, wrote and spoke frequently on public affairs.

1927—Died at San Diego on January 26, 1927.

LESLIE M. SHAW

Secretary of the Treasury
February 1, 1902 to March 4, 1907

(No. 206)

OBV. Bust of Leslie M. Shaw.

REV. Secretary of the Treasury of the United States, February 1, 1902. Keys of the Treasury in saltire. Ribbon inscribed, E Pluribus Unum.

By C. E. Barber.

LESLIE M. SHAW

1848—Born November 2, 1848, at Morristown, Vt., the son of Boardman O. and Lovisa (Spaulding) Shaw. Educated at Cornell College, Iowa, where he re-

ceived a B.S. and M.S. degree, in 1874. Two years later he received an LL.B. degree from the Iowa College of Law at Des Moines.

1876–97—Practiced law in Denison, Iowa, with his firm, Shaw and Kuehnle. It is said he never accepted a criminal case unless he was sure of the innocence of his client; hence his record of acquittal for all criminal actions he handled.

1877—Married Alice Crawshaw of Clinton County, Iowa. They had three children.

1880—Organized a bank and mortgage loan business with branches in Denison, Manilla, and Charter Oak, Crawford County, Iowa.

1888—Lay delegate to the General Conferences of the Methodist-Episcopal Church, 1888, 1892, 1896, and 1900.

1893—One of the founders of Denison Normal and Business College.

1896—Started his political career by delivering forceful speeches in Iowa in support of the gold standard and McKinley's bid for the presidency.

1898—Permanent chairman of the International Monetary Conference held in Indianapolis, at which he delivered an important speech in support of the gold standard.

1898–1902—Governor of Iowa for two terms; followed a policy of thrift and economy during his administration; reorganized the State school system.

1902–07—Appointed Secretary of the Treasury by President Theodore Roosevelt who later commended him for his independence and ingenuity in preventing a money crisis. Shaw did this by placing Government funds in key banks throughout the country and insisting that such funds, together with moneys set aside as bank reserves, be used to meet the needs of commerce. His position was that bank reserves were intended to be accumulated in times of plenty, to be used in times of adversity.

1907–08—President of the Carnegie Trust Company of New York; resigned to make a preconvention bid for the Presidency. Later withdrew and threw his support to William Howard Taft.

1909–13—President, Mortgage Guarantee and Trust Company of Philadelphia.

1913—Retired to Washington, D.C., where he wrote on economic and financial subjects. He had previously collected his speeches and published them under the title, *Current Issues* (1908). In 1919, he published *Vanishing Landmarks: The Trend Toward Bolshevism*.

1932—Died at Washington, D.C., March 28, 1932.

GEORGE B. CORTELYOU

Secretary of the Treasury
March 4, 1907 to March 4, 1909
(No. 207)

OBV. Bust of George B. Cortelyou, Secretary of the Treasury.

REV. Not inscribed.

By George T. Morgan.

GEORGE B. CORTELYOU

1862—Born in New York City, July 26, 1862, the son of Peter C., Jr., and Rose (Seary) Cortelyou.

Educated at the Hempstead Institute at Long Island, from which he graduated in 1879, and the Massachusetts State Normal School at Westfield, Mass., from which he graduated in 1882.

While teaching in Cambridge, Mass., studied at the New England Conservatory of Music at Cambridge.

1883–85—Studied shorthand and became a court reporter, in New York City.

1885–89—Principal of preparatory schools in New York.

1888—Married Lily Morris, daughter of the president of Hempstead Institute. They had five children.

1889—Entered public service as private secretary to the surveyor of the Port of New York. Moved to Washington, D.C., where he served as a secretary to the Fourth Assistant Postmaster General.

After Cortelyou took up residence in Washington, he attended Georgetown University from which he was granted an LL.B. degree, and he followed this training by achieving an LL.M. from the Law Department of George Washington University (then the Columbian College) in 1896.

1895—Cortelyou went to the White House to serve as confidential secretary to President Cleveland and later, in the same capacity, to Presidents McKinley and Theodore Roosevelt. While with Roosevelt, he played a tactful role in labor negotiations between mine operators and miners, which led to his selection as head of a new cabinet post.

1903—Appointed by President Roosevelt as the first Secretary of the newly organized Department of Commerce and Labor. Cortelyou formulated the basic policy which was to guide this new instrument of Government. Many existing Federal activities were transferred to the Department of Commerce and Labor: The Lighthouse Board, the Lighthouse Establishment, Steamboat Inspection Service, Bureau of Navigation, U.S. Shipping Commissioners, National Bureau of Standards, Coast and Geodetic Survey, the Commissioner-General of Immigration, the Bureau of Immigration, the Bureau of Statistics from the Treasury Department, the Bureau of Census from the Department of the Interior, the Bureaus of Foreign Commerce from the Department of State, together with the Commissioner of Fish and Fisheries from the Department of Labor. Also transferred was the Bureau of Corporation and a Bureau of Manufactures.

Cortelyou undertook his new task as Secretary of the Commerce and Labor Department with the view he followed while he continued in this post: How best to serve the American public and, in particular, the businessmen whose activities would contribute to the growth of the American economy.

1904–07—Chairman of the Republican National Committee; managed Theodore Roosevelt's second campaign for the Presidency.

1905–07—Appointed by President Roosevelt as Postmaster General. In his second Cabinet post, Cortelyou endeavored to minimize political patronage and made appointments on a merit basis. He reorganized the Post Office Department on a functional basis, to improve its efficiency.

1907–09—Appointed by President Roosevelt as Secretary of the Treasury. Not long after he took office, the country was threatened by a financial panic, because of an insufficiency in the amount of money in circulation. Using such powers as the Treasury had to act as a central bank, he placed Government funds throughout the country in private banking institutions and made them available to meet the needs of commerce. As Treasury Secretary, he spent much of his term in office to frame legislation for an essential central banking system.

Also as Secretary of the Treasury, Cortelyou improved the quality of personnel in the Revenue Cutter Service and is considered to be one of the founding fathers of the modern U.S. Coast Guard. Throughout his tenure of office, he fought to balance Government expenditures with its income from revenues.

1909—Became president of Consolidated Gas Co. of New York (later, Consolidated Edison Co.), which became one of the largest utility companies in the world.

1924–28—Vice President of the Chamber of Commerce, State of New York.

1935—Cortelyou retired to his Huntington, Long Island estate, where he died 5 years later.

FRANKLIN MacVEAGH

Secretary of the Treasury
March 8, 1909 to March 5, 1913
(No. 208)

OBV. Bust of Franklin MacVeagh, Secretary of the Treasury, 1909–1913.

REV. The Treasury Seal.

By George T. Morgan.

FRANKLIN MacVEAGH

1837—Born on November 22, 1837, near Phoenixville, Chester County, Pa., the son of Major and Margaret (Lincoln) MacVeagh.

1862–64—Graduated from Yale University (A.B. 1862) and from Columbia University Law School (LL.B. 1864). Admitted to the bar and practiced law in New York briefly, abandoning the profession because of ill health.

1866—Married Emily Eames of Chicago, to which city MacVeagh had moved. They had five children, most of whom died in childhood.

Became associated with the wholesale grocery firm of Whitaker & Harmon, which was destroyed by the Chicago Fire of 1871. Together with others, he helped feed thousands of the homeless and destitute. Organized his own firm, Franklin MacVeagh & Co., which became one of the largest wholesale grocery houses in the Nation. Served as president of this firm until 1909, and again from 1925 to 1931.

For many years MacVeagh served as a director of the Commercial National Bank of Chicago, which had been founded by his wife's father.

1874—Became president of a citizens committee to eliminate graft in local government.

While supporting the Republican Party in local civic matters, MacVeagh supported the candidacy of Cleveland for Presidency in 1884, 1888, and 1892.

1894—Running as a Democrat, MacVeagh was defeated in the State legislature which then elected U.S. Senators from Illinois.

1896—Differing with William Jennings Bryan on the free silver issue, MacVeagh left the Democratic Party. He published "A Program of Municipal Reform" (American Journal of Sociology, March 1896).

1896–1904—President of the Chicago Bureau of Charities.

1901–13—Trustee of the University of Chicago.

1909—Appointed Secretary of the Treasury by President Taft; served until the close of the latter's administration.

As Treasury Secretary, MacVeagh endeavored to keep Government receipts and expenditures in balance; he supported legislation for a central banking system; and he instituted many progressive measures to promote the efficiency of the Treasury, particularly in the operation of the Customs Service. Though he seldom made public addresses, those which he did deliver were said to be scholarly and eloquent.

During the course of his life, MacVeagh had a variety of interests. He was one of the founders and officers of the Municipal Art League of Chicago; was active in the Chicago Historical Society, the American Economic Association, the American Historical Association, the American Institute of Sacred Literature, the American Free Art League, the American Political Science Association, the American Statistical Association, the American Red Cross, the National Geographic Society, and many other associations.

1934—Died in Chicago, Ill., on July 6, 1934.

WILLIAM G. McADOO

Secretary of the Treasury
March 6, 1913 to December 15, 1918

(No. 209)

OBV. Bust of William Gibbs McAdoo, Secretary of the Treasury, 1913–1918, with the Treasury Seal.

By George T. Morgan.

REV. America, holding in her hands a cornucopia, representing the response of the Nation to the Liberty Loan Drive. On the pedestal is a plaque, inscribed with PATRIA. In the background is the city of New York with which McAdoo was identified, the railroad system which he administered as a wartime measure, and the Army he helped transport.

By John R. Sinnock.

WILLIAM G. McADOO

1863—Born on October 31, 1863, near Marietta, Cobb County, Ga., the son of Judge William G. and Mary (Floyd) McAdoo.

Educated in rural schools and attended the University of Tennessee at Knoxville.

1882—Deputy clerk of the U.S. Sixth Circuit Court of Appeals.

1885—Married Sarah H. Fleming of Chattanooga, Tenn. (who died in 1912). They had six children.

Having studied law, McAdoo was admitted to the bar in 1885 and practiced at Chattanooga. He became division counsel for the Central Railroad and Banking Co. and the Richmond and Danville Railroad Co., and later was made president of the Knoxville Street Railroad Co. This gave McAdoo a solid background in transportation affairs.

1892—Moved to New York City to practice law, where he was associated with William McAdoo (no relation), who had been Assistant Secretary of the Navy.

While practicing law in New York City, McAdoo became interested in reviving the project of tunneling the Hudson River, which had been conceived as early as 1874 and abandoned as being impractical after a great loss of life. In 1902, he organized the

Manhattan Railway Co. and raised $4 million to undertake this great endeavor. Between 1904 and 1909, he had completed four tunnels radiating from New York City. He served as president of this company until be became active in politics.

1910—Supported the New Jersey gubernatorial campaign of Woodrow Wilson.

1912—Delegate to the Democratic National Convention in Baltimore in 1912; also served as delegate to the conventions of 1932 and 1936. Became vice chairman of the Democratic National Committee in 1912.

1913—Appointed by President Wilson and served as Secretary of the Treasury until 1918. He had marked success in floating four Liberty Loans (1917–18) which raised over $18 billion for the war effort. He is responsible for the war risk insurance law, which was later extended to include life insurance for the Armed Forces.

1914—Married Ellen Randolph Wilson, daughter of the President. (Later divorced.)

1918—Became Director General of the Railway Administration, after the railroads and intercoastal shipping were temporarily nationalized to provide consolidated control of transportation to meet wartime needs.

1919—Resumed the private practice of law.

1920—With substantial support from the West, McAdoo emerged as a prominent nominee for the Presidency. He lost to James L. Cox.

1922—Moved to Los Angeles, Calif., and continued the private practice of law.

1924—Was a leading candidate at the New York Democratic National Convention, for the Presidency. After 100 ballots, the nomination went to James L. Davis.

1932–40—Member of the Democratic National Committee. As chairman of the California delegation, he cast California's vote for Roosevelt on the fourth ballot, resulting in the latter being selected as the Democratic nominee for the Presidency.

1933—Elected as a Democrat to the U.S. Senate and served from March 4, 1933, to November 8, 1938, when he resigned. He supported New Deal policies and specialized in legislation on banking and finance.

1939—Returned to private life. Served as chairman of the board of The American President Lines.

1941—Died while on a visit to Washington, D.C., February 1, 1941.

CARTER GLASS

OBV. Bust of Carter Glass, Secretary of the Treasury. 1918–1920.

REV. The Treasury Seal.

By George T. Morgan.

CARTER GLASS

1858—Born at Lynchburg, Va., January 4, 1858, the son of Robert H. and Augusta (Christian) Glass.

Educated in public and private schools in Lynchburg; was the recipient of many honorary degrees.

Printer's apprentice for 8 years with the Lynchburg Daily Republican; afterwards, he was reporter, city editor, editor and owner of the Lynchburg Daily News and of the Daily Advance.

1881–1901—Clerk of the Lynchburg City Council.

1886—Married Aurelia McDearman of Lynchburg. They had four children.

1898–1906—Member, Board of Visitors, University of Virginia, at Charlottesville.

1899–1903—Member of the Virginia Senate, where he was active in revising the State's suffrage laws. Delegate to the Virginia Constitutional Convention in 1901.

1902–18—Served as a Representative in the Congress of the United States. Becoming especially interested in money and banking, Glass studied for many years, becoming a world authority on this subject. Assigned to the House Committee on Banking and Currency, he became chairman in 1911. He was the principal author of the legislation establishing the Federal Reserve System, and he championed this measure until its passage in 1913.

Glass also served as chairman of the Joint Congressional Committee which drafted and put through the Federal Farm Land Bank Act of 1916.

1918—At the request of President Wilson, Glass resigned his seat in the Congress to accept appointment as Secretary of the Treasury, a post which he occupied from December 1918 to February 1920. He is credited with the success of the Victory Loan of April–May 1919 which was oversubscribed. The legislation authorizing this loan included a provision, recommended by Glass, establishing a $25 billion sinking fund to pay for the country's war debt in 25 years.

1919–46—Glass was appointed by the Governor of Virginia to fill an unexpired term in the Senate of the U.S. Congress. He was elected to the Senate in 1924, and was reelected in 1930, 1936, and again in 1942. He served continuously in the Senate from February 2, 1920, until his death.

While in the Senate, Glass supported U.S. entrance into the League of Nations and he stood with President Wilson in the unsuccessful fight to gain ratification of the Versailles Treaty. In the early days of the New Deal he was active in support of the emergency banking legislation. He was opposed, however, to the legislation which resulted in changing the gold content of the dollar, and to other legislation of a welfare nature. With the outbreak of World War II, he supported the President in amending the neutrality law to permit aid to the British and the French.

Glass was particularly active in various roles connected with the Democratic National Committee. He was chairman of the committee on resolutions at the Democratic National Convention in 1920, and drafted its platform. For many years, he was a prominent candidate before the convention, for the presidential nomination.

1940—Married Mrs. Mary Scott Meade.
1946—Died in Washington, D.C., on May 28, 1946.

ANDREW W. MELLON

Secretary of the Treasury
March 4, 1921 to February 12, 1932
(No. 211)

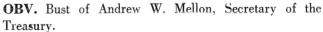

OBV. Bust of Andrew W. Mellon, Secretary of the Treasury.

REV. The Treasury Seal, and the dates, 1921 and 1932.

By John R. Sinnock.

ANDREW W. MELLON

1855—Born in Pittsburgh, Pa., on March 24, 1855, the son of Judge Thomas and Sarah (Negley) Mellon.

Educated at Western University of Pennsylvania (now the University of Pittsburgh), class of 1873.

1874—Joined his father's banking firm, T. Mellon & Sons, becoming senior partner in 1887.

1889—Helped organize the Union Trust Company and Union Savings Bank of Pittsburgh.

In addition to his banking interests, Mellon branched out into industrial activities. In the early 1890's he was one of the organizers of oil producing and refining enterprises, including pipelines from oil fields in western Pennsylvania to Marcus Hook on the Delaware River.

Mellon had a genius for recognizing the potential of many individuals with whom he became associated. He gave assistance to Charles M. Hall, who patented a process for the electrolytic refining of bauxite. From this grew the Aluminum Company of America, with the Mellons as its principal stockholders.

Mellon aided Edward Goodrich Acheson, becoming his partner, in placing the Carborundum Co. on a sound basis; by 1898, Mellon had become the principal owner of this company.

Other projects with which Mellon was identified as one of the chief organizers were the Standard

107

Steel Car Co. (later merged into the Pullman Corp.), the New York Shipbuilding Co., Koppers Gas & Coke Co. of Pittsburgh, and the McClintic Marshall Construction Co. He was also an organizer of the Union Steel Co. with wire mills and other properties on the Monongahela River, later merged with the United States Steel Corporation. In 1901, Mellon helped organize the Gulf Oil Corp., with wells in Texas and Oklahoma.

1900—Married Nora McMullen at Hertford, England. They had two children, Ailsa and Paul Mellon.

1902—The firm, T. Mellon & Sons, was reorganized as the Mellon National Bank, of which Mellon served as president until he entered public life.

1913—With his brother, Richard, Mellon established a memorial to his father, the Mellon Institute of Industrial Research, for the study of physical science and technology as an aid to industry.

Few Americans could match the patriotic civilian activities of Andrew Mellon during World War I. He served on the Executive Committee of the Pennsylvania State Council of National Defense, was a member of the national war work finance committee of the American Red Cross, was chairman of the (Red Cross) War Fund Campaign Committee for Western Pennsylvania, and served with the National War Council of the Y.M.C.A. and the National Research Council of Washington.

1921—Appointed by President Harding, and reappointed by Presidents Coolidge and Hoover to serve as Secretary of the Treasury, a post Mellon held with distinction for many years.

W. H. Smith, in his "History of the Cabinet," gives this account of Mellon's stewardship of the Treasury:

"Mellon's long training and experience as a banker peculiarly fitted him for the work at the treasury, as was immediately demonstrated in his brilliant administration of that department during the difficult period of post-war financial and industrial readjustment. The main outlines of Secretary Mellon's policy were, first of all, to keep the country's finances in order by maintaining the gold standard unimpaired and by balancing the budget, ordinary receipts against ordinary expenditures; second, by carrying out a reasonable program for the gradual liquidation and orderly funding of the war debt; and third, by reducing expenditures and lowering taxes as much as circumstances permitted.

"At the beginning of his administration the treasury was faced with the problem of reducing expenditures and at the same time meeting the fast-approaching maturities of the public debt. When

Mr. Mellon assumed office the cost of running the Government for the preceding fiscal year (1920) had amounted to six billion four hundred and eighty-two million dollars, and obligations in the sum of seven billion five hundred million dollars were maturing within two and a half years. At the end of three years of his administration of the treasury the annual budget had been reduced to three billion five hundred and six million dollars, the seven billion five hundred million dollars of the short-dated debt had been either retired or refunded into more manageable maturities and the public debt had been reduced by about two billion eight hundred million dollars. As the debt had been paid off the interest charges had become less, thus effecting a saving each year in expenditures.

"Secretary Mellon proceeded on the theory that high taxes increase the cost of living and that, so far as the condition of the treasury permits, taxes should be reduced and the cost of living lowered. He repeatedly pointed out that reductions in taxes were dependent on reductions in expenditures and that, with the utmost economy in government, it was not possible to reduce taxes below the amounts required to meet the fixed obligations of the government, such as payment of interest on the public debt. For these reasons he exerted the utmost efforts to reduce the debt and at the same time to lower taxes so far as might be warranted by the condition of the revenues.

"In November, 1923, he called to the attention of Congress, in a letter to the chairman of the Committee on Ways and Means, the need for tax reduction out of surplus revenues and presented a comprehensive and well-balanced program for tax reform which would grant relief from the most burdensome and least productive taxes. This program, which was known as "The Mellon Plan," evoked an unprecedented amount of discussion throughout the country on the subject of taxation. It was subsequently enacted, in part, into law, causing sweeping reductions in taxes but without some of the reforms which Mr. Mellon sought to introduce into the tax system. As a result of this reduction of taxes under the Revenue Act of 1924, the taxpayers' bill was reduced by more than four hundred million dollars annually over the amount which would have been collected if the 1921 rates had remained in force."

In 1922, Mellon served as chairman of a commission which handled the negotiation with foreign countries of war debts due the United States. In 1924, he published a treatise, "Taxation, The People's Business." In 1929, he revised the paper currency, reducing its size and improving its appearance. In 1931, he was a delegate to the seven power economic conference in London.

Mellon reorganized the federal farm loan system, liquidated the assets of the wartime U.S. railroad administration, and handled the return of alien property seized during World War I.

1932—Mellon resigned as Secretary of the Treasury, to accept appointment as U.S. Ambassador to Great Britain, in which capacity he served until the close of the Hoover administration.

In retirement, as well as during his earlier years, Mellon gave generously of his vast wealth to educational, cultural, and philanthropic causes. His greatest public benefaction is the National Gallery of Art.

1937—Died on August 27, 1937, at Southampton, Long Island, N.Y.

OGDEN L. MILLS

Secretary of the Treasury
February 13, 1932 to March 4, 1933

(No. 212)

OBV. Bust of Ogden L. Mills, Secretary of the Treasury.

REV. The Treasury Seal, and the date, 1932.

By John R. Sinnock.

OGDEN L. MILLS

1884—Born on August 23, 1884, at Newport, R.I., the son of Ogden and Ruth T. (Livingston) Mills.

1901–07—Attended Harvard University (A.B. in 1904) and Harvard Law School (LL.B. in 1907).

1908—Admitted to the New York State Bar; practiced law with the firm of Stetson, Jennings and Russell, subsequently becoming a member of that firm.

1911–26—Treasurer of the Republican County Committee, New York.

1912—Unsuccessful candidate for the U.S. Congress.

Delegate to the Republican National Convention in 1912, and again in 1916 and 1920.

1914—Elected a member of the New York State Senate and served until 1917. Distinguished himself for his strong stand in favor of progressive welfare and financial legislation, such as widows' pensions, workmen's compensation, a prison parole commission, and court reforms. Made an exhaustive study of the State's financial and taxation resources and served as President of the New York State Tax Association.

1917—Commissioned a captain in the U.S. Army; later served with the American Expeditionary Forces in France.

1921–27—Served as a Representative in the U.S. Congress. Held an important post on the House Ways and Means Committee where his expertise in taxation helped secure passage of the Mellon Tax Bill of 1926.

1924—Married to Mrs. Dorothy Randolph Fell.

1926—Running against Alfred E. Smith, was unsuccessful in his bid for the governorship of New York.

1927—Appointed by President Coolidge as Under Secretary of the Treasury and served until February 1932.

1932—Appointed by President Hoover as Secretary of the Treasury, and served until the change of administration in 1933.

As Secretary of the Treasury, Mills continued the policies of his predecessor, Andrew W. Mellon. He favored reductions in Government spending, with the purpose of achieving a balanced budget, as well as a general manufacturers' excise tax.

In private life, Mills served as a director of the Atchison, Topeka & Santa Fe Railroad, Mergenthaler Linotype Co., Lackawanna Steel Co., Shredded Wheat Co., Crex Carpet Co., Continental Paper & Bag Mills, and was a trustee of the New York Trust Co.

1937—Died in New York City on October 11, 1937.

WILLIAM H. WOODIN

Secretary of the Treasury
March 5, 1933 to December 31, 1933
(No. 213)

OBV. Bust of William H. Woodin, Secretary of the Treasury.

REV. South view of the Treasury Building in Washingington, D.C. A stylized shield of the United States of America. A tablet carrying the Treasury Shield, and the date MCMXXXIII.

By John R. Sinnock.

WILLIAM H. WOODIN

1868—Born at Berwick, Pa., May 27, 1868, the son of Clemuel R. and Mary (Dickerson) Woodin.

Educated at Woodridge School in New York and

at the School of Mines of Columbia University, New York, from which he graduated in 1890.

1889—Married Annie Jessup of Montrose, Pa. Four children were born to them.

1892–1922—General Superintendent of Jackson & Woodin Manufacturing Co., manufacturers of steel castings, at Berwick, Pa. Became president in 1895. This firm was later absorbed by the American Car and Foundry Co., of which Woodin became its president in 1916, and served in that capacity until 1922.

1922—Appointed State Fuel Director of New York. Controlled the price and distribution of fuel in the entire State of New York throughout the shortage that prevailed in the winter of 1922.

While in private industry, Woodin also served as president of the American Car and Foundry Securities Corp. and of the same concern's export company. He was chairman of the boards of the American Locomotive Co., the American Car & Foundry Motors Co., the J. B. Brill Co., the Railway Steel Spring Co., and the Montreal Locomotive Works.

Woodin held directorates with the Federal Reserve Bank of New York, the Remington Arms Co., the Super Heater Co., Cuba Co., Cuba Railroad, Compania Cubana Consolidated Railroads, American Ship & Commerce Co., Atlantic Mail Corp., and the American Surety Co., besides service on the boards of several real estate companies and banks in New York.

1928–32—Woodin gave staunch support to the Democratic tickets of 1928 and 1932, and was later treasurer of a special committee organized to wipe out a substantial deficit in the party treasury.

1933—Appointed by President Roosevelt as Secretary of the Treasury.

The first act of the new administration was to declare a banking holiday, which closed all financial institutions in the nation for 10 days and then allowed them to reopen only under regulations which the Treasury Department was charged with enforcing. The crisis involved the issuing of millions of new currency in Federal Reserve Bank notes, classification of the closed banks according to liquidity of assets, and a tremendous amount of other detail for the new Secretary of the Treasury.

Scarcely weeks after assuming office, Woodin issued a series of orders, supplementing executive orders of the President, controlling the holding, the use, and the export of gold. The first of such orders was promulgated in April 1933. President Roosevelt later wrote that many useless volumes could be written as to whether in April 1933, the United States had abandoned the traditional gold standard. The President commented:

"In one sense we did not, because the legal gold content of the dollar was unchanged and because the Government and the banks retained all gold as a basis for currency. On the other hand, gold here in the United States ceased to be a medium of exchange. The (gold) order was the turning point. Its result was felt almost immediately. American exchange weakened in terms of foreign currencies, and the price level at home went up substantially. Everyone realized at last that we were serious in our purpose of conserving our own financial resources, that we proposed to maintain our currency, and that at the same time we had determined definitely to seek an increase in all values."

The successful efforts made by Woodin and other members of the administration to restore public confidence in the dollar, at home and abroad, led to a breakdown of his health and he was compelled to resign his office at the year's end.

In private life, Woodin's avocation was music and coins, as well as art. He began serious musical compositions when he was past 60, writing a number of symphonies and popular tunes, as well as the "Franklin D. Roosevelt March," which was played by the service bands in the inaugural parade of March 4, 1933. As a numismatist, he had a fine collection of U.S. pattern coins and was joint author of a publication on "United States Pattern—Trial and Experimental Pieces" published in 1913.

1934—Secretary Woodin died in New York City on May 3, 1934.

HENRY MORGENTHAU, JR.

Secretary of the Treasury

January 1, 1934 to July 22, 1945

(No. 214)

OBV. Bust of Henry Morgenthau, Jr., Secretary of the Treasury.

REV. South view of the Treasury Department, Washington, D.C., with a scroll bearing the date Jan. 1, 1934, and the Treasury Seal.

By John R. Sinnock.

HENRY MORGENTHAU, JR.

1891—Born on May 11, 1891, in New York City, the son of Henry and Josephine (Sykes) Morgenthau.

Attended private schools, including Exeter Academy; studied architecture, and later, agriculture at Cornell University at Ithaca, N.Y.

1913—Purchased a large farm in Dutchess County, N.Y., where he specialized in apple growing and dairying.

During the First World War, he worked with Herbert Hoover's U.S. Food Administration on a plan that sent farm tractors to France. Shortly before the end of the war he was commissioned a lieutenant in the Navy.

1916—Married Elinor Fatman, from which union three children were born. Two years after her death in 1949, he married Mrs. Marcelle Puthon Hirsch of New York.

1922—Purchased the *American Agriculturist*, a farm journal, and was its publisher for 12 years.

1929—Was appointed by his long-time friend, Franklin D. Roosevelt, then Governor of New York, as chairman of the New York State Agriculture Advisory Commission. The following year he was named State Commissioner of Conservation and directed a million-acre reforestation program.

1933—Appointed by President Roosevelt as chairman of the Federal Farm Board, and its successor, the Farm Credit Administration. His assignment in these posts was to expand credit, thus easing the burden of mortgages and other debts contracted by farmers prior to the depression. He counseled the President on basic fiscal policy involving abandonment of the traditional gold standard, devaluation of the dollar, and the purchase of gold abroad.

1934—Appointed Secretary of the Treasury. Serving in this post for 11 years, Morgenthau is credited with having exercised a stabilizing effect on administration monetary policies. When he took office, national expenditures were $7.1 billion a year; when he left the Secretaryship, expenditures were at a World War II high of $93.7 billion a year.

Morgenthau defended the dollar against competitive devaluation by other nations. He did this by intervening in the financial markets of the world by buying and selling foreign currencies, gold and dollars. Nazi Germany had set up a system of blocked currencies with marks of different exchange value for various types of trade, producing anarchy in the foreign exchange markets. Operating with a large stabilization fund (derived from the increment coming about as a result of the new value placed on gold) Morgenthau defended the dollar until after the Munich conference of 1938, when a stabilization agreement was reached. The U.S. dollar became the strongest currency in the world.

1939—When Poland was taken over by Germany in 1939, Morgenthau established a procurement service in the Treasury, to facilitate the purchase of American munitions by Britain and France, and he geared the American economy to meet expanded needs following Pearl Harbor.

Morgenthau had previously taken a strong stand against supplying scrap metals to Japan and he had assisted private efforts of Brig. Gen. Claire L. Chennault to obtain his first 100 fighter planes for China's Flying Tigers. (He later aided in providing credit to Nationalist China, and having aid sent to China over the Burma Road.)

1942—Financing the war effort was one of Morgenthau's chief responsibilities. He established a program for the sale of defense (later, war) savings bonds which in 1942, alone, amounted to a billion-dollar distribution of these securities. The bonds not only made possible the extensive war effort, but they also siphoned off excess funds which otherwise would have had a serious inflationary effect.

1944—Morgenthau suggested a plan, which bore his name, under which postwar Germany would have been stripped of industry and reduced to an agricultural nation. This was initiated at the second Quebec conference in 1944, but was later dropped.

In the Bretton Woods conference of 1944, Morgenthau took a leading role in establishing postwar economic policies and currency stabilization which, since depression days, had been one of his major goals. As a result of this conference, the United States now participates in the International Monetary Fund and the Bank for Reconstruction and Development (World Bank).

1945—Morgenthau resigned his office in July 1945, 3 months after the death of President Roosevelt.

1947–50—General chairman of the United Jewish Appeal, which raised $465 million under his direction.

1951–54—Chairman of the board of governors of the American Financial and Development Corporation for Israel, which handled a $500 million bond issue for the new nation.

1967—Died on February 6, 1967, at Poughkeepsie, N.Y.

FRED M. VINSON

Secretary of the Treasury
July 23, 1945 to June 23, 1946
(No. 215)

OBV. Bust of Fred M. Vinson, Secretary of the Treasury.

REV. Secretary of the Treasury, July 23, 1945–June 23, 1946.

By John R. Sinnock.

FRED M. VINSON

1890—Born on January 22, 1890, the son of James and Virginia Vinson, in Louisa, Lawrence County, Ky.

1908–11—Graduated from Kentucky Normal College (1908); B.A. (1909) and LL.B. (1911) from Centre College, Danville, Ky.

1911—Admitted to the Kentucky State Bar and practiced law at Louisa, Ky.

1913—City Attorney at Louisa, until he left to serve in the U.S. Army during the First World War.

1921–24—Commonwealth Attorney of Kentucky's 32d judicial district.

1923—Married Roberta Dixon, from which union two sons were born.

1923–38—Served as a Representative from Kentucky, in the U.S. Congress from 1923 to 1929, and from 1931 to 1938. He made an unsuccessful bid for reelection in 1928, when he managed the Al Smith presidential election in Kentucky.

In Congress, Vinson became a student of Federal taxation, and his knowledge of tax matters received recognition from his colleagues during his service as a member of the House Ways and Means Com-

mittee; duties to which he was assigned including membership on a joint House-Senate committee on tax evasion and avoidance, and chairmanship of a subcommittee of the Ways and Means Committee on internal revenue taxation.

Vinson's other work in Congress included co-authorship of the Vinson-Guffey Coal Act to stabilize the soft coal industry, support of social security legislation, and support of legislative authority for Secretary of State Hull's program of reciprocal trade agreements.

1938–43—Appointed by President Franklin D. Roosevelt as Associate Justice of the U.S. Circuit Court of Appeals for the District of Columbia. Just before accepting this appointment, Vinson had secured congressional approval of the Revenue Bill of 1938.

On March 2, 1942, Chief Justice Stone designated Vinson as chief judge of the Emergency Court of Appeals. This court was established under the Price Control Act to hear cases involving the legality of price control orders.

1943–45—Appointed by the President, as Director of the Office of Economic Stabilization, serving from May 27, 1943, until March 5, 1945.

On March 5, 1945, President Roosevelt transferred Vinson to the post of Federal Loan Administrator, in charge of the Reconstruction Finance Corporation and its subsidiaries, these agencies having been removed from the Department of Commerce.

On April 2, 1945, in one of the last major appointments made by President Roosevelt, Vinson was named Director of the Office of War Mobilization and Reconversion—the "economic czar" of the country.

A report, "The Road to Tokyo and Beyond," which as Director of War Mobilization and Reconversion, he submitted to the President and Congress reflected the scope of his work. It dealt with such broad matters as continued war production, reconversion, surpluses, price and wage controls, food supply, and aid to liberated Europe, and such specific domestic concerns as taxation, small business, competition, labor and management, foreign trade, social security, farm program, public works, and fiscal policy.

1945–46—Appointed Secretary of the Treasury by President Truman; served from July 23, 1945 to June 23, 1946.

1946—Appointed 12th Chief Justice of the United States, and took oath of office on June 24, 1946.

1953—Died at Washington, D.C., on September 8, 1953.

JOHN W. SNYDER

Secretary of the Treasury
June 25, 1946 to January 20, 1953
(No. 216)

OBV. Bust of John W. Snyder, Secretary of the Treasury.
By John R. Sinnock.

REV. The Treasury Seal.
By Gorge T. Morgan.

JOHN W. SNYDER

1895—Born in Jonesboro, Ark., on June 21, 1895, the son of Jerre H. and Ellen (Hatch) Snyder.
Educated in elementary and high schools in Jonesboro, and attended Vanderbilt University.

As a young man, Snyder's initial business experiences were with his uncle, Judge E. A. Rolfe, in farming, the timber business and banking.

1917—Entered the Army, and after training at Fort Logan H. Roots, was assigned to the 32d Division at Waco, Tex. He received further artillery instruction at Samur and Coetquidan, France. He rose to the post of Operations Officer of the Headquarters Staff, 57th Field Artillery Brigade, served in five sectors at the front, and was decorated by the French and United States Armies. He served in the Army of Occupation in Germany and was honorably discharged in 1919, with the rank of captain in the Field Artillery Reserve. He now holds the rank of colonel in the Reserve Corps of that organization. While in the service, he was associated with Harry S. Truman, then an artillery captain.

1919—Began his career in the banking business with the First National Bank of Forrest City, Ark. During the following years, he added to his knowledge of financial management and bank credit through posts he held in banks in Arkansas and Missouri, and his participation in their lending and investment activities.

1920—Married Evlyn Cook. They have one daughter, Mrs. John E. Horton.

1930–36—Snyder was appointed to his first public office, when the national economy and the banking system were experiencing the severe impact of the depression. He served in the field service of the Office of the Comptroller of the Currency to aid in liquidating and reorganizing insolvent banks in the St. Louis area. As a conservator and receiver of these institutions, he followed a policy of aiding the borrowers of insolvent banks by helping them to obtain the credit they needed to continue in business rather than undergo foreclosure or bankruptcy through forced liquidation. This policy resulted in minimum losses to bank depositors and shareholders, because of the high percentage of collections and recoveries on the loan assets of the insolvent banks.

1937-43—Appointed manager of the St. Louis agency of the Reconstruction Finance Corporation, and continued in that post until 1940. He directed the work of this agency in making loans to business and industry in the St. Louis area, which enabled many firms to reestablish their financial stability and credit standing. As the RFC borrowers regained their credit standing, Mr. Snyder encouraged banks and other private lenders to take up the RFC loans and to resume their normal function of providing business and industrial credit to RFC borrowers and other companies. He also supervised the operations of the Disaster Loan Corporation, an RFC subsidiary, in making loans to individuals and business concerns whose property was damaged during the Ohio River floods in 1937.

1940–44—Became Special Assistant to the Chairman of the Board of the RFC, and meanwhile continued to head the St. Louis agency. He assisted in organizing the Defense Plant Corporation, a vital war production financing agency of the RFC, and was appointed Executive Vice President and Director of this agency. In this capacity, he aided in the development of programs to provide financing for building, equipping, and expanding defense industries and war production plants and facilities. By 1944, the Defense Plant Corporation had extended war production financing commitments to business and industry of more than $10 billion, had established nearly a thousand defense production factories, and had financed the expansion of privately owned companies producing aircraft, steel, machine-tools, aluminum, synthetic rubber, chemicals, aviation gasoline, and other war essentials. The activities of this agency extended into 46 States and into many allied countries where vital war materials were produced.

When the Defense Plant Corporation construction program was nearing completion toward the close of the war, Snyder desired to return to the banking business. He was Executive Vice President of the First National Bank in St. Louis, but continued to aid the RFC until August 1944, when he resigned all Federal posts to devote full time to banking and the civic, commercial, and industrial progress of that city.

Assisted in the formation of bank credit pools established throughout the country to provide credit for small and large business, and aided in the formation of the St. Louis Bank Credit Group. He was chairman of the St. Louis Chamber of Commerce War Surplus Disposal Committee, a member of its War Contract Termination and Cancellation Committee, a trustee of the Governmental Research Institute, St. Louis, and a member of the Department of Commerce Business Advisory Council.

1945—Snyder was recalled to Washington as Federal Loan Administrator in April 1945, when the Country was taking the first steps toward returning to a peacetime economy. His primary task was to coordinate and direct the work of Government lending agencies in helping to meet the credit needs of business and industry during the period of reconversion. In addition, many of the RFC's wartime lending agencies required consolidation at the end of the war, and Snyder recommended legislation, which Congress enacted, to absorb the Metals Reserve Corporation, the Disaster Loan Corporation, the Rubber Reserve Corporation and the Defense Plant Corporation into the parent organization. The War Damage Corporation, which had been created to insure private property against damage from enemy attack, was no longer needed, and Snyder felt that its functions should be terminated. He recommended legislation to effect this, and the corporation's business was subsequently liquidated.

1945–46—In July 1945, Snyder was appointed Director of the Office of War Mobilization and Reconversion. He immediately initiated a program to deal with the major adjustments in production and employment during the period of economic transition from war to peace. He coordinated the requirements of the Armed Forces and those of civilian agencies, reconciled transportation difficulties which arose from reversal of the flow of war supplies and personnel at the end of the war in Europe, and expedited the release of skilled manpower from the armed services to meet the critical shortage of manpower in the fuel industry.

Prior to the end of the war in the Pacific, Snyder directed the formulation of plans to remove wartime restrictions over the construction industry after V–J Day, and to ease or eliminate other wartime controls over the economy. He also assisted in meeting labor difficulties in essential industries, including steel and coal mining, to expedite the reconversion program.

Since 1945, the duties of his offices required Snyder's frequent participation in international financial conferences and other foreign relationships and events. In April of that year, he was a delegate to the United States-Mexican Foreign Exchange Conference, and in September 1945, as Director of the Office of War Mobilization and Reconversion, he took part in conferences in Europe with government and military representatives of foreign countries to work out the distribution of surplus war material.

1946—Attended the inauguration of President Aleman of Mexico, representing the President of the United States. He served as Chairman of the International Monetary Fund and International Bank Conference in Washington in 1946, was Vice Chairman of similar conferences in London in 1947, in Washington in 1948 and 1949, in Paris in 1950, again in Washington in 1951, and in Mexico City in 1952.

1947—At the invitation of the President of Brazil, Secretary Snyder visited that country to assist in a survey of economic conditions in the neighbor Republic. He participated in discussions out of which developed the joint Brazilian-United States Technical Commission, which convened in Rio de Janeiro in September 1948. Also in 1947, Snyder participated in a conference in Washington which dealt with British economic conditions and their relationship to the Anglo-American Financial Agreement.

1949—Snyder visited Europe, Africa, and Asia in July 1949, consulting with Treasury, diplomatic and ECA representatives, and officials of foreign governments, on economic and financial conditions in the countries he visited. During this trip, he participated in the Balance of Exchange Conference in London, which was attended by the Foreign and Finance Ministers of the United States, Britain, and Canada, and later was Chairman of the Balance of Exchange Conference in Washington in September 1949, attended by representatives of the same countries.

In November 1949, his official duties took him to Alaska and the Western Pacific. He inspected Coast Guard long-range aids to navigation installations in Alaska, the Aleutians, the Philippines, Guam, and Honolulu. From this inspection trip, there resulted improvements in sea and air navigation equipment and methods which have been of very material aid to the Armed Forces throughout the war in Korea. He also conferred during this trip with the Governors of Alaska and Hawaii on legislative and economic problems. In the Philippines, he discussed economic conditions with the President and Cabinet of that Republic and studied plans for meeting its financial problems.

1950—In Washington, in October 1950, he was one of the conferees in consultations with the Foreign, Financial, and Defense Ministers of France concerning the rearmament program for the democratic nations. In December 1950, he participated in a conference of United States and British Government officials dealing with the Anglo-American economic defense program.

1951—Snyder was one of the American representatives in the United States-French conference held in Washington in January 1951, to discuss economic and military problems in the Far East and Europe. He also attended the meetings of the Council of the North Atlantic Treaty Organization in Ottawa, Canada, in September 1951; in Rome, November 1951, and in Lisbon in February 1952. The Council is composed of the Foreign Ministers, Finance Ministers, and Defense Ministers of the NATO countries.

*　　*　　*　　*　　*

When Snyder was appointed Secretary of the Treasury in 1946, he established, a program of Federal financial management designed to help maintain a stable economy. Among the chief points in this program were: Maintaining confidence in the credit of the Government; reduction of Federal debt during years of budget surpluses; reducing the ownership of Government securities by the banking system; widening the distribution of the debt by spreading its ownership as broadly as possible among individuals and nonbank investors; encouraging the public to practice thrift in all its forms, including investment in U.S. savings bonds;

and developing programs to promote economy and efficiency in the operations of the Treasury Department and its bureaus.

Under Secretary Snyder's administration, the Treasury's postwar management of the national debt contributed materially to successful reconversion and readjustment of the economy after World War II, and helped maintain high levels of production and employment during the period of business readjustment in 1949 and 1950. The bank-held portion of the debt was reduced substantially during the 5 fiscal years ended June 30, 1951. The Treasury retired nearly $27 billion of the holdings of Government securities by the commercial and Federal Reserve Banks during this period. This reduction was made possible by almost $8 billion of net budget surpluses during the 5-year period, an increase of approximately $12 billion in the ownership of Federal securities by Government trust funds and by use of $7 billion of the Treasury's cash balance. There also was brought about during this 5-year period a net reduction of the total Government debt of nearly $15 billion.

Secretary Snyder vigorously promoted a program of thrift, of which the sale of U.S. Savings Bonds is an integral part. Individual ownership of savings bonds increased very substantially during the postwar years.

Shortly after taking office, Secretary Snyder initiated a program to improve the efficiency of the Treasury Department's operations. The program was carried forward steadily under his direction through a Departmental Management Committee composed of representatives of the Treasury's various bureaus. The advice of private management experts outside the Treasury was sought and many efficiency promoting recommendations were adopted. Substantial savings in the cost of operating the Treasury Department were effected, in the view of the Treasury's tremendously increased workload during the postwar years in issuing and redeeming Government securities, currency and coins, and handling a vastly greater number of tax returns than during the years prior to World War II. Modern business machines and equipment were installed, saving thousands of man-hours of work and simplifying the Treasury's recordkeeping tasks. Improved accounting techniques were adopted, and job classification and work simplification practices were utilized in all of the Treasury's bureaus, the Coast Guard, and the Secret Service. A program of employee awards for management improvement suggestions also resulted in increased operating efficiency within the Department.

In later years, Secretary Snyder also successfully urged the Congress to enact reorganization plans to streamline and coordinate the Treasury Department's operations. Reorganization Plan No. 26 of 1950 enabled the Secretary to shift functions among the Treasury's various bureaus and to transfer records, property, and personnel within the Department to improve the Treasury's services and promote internal operating efficiency. The Secretary also sponsored the development and advocated congressional adoption of Reorganization Plan No. 1 of 1952, under which the internal organization and functions of the Bureau of Internal Revenue were comprehensively reorganized to attain maximum economy and effectiveness.

GEORGE M. HUMPHREY

Secretary of the Treasury
January 21, 1953 to July 29, 1957
(No. 217)

OBV. Bust of George M. Humphrey.

By Gilroy Roberts.

REV. An American eagle, with displayed wings, emblazoned with the Treasury Department Seal. Clouds, and 13 stars, forming a constellation. A scroll upon which is inscribed, E. Pluribus Unum. A band of oak leaves binds the central motif, denoting unity and strength. Secretary of the Treasury. United States of America.

By Frank Gasparro.

GEORGE M. HUMPHREY

1890—Born March 8, in Cheboygan, Mich., the son of Watts S. and Caroline (Magoffin) Humphrey.
Public and high school education, Saginaw, Mich.

1908–12—LL.B. from the University of Michigan; admitted to the Michigan State Bar in 1912.

1912–17—Practiced law at Saginaw with his father's firm of Humphrey, Grant & Humphrey. Married in 1913 to Miss Pamela Stark of Saginaw, of which union four children were born.

1917–52—General Counsel of M. A. Hanna and Company, Steel Manufacturers, at Cleveland, Ohio. Made a partner in 1920, vice president in 1922, executive vice president in 1925, president in 1929, and chairman of the board in 1952.

The M. A. Hanna Co., at first a relatively small corporation engaged in the shipment of coal and iron, expanded into a great industrial complex with interests in banking and the production and distribution of copper, steel, coal, rayon, plastics, and natural gas.

Mr. Humphrey was also instrumental in the following industrial activities: organization of National Steel Corporation in 1929, combining Weirton Steel Co., Great Lakes Steel Corp., and Hanna interests in iron ore mines, lake vessels and blast furnaces properties; organization of the Pittsburgh Consolidation Coal Co. in 1945, to form the world's largest bituminous coal producing company.

1946—Chairman, Business Advisory Council, Department of Commerce.

1947—Helped negotiate a coal contract with John L. Lewis of the United Mine Workers of America.

1948–49—Headed the Reparations Survey Committee of the Economic Cooperation Administration.

1950—Was instrumental in organizing the Iron Ore Company of Canada, to develop Labrador-Quebec iron ore deposits.

1952—In addition to serving as chairman of the board of the M. A. Hanna Co., Humphrey was a director of many subsidiary and affiliated companies. He was also chairman of the board, Pittsburgh Consolidation Coal Co.; chairman of the executive commit-tee, National Steel Corp.; and of the Industrial Rayon Corp. He was president of the Iron Ore Company of Canada.

1953—Appointed by President Eisenhower, he became Secretary of the Treasury on January 20, 1953. He served until 1957, when he became chairman of the board of the National Steel Corp.

ROBERT B. ANDERSON

Secretary of the Treasury
July 29, 1957 to January 20, 1961
(No. 218)

OBV. Bust of Robert B. Anderson.

REV. Secretary of the Treasury. United States of America. An American eagle, with displayed wings, emblazoned with a seal carrying the Treasury scales and key. A ribbon inscribed E Pluribus Unum. Below the eagle: In God We Trust.

By Frank Gasparro.

ROBERT B. ANDERSON

1910—Born in Burleson, Johnson County, Tex., on June 4, 1910, the son of Robert L. and Elizabeth (Haskew) Anderson.

1917–28—Attended high school in Godley, Tex., in 1917, Weatherford College (a unit of Southwestern University) in 1927, and the University of Texas, in 1928.

1929–32—Taught at Burleson High School; entered the University of Texas Law School and was graduated with highest honors and received the degree of Bachelor of Laws in 1932.

1932—Elected to the Texas Legislature; was admitted to

the bar of Texas, and began the practice of law in Fort Worth.

1933—While a member of the legislature, Anderson accepted a position as Assistant Attorney General of Texas, and that year also served as adjunct Professor of Law at Texas University.

1934—Appointed State Tax Commissioner, and as such was an ex officio member of the State Racing Commission and of the State Tax Board.

1935—Married Ollie May Rawlings. They have two sons.

1936—Chariman and executive director of the Texas Unemployment Commission, having written the bill passed by the State legislature, setting up the State's first Social Security Agency. Anderson also served as a member of the Texas Economy Commission, on the executive committee of the Texas Research Council and as chairman of the State Board of Education.

1937—General counsel for the Waggoner Estate, made up of extensive ranching and oil properties of the late W. T. Waggoner. Four years later he became general manager of the estate and, as such, operating head of the second largest ranch in Texas, stretching over six northwest Texas counties and producing and refining oil as well as producing livestock and farm crops on thousands of acres. He remained actively in charge of the Waggoner estate until 1952.

1952—Excluded from military service because of an attack of poliomyelitis in his youth, Anderson became a civilian aide to the Secretary of the Army.

1953–54—Secretary of the Navy, by appointment of President Eisenhower.

1954–55—Deputy Secretary of Defense. In August 1955, President Eisenhower bestowed upon Mr. Anderson the Medal of Freedom, the Nation's highest award—in recognition of his service.

1955—Became president of Ventures, Ltd., a Canadian firm with worldwide oil and mining interests.

1957—Appointed Secretary of the Treasury, a post he held until 1961.

Mr. Anderson has served as a director of the Vernon Times Publishing Co., the Vernon Transit Co., Better Business Bureau of Texas, Texas Industrial Conference, American Petroleum Institute, Independent Petroleum Association of America, Texas and Southwestern Cattle Raisers Association, Southwestern Bell Telephone Co. and Northwest Broadcasting Co., Inc. He also served as director and deputy chairman of the board of the Federal Reserve Bank of Dallas. He resigned his Federal Reserve Bank post on January 13, 1953. He was vice president of Associated Refineries, Inc., during World War II and was president of the Texas Mid-Continent Oil and Gas Association for 4 years. He has been a member of the National Manpower Commission and the National Advisory Heart Council.

Mr. Anderson's residence is at Deer Park, Greenwich, Conn.

DOUGLAS DILLON

Secretary of the Treasury
January 21, 1961 to April 1, 1965

OBV. Bust of Douglas Dillon.
By Gilroy Roberts.

REV. Secretary of the Treasury. United States of America. Seated figure of Alexander Hamilton; standing, David Rittenhouse and Robert Morris, founders of the Treasury Department. The Treasury Seal. 1789–1961.

By Frank Gasparro.

DOUGLAS DILLON

1909—Born on August 21, 1909, in Geneva, Switzerland, the son of Clarence and Ann (Douglass) Dillon.

1927—Graduated from Groton School, of which he later became a trustee.

1931—Graduated from Harvard University, A.B., magna cum laude. Member of the Board of Overseers of Harvard University, 1952–58.

Married to the former Phyllis Ellsworth. They have two daughters.

1931–36—Became associated with his father's firm, Dillon, Read & Co., a member of the New York Stock Exchange.

1936—Director of the United States and Foreign Securities Corporation.

1938—Elected vice president and director of Dillon, Read & Co.

1940—Commissioned as ensign in the Naval Reserve. Rose to the rank of lieutenant commander during 4 years of active duty. For his service at Guam, Saipan, and in the Philippines, he received the Legion of Merit, with combat device, the Air Medal, and the Navy Commendation ribbon. Released from active duty in 1945.

1946–53—Chairman of the board of Dillon, Read & Co., president of the United States and Foreign Securities Corporation, and (from 1947) a director of Amerada Petroleum Corp.

1953—Appointed by President Eisenhower as U.S. Ambassador to France. Served from February 1953, until March 1957.

1957—Directed the State Department's economic activities from March 1957, when he was appointed Deputy Under Secretary for Economic Affairs, a position that was elevated to the Under Secretary level by the Congress in 1958.

1959–61—Served as Under Secretary of State from June 12, 1959, to January 4, 1961. In that position, Dillon was responsible for the economic policies and programs of the Department of State and for coordinating the Mutual Security Program, both in its military and nonmilitary aspects. These duties were in addition to the Under Secretary's traditional responsibilities.

He was one of the founders of the Inter-American Development Bank, established in 1959, to promote the economic development of Latin America.

While in the State Department, Dillon attended several Foreign Ministers' meetings and headed a number of U.S. delegations to international conferences. The latter include the meeting of the Committee of 21 of the Organization of American States which, in September 1960, concluded the Act of Bogota, and the Ministerial Meeting in Paris in December 1960, which put into final form the Convention for the Organization for Economic Cooperation and Development.

The Organization for Economic Cooperation and Development (OECD) came about as a merger, which Dillon helped achieve, of the six nations comprising the European Common Market and the seven nations comprising the European Trade Association. Today, OECD includes the United States, Canada, and European nations not originally associated with the two major trading blocks. The purpose of OECD is to reduce trade barriers, aid underdeveloped countries, and to cushion large, sudden capital movements from one country to the other.

1961—Appointed by President Kennedy as Secretary of the Treasury. He took office on January 21, 1961, and served until April 1, 1965.

HENRY H. FOWLER

Secretary of the Treasury
April 1, 1965 to December 20, 1968
(No. 220)

OBV. Bust of Henry H. Fowler.

By Frank Gasparro.

REV. Symmetrical design employing the insignia and seals, linked together by dates and offices, significant to the life and career in Federal service of Secretary Fowler.

By Edgar Z. Steever.

HENRY H. FOWLER

1908—Born in Roanoke, Va., on September 8, 1908, the son of Mack J. and Bertha (Browning) Fowler.

1925—Graduated from Jefferson High School, Roanoke, Va. Four years later, graduated from Roanoke College.

1932—Graduated from Yale Law School (LL.B.); J.S.D. in 1933.

1934–40—Joined the legal staff of the Tennessee Valley Authority where he assisted in the preparation and successful conduct of the 4-year litigation establishing the continuity of that program. By 1939, he had risen to assistant general counsel of the TVA. In 1939, served as chief counsel of a subcommittee of the Senate Committee on Education and Labor.

1938—Married Trudye Pamela Hathcote of Knoxville, Tenn. They have two daughters.

1940—Special counsel to the Federal Power Commission.

1941–44—Prior to and during World War II mobilization,

he was an assistant general counsel of the Board of the Office of Production Management and afterward, of the War Production Board.

1944—Economic advisor, U.S. Mission for Economic Affairs, London.

1945—As special assistant to the administrator, Foreign Economic Administration, he gathered data on the German war potential.

1946–51—Private law practice as senior member of Fowler, Leva, Hawes & Symington, Washington, D.C.

1951—Deputy, and later, administrator of the National Production Authority, with responsibility for planning and programing the distribution of scarce materials for defense and essential civilian needs.

1952–53—Administrator, Defense Production Administration and Director of the Office of Defense Mobilization. Also a member of the National Security Council.

1953–61—Resumed private law practice in Washington, D.C.

1958–61—Members of the Commission on Money and Credit.

1960–61—Member of the National Committee on Government Finance, Brookings Institute.

1961—Served as Under Secretary of the Treasury from February 3, 1961, until April 10, 1964. Played a crucial role in shaping and in the enactment of the Revenue Acts of 1962 and 1964, the liberalization

123

335-478 O - 69 - 9

of depreciation procedures, and the coordination of related programs designed to promote economic expansion.

1963—Appointed head of a Presidential Task Force to seek ways of meeting our balance of payments problem by encouraging greater foreign investment in American securities as well as greater financing for American corporations operating abroad.

1964—On April 27, 1964, the Fowler Task Force reported its recommendations to President Johnson. The President submitted to Congress legislative proposals issuing from that report, and a large measure of a voluntary program to meet the balance-of-payments problem was based on its recommendations.

1964—Returned to private law practice, in Washington, D.C.

1965—Took the oath of office as Secretary of the Treasury on April 1, 1965; served until December 20, 1968.

1969—Joined the investment banking firm of Goldman, Sachs & Co., New York City, as a general partner.

JOSEPH W. BARR

Secretary of the Treasury
December 23, 1968 to January 20, 1969
(No. 222)

OBV. Bust of Joseph W. Barr.

By Frank Gasparro.

REV. Secretary of the Treasury, December 23, 1968 to January 20, 1969. Four smaller seals around a dominant Treasury Department seal. Each seal represents highlights and achievements in the Secretary's life.

By Edgar Z. Steever.

JOSEPH W. BARR

1918—Born in Vincennes, Ind., on January 17, the son of Oscar L. and Stella F. (Walker) Barr.

Educated at DePauw University (A.B., 1939);

Harvard University (M.A., 1941, in theoretical economics).

1939—Married Beth Ann Williston. They have five children.

1942–45—U.S. Navy, May 1942 to October 1945. Awarded Bronze Star at Anzio Beachhead. Released with the rank of lieutenant commander.

Treasurer, O. L. Barr Grain Co., Indiana, and Barr Development Corp., Illinois. Executive vice president, Merz Engineering, Indianapolis, Ind.

1958–60—Member of Congress. Served on the House Banking and Currency Committe, where he helped write and defend legislation creating the Inter-

American Bank and the International Development Association. Also worked with the Hoover Commission on Accounting Procedures.

1961–64—Assistant to the Secretary of the Treasury, handling congressional relations.

1964–65—Chairman, Federal Deposit Insurance Corporation.

1965—Under Secretary of the Treasury, April 29, 1965, to December 23, 1968.

1968–69—Appointed by President Johnson as Secretary of the Treasury. Served until the change of administration.

1969—Vice Chairman of the Board of the American Security & Trust Company, Washington, D.C.

Directors of the Mint

DAVID RITTENHOUSE

OBV. David Rittenhouse 1st Director U.S. Mint, 1792–1795. Bust of Dr. Rittenhouse.

REV. "He belonged to the whole human race." Born 1732. Died 1796. Exergue: Medal Series of the U.S. Mint. 1871. J. Pollock, Director.

By William Barber.

DAVID RITTENHOUSE

1732—Born in Germantown, Pa., on April 8, the son of Mathias R. and Elizabeth (Williams) Rittenhouse, of Dutch and Welsh extraction.

Spent his youth on his father's farm. At the age of eight, he constructed a complete working model of a water mill. At the age of 12 he inherited a chest of tools, together with some books on arithmetic and mathematics. Self-educated, he went on to become one of the country's most distinguished scientists of his day—astronomer, mathematician, a mechanical construction genius, and a world famous philosopher.

1750—At the age of 17, Rittenhouse made a wooden clock which included an innovation in the operation of the pendulum. A year later, he went into the clockmaking business.

To further his study of astronomy, he erected an observatory as part of his clock shop. Some of the instruments of astronomy were made with his own hands.

1763—Again, making his own instruments, he determined the boundary line between Pennsylvania and Maryland. His observations were accepted by Mason and Dixon when they extended the line.

1766—Married Eleanor Colston. They had two daughters.

1767—Constructed his celebrated orrery, an apparatus that illustrates the relative positions and motions of bodies in the solar system by rotation and revolution of balls moved by wheelwork. This was sold to Princeton College and a copy to the College of Philadelphia (University of Pennsylvania).

1768—Awarded the degree of Master of Arts, conferred by the University of Pennsylvania.

His observation of the transit of Venus, that was to occur in 1769, exhibited in a remarkable degree his great astronomical knowledge and also his skill. To make this observation, Rittenhouse built a transit telescope, believed to be the first telescope made in America.

1769—Established the boundary line between New York and New Jersey. Soon afterward he made a thermometer on the principle of the expansion and contraction of metals.

1770—Moved to Philadelphia and took his shop and observatory with him, to be nearer to library sources and to materials used in making his clocks.

Continued his studies of scientific matter, as well as philosophy, from books brought to him from England. A year after he moved to Philadelphia, his wife Eleanor died. A year later, he married Hannah Jacobs of Philadelphia.

Appointed one of three commissioners of the Loan Office.

1771—Elected Secretary of the American Philosophical Society.

1772—Awarded the degree of Master of Arts from Princeton (a doctorate from Princeton followed, in 1789). Surveyed and ascertained the levels of the country between the Susquehanna and the Delaware Rivers.

1774—Ran the northwestern boundary line between New York and Pennsylvania.

1775—Chosen a member of the Assembly of Pennsylvania, to fill the vacant seat of Benjamin Franklin. Elected that same year as a member of the convention called for the purpose of forming a State constitution.

Appointed "to prepare moulds for the casting of clock-weights, and send them to some iron-furnace, exchanging them with the inhabitants for their leaden clock-weights." This was his first Revolutionary War service.

In October 1775, Rittenhouse was appointed as engineer of the Committee on Public Safety, and was charged with responsibility for manufacturing and storing ordnance equipment, as well as to "fix upon a method of fastening chain for the protection of the river." He became vice president of this committee in 1776, and its president in 1777.

1776—Upon adoption of the Philadelphia State Constitution, Rittenhouse was elected Treasurer of the Commonwealth, a position he continued to fill by annual election until 1789, when he declined further service.

1779—First professor of astronomy at the University of Pennsylvania, a post he held until 1782.

Appointed by the Legislature of Pennsylvania to adjust a dispute between that State and Virginia; effected a satisfactory determination of that controversy.

1782—Elected a Fellow of the Academy of Arts and Sciences of Boston.

1784—Awarded a Master of Arts degree by William and Mary College of Virginia. It was in this year that he ground lenses and made a pair of spectacles for George Washington.

1786—After participating in a determination of the western limits of Pennsylvania, Rittenhouse was employed in fixing the northern line which divides Pennsylvania from New York. The following year, he performed his last big survey, in settling a boundary dispute that had arisen between the States of Massachusetts and New York.

1789—Received the degree of Doctor of Laws from the College of New Jersey (now Rutgers University).

1791—Appointed by President Washington on the commission to receive subscriptions in Pennsylvania for the Bank of the United States.

Rittenhouse succeeded Benjamin Franklin in 1791 as president of the American Philosophical Association. Thomas Jefferson, who succeeded Rittenhouse in that office, said of him: "We have supposed Mr. Rittenhouse second to no astronomer living; that in genius he must be first, because he is self-taught."

1792–95—Although his health was failing rapidly, Rittenhouse consented, at the urgings of Thomas Jefferson and Alexander Hamilton, to accept the appointment by President Washington, as Director of the Mint.

The national coinage was established by Act of April 2, 1792. The appointment of Dr. Rittenhouse as Mint Director is April 14, 1792.

The mechanical and philosophical nature of David Rittenhouse stood him in good stead during the difficult formative days, in launching the fledgling mint upon its historic course and guiding it through a crucial period of organization. To Rittenhouse fell the responsibility of purchasing the ground; erecting the necessary buildings; procuring and assembling machinery, implements, and apparatus; and the employment of skillful artists and mechanics. It has been said that his interest in the new mint even caused him, upon occasion, to make advances from his personal funds for work to be performed.

The first coins of the United States struck under the direction of Rittenhouse, for general circulation, were copper cents and half cents, minted in 1793. Silver coinage commenced in 1794, with the issuance of dollars, half dollars, and half dimes, the 5-cent denomination.

The legislation establishing the Mint made provision for an Assay Commission, the yearly testing of our coinage, under the careful eye of such notables as the Chief Justice of the United States, the Secretary and Comptroller of the Treasury, the Secretary for the Department of State, and the Attorney General of the United States. Required to be present at this "Trial of the Pyx" is the Director of the Mint, since the days of David Rittenhouse.

During Rittenhouse's tenure, foreign gold and silver coins were made legal tender at certain stipulated rates, and persons were at liberty to bring gold and silver into the mint to have it struck into coin, free of expense.

1795—Resigned as Director of the Mint because of ill health. This same year, he was elected as a foreign member of the Royal Society of London.

1796—Dr. Rittenhouse died on June 26, 1796, in the 65th year of his life. His body was buried in the garden adjoining his home in Philadelphia, but was later moved to the cemetery adjoining the Presbyterian Church on Pine Street, in Philadelphia.

ROBERT MASKELL PATTERSON, M.D.

Director of the Mint
July 1835 to July 1851
(No. 302)

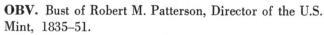

OBV. Bust of Robert M. Patterson, Director of the U.S. Mint, 1835–51.

REV. A parting token of regard from the officers and clerks of the Mint. 1851; above, on a scroll, Codex Monetae 1837; the whole within serpent, palm, and laurel wreath.

By Charles Cushing Wright.

ROBERT MASKELL PATTERSON, M.D.

1787—Born in Philadelphia, Pa., March 23. His father was Prof. Robert Patterson, fourth Director of the Mint.

1804—A.B. degree from the University of Pennsylvania in 1804, and an M.D. degree from this university in 1808.

1809–11—Studied physical sciences in Paris, and in 1811 completed his education as a chemist under Sir Humphrey Davy in London.

The American Philosophical Society accepted him as a member at the age of 22, the youngest man ever to have been admitted. In 1843, he delivered the discourse at its centennial celebration. In 1849, he became its president.

1812—Patterson returned to the United States from abroad, and became a professor of mathematics in the University of Pennsylvania. (He served as vice provost from 1814 to 1823, and as a professor of natural philosophy, chemistry, and mathematics until 1828.)

1828—Accepted a professorship with the University of Virginia, and remained until 1835.

1835-51—By appointment by President Andrew Jackson, Patterson became Director of the Mint in July, remaining until ill health forced his retirement in July of 1851.

Dr. Patterson's term of office was one of great interest in the history of the Mint. He took an active interest in coin designs and one of his first acts after entering upon office was to introduce changes which might make the coinage more creditable specimens of taste and art.

Legislation authorizing mints at New Orleans, La., Dahlonega, Ga., and Charlotte, N.C., had been passed by Act of March 3, 1835, at the close of the term of his predecessor, Dr. Samuel Moore. However, the organization and development of these branches fell to Dr. Patterson.

Many important improvements were made in every department of the Mint, not the least of which was the introduction of steam powered coining presses. The first coinage took place on March 23, 1836.

Patterson prepared the Act of January 18, 1837, which revised all previous laws and regulations, and introduced some very beneficial modifications. The standard fineness of U.S. coins was fixed by this law.

Gold was discovered in California during the closing years of Patterson's term, and it was his responsibility to administer the increased operations necessitated by the processing of the vast deposits of gold which came to the mints.

The Act of March 3, 1849, authorized the coinage of gold dollars and $20 pieces. The Act of March 3, 1851, authorized the coinage of silver 3-cent pieces, which were first issued while Patterson was still Director.

1854—Dr. Patterson died in Philadelphia, September 5.

JAMES ROSS SNOWDEN

Director of the Mint
June 1853 to April 1861
(No. 303)

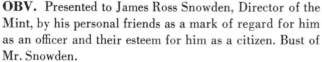

OBV. Presented to James Ross Snowden, Director of the Mint, by his personal friends as a mark of regard for him as an officer and their esteem for him as a citizen. Bust of Mr. Snowden.

REV. The Mint of the United States of America, Philadelphia. Front view of the building. Built 1832, Rendered Fireproof 1856.

By Anthony Paquet.

JAMES ROSS SNOWDEN

1809—Born December 9, in Chester, Pa., the son of the Rev. Nathaniel Randolph Snowden, curator of Dickinson College and Sarah (Gustine) Snowden.

1830—After attending Dickinson College and studying law, was admitted to the bar at 19. Served in the State militia, elected a colonel of a local regiment, and presided at a State military convention in 1845. Snowden began his practice in Franklin, Venango County, Pa., and later served as district attorney in that county.

1838—Elected to the State legislature of Pennsylvania, serving until 1844. Speaker of the House of Representatives, 1842–44.

1845—Elected Treasurer of the State of Pennsylvania, serving two terms; improved the character of State loans.

1848—Appointed Treasurer of the U.S. Mint, and served also as Assistant Treasurer of the United States in Philadelphia.

Married Susan Engle Patterson of Philadelphia; they had five children.

1850—Resumed the practice of law, in Pittsburgh, Pa., where he was a solicitor for the Pennsylvania Railroad Co.

1853–61—Snowden assumed the duties of Director of the Mint under an appointment by President Franklin Pierce, remaining until April of 1861.

Early in his tenure he advocated "a lighter and more convenient coin for the cumbrous cent" then in use. The Act of February 21, 1857, authorized a reduction in the size of the cent and changed the alloy to copper-nickel. This same legislation also ended the coinage of half cents and directed that the Director's annual report be made to the Secretary of the Treasury on a fiscal year basis so that the information could appear in his annual report to the Congress on the finances. Until 1857, Mint reports were made on a calendar year basis.

The mint building was made fireproof during Snowden's term of office, and a medal department was formally established at the Philadelphia Mint in 1855, through which medals of national historical interest have been manufactured and sold to the public for over 100 years.

To Snowden, also, is given the credit for having first used the term "proof" coins, to designate these special collectors' pieces.

While the Act of March 3, 1853, authorizing the establishment of an Assay Office in New York City, was passed while his predecessor was in office, to Snowden fell the responsibility of its erection. The doors were opened for business October 10, 1854, for the assaying of gold and silver bullion and foreign coin, and for casting the same into bars, ingots or disks. The Congress, responsive to the fast-growing demands of the country's great commercial and financial center, passed this legislation to provide for the establishment in the city of New York of a Government institution for the ready redemption of currency for specie, and to receive and disburse gold and silver bullion.

The first mintage of U.S. nickel coins took place, with the issuance of the copper-nickel cent authorized by the Act of February 21, 1857.

1861—Snowden resigned as Director of the Mint in April, and was appointed prothonotary of the Supreme Court of Pennsylvania, which position he held for 12 years.

1873—Returned to the practice of law, but continued to contribute for publication numerous articles on coins and the monetary system.

1878—James Ross Snowden died March 21, at Hulmesville, Pa.

JAMES POLLOCK

OBV. The Hon. James Pollock, L.L.D. Bust of Governor Pollock.

REV. Governor of Pennsylvania 1855–1858. Director of the U.S. Mint 1861. Resigned 1866. Reappointed 1869. A wreath of oak and laurel frames the inscription.

By William Barber.

JAMES POLLOCK

1810—Born in Milton, Northumberland County, Pa., on September 11, the son of William and Sarah (Wilson) Pollock.

1831—Was graduated from Princeton University. Studied law under Samuel Hepburn, at Milton, Pa.

1835—Appointed district attorney of Northumberland County, having been admitted to the county bar 2 years previously.

1844—Was sent to the 28th Congress as Whig Representative and served, through reelection, until 1849. His committee appointments were territories, claims, and ways and means. In 1848, he introduced a bill and later headed a committee favoring the construction of a railroad to the Pacific Coast. He also assisted Samuel Morse in obtaining Government assistance in connection with the invention of the telegraph.

1850—Became president judge, 8th judicial district of

Pennsylvania; declined renomination and returned to private law practice.

1854—Elected Governor of Pennsylvania and served until January of 1858. While Governor, Pollock laid the foundation for a public school system, reduced the State debt and thus reduced State taxes. He declined reelection and returned to the practice of law.

1857—During the financial crisis in Pennsylvania, Governor Pollock called a special session of the legislature and obtained a statute which restored specie payments, thereby restoring public confidence.

1860–61—Together with other prominent men of his time, and as a representative of Pennsylvania, Pollock attended the Peace Conference which met in Washington, D.C., to discuss means of adverting war between the North and the South.

1861–66—President Abraham Lincoln appointed Pollock Director of the Mint in May, to guide the Mint through an eventful 5 years.

The mint at Denver, established by Act of Congress approved April 21, 1862, was intended exclusively for the coinage of gold. However, due to difficulties in finding a suitable location, and setting up the operation, the opening was delayed until the latter part of September 1863. Operations were confined to the melting, refining, assaying, and stamping of bullion, and the return of the bullion to depositors in unparted bars, stamped with the weight and fineness. No coinage was executed at Denver until 1906.

An act was passed March 3, 1863, authorizing a branch mint at Carson City, but operations did not commence there until 1870, even though preparations for its erection were started.

In 1864, a new denomination was introduced into the coinage system in the form of a copper 2-cent coin. The motto IN GOD WE TRUST was adopted during Pollock's term of office and it is upon this 2-cent coin that it first appeared.

A nickel 3-cent piece was authorized by Act of March 3, 1865, and a 5-cent nickel piece was authorized by Act of May 16, 1866.

Pollock was faced with an unparalleled demand for coins, brought about by the Civil War conditions, which added greatly to his responsibilities. The mints at Charlotte, Dahlonega, and New Orleans had been closed because of war activities in the South, and the increased demand for coins placed a burden on the remaining mints which could not be successfully met. As a result, such an acute shortage developed that many privately issued tokens were manufactured to supply the necessary small change.

1866—Pollock's tenure as Director ended in September and he returned to private life.

1869–73—Pollock was reappointed Director of the Mint by President Ulysses S. Grant and commenced his second term in May. He remained until 1873. The mint at Carson City opened its doors January 8, 1870; an assay office was opened at Boise, Idaho, and received the first deposits in March of 1872.

A most important piece of legislation known as the Coinage Act of 1873 was passed February 12th of that year, which revised and amended existing laws pertaining to the mints and assay offices, and coinage. It provided for formation of the Bureau of the Mint as an agency of the Treasury Department, with headquarters in Washington, D.C.

The motto E Pluribus Unum had appeared on U.S. coins from time to time since 1795. This act now made its use mandatory on certain of the gold and silver coins.

1873—Pollock resigned in March as Director of the Mint, choosing to remain at the mint in Philadelphia as Superintendent. Henry R. Linderman, who had worked extensively on the 1873 act, was reappointed by President Grant as Director and took up his duties in the newly established headquarters in Washington, D.C.

1880—Pollock was appointed Naval Officer of Customs at Philadelphia and served until 1884, when he again resumed his law practice.

1886—Served as Federal Chief Supervisor of Elections.

1890—Governor Pollock died in Lock Haven, Pa., April 19.

HENRY RICHARD LINDERMAN

Director of the Mint
April 1867 to May 1869
April 1873 to December 1878

(No. 305)

OBV. Bust of Dr. Henry R. Linderman.

REV. H. R. Linderman, Director of the U.S. Mint from April, 1867 to May, 1869. A wreath of oak and laurel frames the inscription.

By William Barber.

HENRY RICHARD LINDERMAN

1825—Born December 26, in Pike County, Pa., the son of Dr. John Jordan and Rachel (Brodhead) Linderman. Self-educated, Linderman studied medicine under his father, and later received a diploma from the New York College of Physicians and Surgeons.

1855—In addition to being a practicing physician, Linderman took an active interest in politics. President Pierce appointed him as Chief Clerk of the Mint in Philadelphia, where he stayed until 1864, before resigning to become a partner in a firm of stockbrokers in that city.

1867—President Andrew Johnson appointed Linderman to be Director of the Mint, succeeding William Millward, whose term was ended by death after only 6 months in office.

The Mint Director's Report for 1867 carries a reference to the acquisition of "an important and interesting machine," for making reduced copies of bas reliefs "by which all the freedom of execution

of which the larger model is susceptible in the hands of the artist, can be preserved in the most minute proportions in its application to the face of the coin for which it may be designed."

The reopening of the Charlotte Mint as an assay office took place in 1868.

1869—Linderman resigned his position as Director of the Mint in May of this year, because of conflicting political views. However, because of his grasp of Mint affairs and vast knowledge in the monetary field, the Secretary of the Treasury continued to call upon him to perform numerous important mint and monetary missions, both at home and abroad.

1870—Commissioner of the Government to the Pacific Coast to investigate the San Francisco and Carson Mints, and to adjust some intricate bullion questions.

1871—Commissioner to Europe, to examine the coinage systems of the great powers.

1872—Commissioner, with Dr. Robert E. Rogers of the University of Pennsylvania, for fitting up the Government refinery at the San Francisco Mint. In the same year, he wrote an elaborate report on the condition of the gold and silver markets of the world.

1873—Together with Comptroller of the Currency, John Jay Knox, Linderman authored the Coinage Act of 1873, passed February 12, which codified and amended existing laws pertaining to the mints and assay offices, and coinage. There had been no revision of these laws since 1837. The trade dollar, a project close to Linderman's heart, was authorized by this act and first coined in 1873, for circulation in the Orient. This act discontinued the minting of the half dime and 2-cent bronze coins.

The Act of February 12, 1873, consolidated all mint institutions throughout the country into a bureau of the Treasury Department. The title of Director of the Mint was reserved for the chief officer of the Bureau, and the heads of the various mints were designated as Superintendents.

President Grant appointed Linderman as the first Director of the Bureau of the Mint. His 5-year term began in April of 1873 and expired December 7, 1878.

1874—The Congress approved legislation to correct the par of exchange between Great Britain and the United States, based on an exhaustive study made by Linderman of the relationship between these two moneys, since colonial times.

1875—The Act of March 3, 1875, authorized the coinage of a silver 20-cent piece but its use was discontinued by authority of the Act of May 2, 1878, before Linderman left office.

1876—The U.S. Mint was authorized to make foreign coinage by the Act of January 29, 1874. A coinage order for Venezuela, in 1876, was the first foreign coinage to be executed.

Assay office operations were resumed at the New Orleans Mint in 1876, the first activity there since the Civil War forced suspension of operations at that institution.

The Act of March 3, 1878, allotted funds for a laboratory in the Office of the Director of the Mint at Washington. It has been here, through the years, that representative samples of coinage from all the mints have been tested to assure the coinage meets specified standards. The laboratory also performs work for the Treasury agencies, and others, for the purpose of detecting and preventing counterfeiting, and for customs requirements.

1877—Linderman published a book, *Money and Legal Tender in the United States,* giving his views on financial questions.

1878—Linderman's work was highly regarded by others. The Japanese Government offered him $50,000 per year to organize a mint service, an offer he declined. The Director of the French Mint stated that Dr. Linderman's name was as celebrated on the continent of Europe in connection with his opinions on the double standard of metallic currency as that of Garibaldi in connection with the Italian Revolution.

1879—Dr. Henry R. Linderman died in Washington, D.C., on January 27, 1879.

HORATIO CHAPIN BURCHARD

Director of the Mint
February 1879 to June 1885
(No. 306)

OBV. Bust of Horatio C. Burchard.

REV. Director of the Mint of the United States. Appointed Feb. 22, 1879. A laurel wreath frames the inscription.

By Charles E. Barber.

HORATIO CHAPIN BURCHARD

1825—Born at Marshall, N.Y., September 22.

1850—Graduated from Hamilton College, New York; studied law.

1852—Admitted to the State bar.

1854—Began the practice of law in Freeport, Ill., where he also became interested in the public affairs of the municipality.

1857—Was school commissioner for 3 years.

1863—Member of the Illinois State House of Representatives, serving until 1866.

1869—Elected to the 41st Congress to fill the vacancy caused by the resignation of Elihu B. Washburne, and served by reelection until 1879.

1879–85—President Rutherford B. Hayes appointed Burchard Director of the Mint in February 1879, and Chester A. Arthur reappointed him in February 1884. His tenure of office ended in 1885, when he resigned to resume the practice of law.

In 1879, he made the recommendation that the 3-cent nickel piece be discontinued as serving no useful purpose. A change in the design of the 5-cent nickel piece took place when the Liberty Head type was issued January 8, 1883. During this year, also,

the Director recommended that coinage of the gold dollar be discontinued as the coin was too small for monetary use, and virtually out of circulation. It was also urged that the act authorizing the coinage of trade dollars be repealed.

Application having been made by the Government of Hawaii for coinage at the San Francisco Mint of $1 million in silver coins, the necessary authorization was granted by the Secretary of the Treasury and the coinage was commenced on November 17, 1883. It was executed and completed before the close of the fiscal year.

In 1872, the assay office at Boise, Idaho, which had been authorized in 1869, received its first deposits; and an assay office was established in 1881 at St. Louis, Mo.

Congress had earlier authorized the reopening of the New Orleans Mint and operations commenced February 20, 1879.

The regulations governing the mints and assay offices were revised to bring their directives into harmony with the then current provisions of the statutes.

1885—After his resignation as Mint Director in June, Burchard became a member of the commission to revise the Illinois State revenue laws.

1893—Was placed in charge of awards for mines and metallurgy at the World's Columbian Exposition at Chicago.

1908—Mr. Burchard died in Freeport, Ill., May 14.

JAMES PUTNAM KIMBALL

Director of the Mint

July 1885 to October 1889

(No. 307)

OBV. Bust of James P. Kimball.

REV. Within a laurel wreath, the inscription, Director of the Mint of the United States. June, 1885.

By Charles E. Barber.

JAMES PUTNAM KIMBALL

1836—Born at Salem, Mass., April 26.

Educated at the Lawrence Scientific School of Harvard; continued his studies abroad in the fields of engineering, mining and metallurgy.

1859—Took part in geological surveys of the Upper Mississippi Regions of Illinois and Wisconsin and the southeastern part of Iowa.

1861—Professor of chemistry and economic geology at New York State Agricultural College, at Ovid.

1862—Commissioned by the President of the United States as Assistant Adjutant General of Volunteers with the rank of captain. Served on the staffs of Generals McClelland, Burnside, Hooker, and Meade, thus taking part in campaigns of the Army of the Potomac and of the Rappahannock. Ill health forced his resignation from the Army in December of 1863. He was breveted major in 1865, for "gallant and meritorious services."

1864—Resumed his mining practice in New York City for the next 10 years, receiving wide acclaim in this field.

1874—Received the honorary appointment of Professor of Geology at Lehigh University, Bethlehem, Pa., and was associated with that institution for another 10 years, even while continuing his business in New York City.

1881—Vice president of the American Institute of Mining Engineers.

1885–89—Dr. Kimball's appointment as Director of the Mint was made by President Grover Cleveland. At the time of his appointment, Kimball was president of the Everett Iron Co., one of the most extensive blast furnaces in Pennsylvania.

The Act of March 3, 1887, provided for the redemption of trade dollars for a 6-month period in exchange for a like amount of standard silver dollars, or of subsidiary coins of the United States; provided that those so exchanged should not again be paid out, and also repealed the provision of law authorizing coinage of trade dollars.

The Mint Regulations of Business were revised in 1887, to incorporate important changes in the method of reporting the business of the institutions in the schedule of charges on deposits of bullion, and in the method of reporting on bullion at the mints and assay offices.

A proposal was made for the discontinuance of the $3 gold piece due to its unpopularity as a circulating medium.

Special consideration was given enlargement of

139

the Philadelphia Mint, which resulted in an appropriation approved by the Congress October 2, 1888, for an additional story, enlargement of the building, including vault, alterations, and other necessary work.

1889—Dr. Kimball resigned October 15, 1889. He had a wide reputation in the scientific and technical fields and was the author of many papers which were published both at home and abroad.

1913—Dr. Kimball died October 23.

EDWARD OWEN LEECH

Director of the Mint
October 1889 to May 1893
(No. 308)

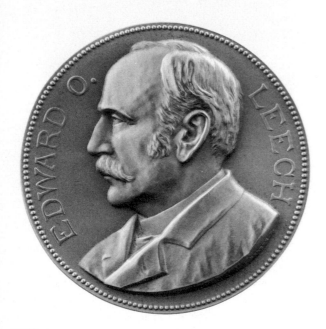 

OBV. Bust of Edward O. Leech.

REV. Edward Owen Leech. Director of the Mint. Appointed in Mint Bureau upon its organization, 1873. Director, October 16, 1889. An olive wreath frames the inscription.

By Charles E. Barber.

EDWARD OWEN LEECH

1850—Born December 9, in Washington, D.C., the son of Daniel D. Tompkins and Eliza (Owen) Leech.

1869—Employed by the Bureau of Statistics in the Treasury Department, as a clerk, following his graduation from the Columbian University.

1873—Transferred to the Bureau of the Mint as an assay clerk, under Dr. Henry R. Linderman. Some years later, in the capacity of computer of bullion, his efficiency and responsibilities were recognized by a substantial increase in salary granted through an act of Congress.

1886—Graduated from National Law University, with the degree of LL.M.

For a long while prior to his appointment as Director of the Mint, Mr. Leech was in charge of preparing the widely read important national and international monetary statistics published in the Annual Report of the Director of the Mint, as well as information on the gold and silver production in the United States and foreign countries.

1889—President Benjamin Harrison appointed Leech to the position of Director of the Mint. He took office October 16.

Through his continuing work in the monetary and precious metals fields, he acquired the reputation of being one of the best informed men in the United States on the subject of the monetary systems of the different countries of the world.

1890—Coinage of the $3 gold and $1 gold coins was discontinued by provisions of the Act of September 26,

1890, which also discontinued the coinage of the 3-cent nickel coins.

Mr. Leech's Annual Report for 1890 deals with the desirability of new designs for our coins, mentioning that there had been none for half a century and that existing legislation precluded any change. Legislation was enacted September 26, 1890, authorizing changes. Invitations were then issued for new designs. A jury decided none submitted were worthy, and Mint Engraver Charles E. Barber was asked to prepare designs for the half, quarter, and dime, which were issued in 1892.

1891—The Act of March 3, 1891, authorized the erection of a new mint building in Philadelphia, but it was to be 10 years before these plans culminated in the transfer of operations to new quarters.

1892—The Act of August 5, 1892, authorized the first commemorative coin issued by the U.S. Mint, that for the Columbian Exposition in Chicago in 1892 and 1893. The first commemorative coin was struck November 19, 1892.

In order to facilitate the striking of medals, a powerful hydraulic press was substituted for the old-fashioned and ponderous screw press in use for many years.

1893—Leech resigned as Director of the Mint effective on June 1, to become vice president of the National Union Bank in New York City.

1900—Mr. Leech died in New York City on May 1.

ROBERT E. PRESTON

Director of the Mint
November 1893 to February 1898

(No. 309)

OBV. Bust of Robert E. Preston.

REV. Upon a tablet suspended from a laurel wreath, appear the inscriptions: Appointed Clerk First Auditor's Office April 1856. Examiner Mint Bureau July 1874. Director of the Mint November 1893.

By Charles E. Barber.

ROBERT E. PRESTON

1836—Born in Tennessee.

1856—Preston joined the Bureau of the Mint on April 1,

when he was appointed as a clerk in the First Auditor's Office.

1874—Appointed Examiner.

1893—President Grover Cleveland appointed Mr. Preston as Director of the Mint and he took office in November of this year. At the time, the following article appeared in the New York Times:

"Robert E. Preston, appointed * * * to be the Director of the Mint, has been connected with the Bureau of the Mint since it was organized.

Entering it under Director Linderman in 1873, he was continued under all the succeeding administrations and has become thoroughly familiar with its operations and is a trustworthy and businesslike officer.

"Adverse political fortune has kept him hitherto from public office to which he has been promoted, but he has been an able assistant to all the men who have ever held the chief place. He has never used his position to celebrate himself, nor has he vexed the souls of his superior officers by startling suggestions calculated to magnify Preston.

"Since the departure of the last Director he has conducted the Mint on plain business principles and without any very settled expectation that he would be selected to succeed Mr. Leech. * * *."

Edward O. Leech, whom Preston succeeded as Director of the Mint, was quoted as having said no better appointment, in his opinion, could have been made. His best work in the Mint, according to Leech, was statistical. Great care had been taken by Directors for many years in the compilation of facts and figures about finance and coinage until it was generally admitted that the statistical papers of the Mint were the best issued anywhere.

Preston was Director of the Mint at a time when there was great activity in the monetary metals field and was a contributor to publications on the subjects of silver and coinage, and the monetary field in general.

Consideration was given to changing the alloys of the minor coins during Preston's tenure. To this end, experimental pieces were struck in the 1-cent and 5-cent denominations. In December of this year, pure aluminum and nickel alloy coins were made but proved unsatisfactory, either because they were no improvement over alloys then being used, or because they were not adaptable for coinage purposes, i.e., too soft or too hard. In February of 1897, further experiments were conducted during the session of the Annual Assay Commission, but the results were not favorable.

1898—Mr. Preston resigned from the Director's position in February, and immediately reentered the Mint Service as an Examiner.

1911—Mr. Preston died June 24.

GEORGE EVAN ROBERTS

Director of the Mint
February 1898 to July 1907
July 1910 to November 1914

(No. 310)

OBV. Bust of George E. Roberts.

REV. On a tablet within an oak wreath: Director of the Mint of the United States. Appointed Feb. 14, 1898.

By Charles E. Barber.

GEORGE EVAN ROBERTS

1857—Born in Colesburg, Delaware County, Iowa, August 19, the son of David and Mary (Harvey) Roberts.

1878—Became the owner of the Fort Dodge Messenger, which interests he retained until 1909.

1883—Elected State Printer of Iowa and held this office for 6 years.

1894—Author of "Coin at School in Finance," written in reply to the free-silver document, "Coin's Financial School." This was followed by "Money, Wages and Prices" which Roberts published in 1895, and "Iowa and the Silver Question" published in 1896. These pamphlets were circulated widely by the National Sound Money League, and they exercised a large influence on the presidential campaign of 1896. McKinley won this campaign on a platform of adherence to the gold standard, over William Jenings Bryan who campaigned for the free coinage of silver.

1898—Roberts took an active part in State politics. Notice of his ability as a financial writer and speaker was

brought to the attention of President McKinley by Treasury Secretary Lyman J. Gage. He was appointed Director of the Mint in February 1898, and again by President Theodore Roosevelt in 1903, serving in all, 9 years.

Accounting for his stewardship of the Mint, Roberts reported in 1907:

"The organization of the service has expanded to the extent of one new coinage mint, opened in 1906 in Denver, and one important assay office, opened in 1898 in Seattle. The capacity of all the mints was greatly increased by the introduction of new and improved machinery. The old mint at Philadelphia, built in the early thirties, has been replaced by a splendid new one, undoubtedly the finest building ever constructed for coinage uses, and thoroughly equipped with machinery of the most approved type. The new mint at Denver, although of smaller capacity than the one at Philadelphia has thoroughly modern and perfect equipment.

"By the originality and interested labors of the workmen and officers practically every process in the preparation and treatment of the metals has been changed in this time.

"Contrary to the policy of the European mints, it has always been the practice here to conduct refineries in connection with coinage operations, being thus enabled to receive crude bullion.

"In 1898 the time-honored acid-parting methods were used in all the mints and in the assay office at New York. The partial suppression of acid fumes (it could be made only partial) was expensive and they remained a constant source of complaint from Wall Street.

"In 1907 all is done by electrolysis. Experiments in refining gold by the electric current were conducted by the melter and refiner of the mint at Philadelphia as early as 1898, with such satisfactory results that a plant for actual work was about to be installed when an inspection of the records of the Patent Office showed that his process was covered by a patent issued to Dr. Emil Wohlwill, of Hamburg, Germany. The facts were reported to the Mint Bureau and negotiations opened with the patentee which resulted in the purchase of a right to use the process in the mint at Philadelphia. A small plant was installed in the old mint, and in August of 1900, 20,000 ounces of electrolytic refined gold was produced of almost absolute purity. Experiments looking to an equally efficient method for refining silver were prosecuted, but the problem here was a more difficult one, since in the parting of mint deposits considerable quantities of base metal have to be reckoned with, such as copper, lead, etc. In the Moebius process, then coming into extended use in private refineries, all bullion to be treated by electrolysis was, and still is, submitted to a preliminary cupellation, by which it was brought to so-called Dore bars, consisting of practically pure silver, with only a small percentage of gold as an impurity. The problem in mint practice was to adapt the electric current to the quartation process—that is to part bullion containing say one-third gold and two-thirds silver and base metals. To have accomplished this result and on a large scale, reflects great credit on the melting and refining department of the mint at Philadelphia. Only an untiring devotion to the work, directed by high scientific training, could have produced the results which have been realized. Parting and refining is now done entirely by electrolysis in the mints at Philadelphia and Denver. The process had a successful trial in the assay office at New York, and will be installed in the new structure, now in process of building on Wall Street. The acid plant in the mint at San Francisco is now being replaced by one in which electricity is to do the work of tons of acids.

"A great saving has been effected in the cost of parting and refining; valuable byproducts, principally platinum, are recovered in important quantities. The refined metals, gold and silver, are almost chemically pure; the acid fumes are eliminated and the process is a cleanly, healthy one, of scientific as well as commercial interest. Surely such results mark an era in mint methods.

"Melting is now entirely done by gas, which has many advantages over coal as fuel beyond the mere absence of ashes. A special form of furnace suitable for mint melting had to be devised. This was done and the results are satisfactory. Gas furnaces were installed for annealing the strips and blanks—a marked improvement over the former cumbersome wood-burning ovens. It has been found, however, that with the improved quality of the bullion resulting from refining by electricity and with care in rolling, the annealing of strips can be dispensed with, and only the planchets are annealed preparatory to stamping.

"All machinery in the mints is driven by direct-connected motors after the most approved engineering methods. The rolling mills are from improved patterns and do more accurate work than the old type. The cutting and upsetting machinery is of new and improved patterns. Where formerly only one blank was punched at a stroke, two, and even three, are now punched at once by this heavier machinery—a distinct economy.

"Nine years ago every coin blank was weighed singly by hand, and the pieces a trifle overweight were filed down by hand, this work being done by women known as 'adjusters.' An automatic weighing machine has been developed which rapidly and accurately selects and assorts by weight. One of these machines is on exhibition at the Jamestown Exposition.

"Important and successful experiments have been made at the Philadelphia and Denver Mints, independently, upon a process for automatically adjusting the heavy blanks by passing them under a shaving device which has been introduced into the upsetting machine. These experiments are very promising, and this device, together with the automatic weighing and selecting machine previously described, will accomplish a very large annual saving in wages.

"Nine years ago the ready-made blanks for 1 and 5 cent pieces were all purchased from contractors. These coins are now to a great extent made in the mints from pig metal. All difficulty in the treatment of these metals has been overcome, and with the installation of additional machinery designed specially for economical production, these coins will be wholly made in the mints.

"Upon two different occasions during the period

under review, experts have been sent to visit the principal mints of Europe in order that we might keep in touch with any improvements being made in coinage methods.

"Nine years ago we had practically no medal department. The few medals made at the mint were struck in the coiner's department, and the equipment for that purpose was incomplete and inferior. Upon removal to the new mint at Philadelphia, the making of medals was placed under the supervision of the engraver, and ample quarters and first-class equipment were provided. The result has been some exceedingly creditable work, and a prospect that in the future the mint will make all medals conferred by the Government as it surely should do.

"A complete system of costkeeping has been introduced in the mints by which the cost of each process in coinage operations per ounce of metal handled and per dollar of product is calculated monthly, and a statement of the same at each institution is supplied to all the others."

1907—Roberts resigned the Director's position to become president of the Commercial National Bank of Chicago, but retired in 1910 when the bank merged with the Continental National Bank.

1910–14—Roberts' third term as Director of the Mint commenced in July, when he was again appointed to the position, this time by President William Howard Taft.

The first coinage of bronze cents made in Denver took place on May 20, 1911. The first delivery of 5-cent coins took place on February 5, 1912.

The assay office at St. Louis was discontinued by Act of June 20, 1911, because the volume of business was insignificant. Of benefit to the miner at the outset, with placer production becoming insignificant, the service rendered was not considered of sufficient importance to justify the cost of maintenance.

A catalog of the Mint coin and medal collection was issued during 1912, 1913, and 1914, and in 1913 an abbreviated edition more in the nature of a guidebook, also was issued.

The New York Assay Office vacated its quarters at 32 Wall Street and moved into temporary housing pending completion of a new building to be erected.

James E. Fraser's design for the 5-cent nickel coin was placed in circulation in 1913.

Due to admission of two new States to the Union, it was necessary in 1912 to change the design on the edge of the $10 gold coin from 46 to 48 stars.

1914—Mr. Roberts resigned as Director of the Mint to accept the position of assistant to the president of the National City Bank of New York; served as vice president from 1919 to 1931.

1930—For a 2-year period was a member of the Gold Delegation of the Financial Committee of the League of Nations.

1949—Mr. Roberts made his home in Larchmont, N.Y. He died June 7.

F. J. H. von ENGELKEN

Director of the Mint
September 1916 to February 1917
(No. 311)

OBV. Bust of F. J. H. von Engelken. Director of the Mint. 1916.

REV. America, holding the torch of enlightenment, giving forth the fruits of her wealth and artistry. In the background, the U.S. Mint at Philadelphia.

By George T. Morgan.

F. J. H. VON ENGELKEN.

1881—Born in the Province of Schleswig-Holstein, Germany, on April 26, the son of Ludwig Herman von Engelken, a Doctor of Medicine, and Amelia Deorderlin, his wife.

Attended elementary schools in St. Louis, Mo., and Grand Island, Nebr., and high school in Winona, Minn.

Entered the service of Chicago Northwestern Railroad where he engaged in engineering work.

1900—Went to Hong Kong as assistant to the general agent of the Portland & Asiatic Steamship Co. Transferred in 1902 to Kobe, Japan, and there had charge of steamers, in and out of port, with supervision of cargo, lightering, and ships' papers.

1904—Returned to America and farmed in East Palatka, Fla., until 1908, when he became associated with the Gulf, Colorado & Santa Fe Railroad in Galveston, Tex. Thereafter, and until the close of 1909, he was in agency work in Clifton, Tex., and Ardmore, Okla., for the same railroad.

After leaving the Santa Fe, he was in business in New York for about 2 years and then returned to his farm in Florida, where he remained until 1913.

1913—Appointed Member from Florida of the Fact Finding Commission, created by the U.S. Senate, to study European methods of rural credits. The Commission traveled in Europe for several months and, on its return, Von Engelken authored the minority report which became the basis of the Hollis-Buckley Act creating the Federal Land Bank System.

1914—Assisted the American Counsel General at Munich in relief for American refugees fleeing Europe. Returned to East Palatka, Putnam County, Fla., and resumed farming.

1916—Appointed by President Wilson as Director of the Mint, in recognition of his work on the Rural Credits Commission and in legislative hearings leading to the enactment of the Federal Land Bank Act. In February 1917, Von Engelken left the Mint to assume the presidency of the Federal Land Bank for the Third District at Columbia, S.C.

Though his term of office in the Mint was of relatively short duration, it represented a period marked by an unprecedented demand for coins of the smaller denominations. The coinage executed approached the half billion mark in the number of pieces, against approximately 155 million pieces in the previous year. This was the largest year's coinage in the history of the Mint Service. Over

17 million pieces were coined for foreign governments. This heavy coinage program was completed as a result of improved methods instituted by Von Engelken (the first in some 40 years) for melting coinage metals. During his tenure, he also handled approximately a billion dollars in gold received from the Allies.

1917—Organized the Federal Land Bank at Columbia, an institution with an authorized capital of $2 million. Resigned in May 1918, when he went to Washington to take over the work of organizing a Bond Sales Department for the Twelve Associated Federal Land Banks. Withdrew from this work when the Liberty Bond Drive was inaugurated.

1918—The victim of anti-German sentiment which swept the United States, and of false allegations of disloyalty, Von Engelken appealed to the President of the United States to clear his name. On November 18, 1918, President Woodrow Wilson sent him a letter in which he stated:

"My attention has been called to the very distressing experiences you have recently had, and I have acquainted myself very fully with the real facts of the case. It affords me real pleasure, therefore, to say that the fullest investigation having been made, there can be no reasonable doubt of your entire loyalty and zeal as a patriotic American citizen. I am glad to have an opportunity to tell you that this is my unhesitating opinion and that I hope the clouds that have gathered about you will presently clear happily away."

1919—Went to France as a representative of American bankers, in connection with a proposed loan to that country. Later served as a consultant for business reorganizations.

1947—Retired to his home at East Palatka, Fla., where he married an attorney, Kate Lee Walton, in 1952.

Von Engelken maintained an active interest in civic affairs during his years of retirement. He was appointed to the Advisory Board of the St. Johns River Junior College at Palataka, Fla., when the college was created in 1957. He was named chairman of the boad and served in such capacity until he suffered a heart block in the fall of 1959.

1963—Mr. Von Engelken died at his home in East Palatka on February 12, 1963.

ROBERT WICKLIFFE WOOLLEY

Director of the Mint
March 1915 to July 1916
(No. 312)

OBV. Bust of Robert W. Woolley.

REV. Laurel branch, scales, lamp, and inscription, Director of the Mint 1915–1916.

By George T. Morgan.

ROBERT WICKLIFFE WOOLLEY

1871—Born April 29, at Lexington, Ky., the son of Frank W. and Lucy (McCaw) Woolley, of a family of political traditions.

1886–87—Student at the University of Kentucky.

1887–89—Attended Fordham University.

1893—Started as a reporter with the Lexington Leader, and in 1896, at 25 years of age, became sports editor of the Chicago Tribune. Was on the staff of the New York World from 1897 to 1905, and again from 1907 to 1909. Woolley helped found the National Press Club.

1911—In this year and the one following, he served as chief investigator for the Stanley Committee, investigating the affairs of the U.S. Steel Corporation.

1912—Chief, Bureau of Publicity, Democratic National Committee, and editor of the 1912 and 1914 democratic campaign textbooks.

1913–15—Auditor of the Treasury for the Department of the Interior.

1915—Under an appointment by President Woodrow Wilson, Woolley assumed the duties of Director of the Mint.

The volume of the Mint's activity in gold increased so steadily and so rapidly, commencing July 1, 1915, that the records show the total value of the gold deposits at the New York Assay Office for the first 4 months of the fiscal year 1916 to be nearly that of the deposits for the whole of 1908, heretofore this office's banner fiscal year, and amounted to $126,224,600.

Mr. Woolley handled the receipt of more than $50 million in foreign gold coin and bullion from Australia, Japan, and China, as compared with $4.3 million during the entire calendar year 1914. Most of it required melting and storing, calling for extraordinary energy and some ingenuity to surmount prompt melting and storage problems.

In connection with the special commemorative coinage for the Panama-Pacific International Exposition, Mr. Woolley arranged for the striking at the San Francisco Mint of the only $50 gold coin issue ever struck by the Government. It was a memorable event, marked by appropriate ceremonies. The coin was struck on the large hydraulic press which had been forwarded from the Philadelphia Mint for this special coinage.

Designs were selected early in 1916 for the dime, quarter, and half dollar, marking the first time in the history of our coinage that there were separate designs for each of these three denominations.

1916—Mr. Woolley resigned as Director of the Mint in July to become Director of Publicity and member of the Democratic National Campaign Committee. President Wilson's biographers credited Mr. Woolley with the slogan, "He has kept us out of war." Mr. Woolley was said to have objected to the shortened version of his original, "With honor he has kept us out of war," declaring the former implied promise to continue the status quo.

1917—Served as publicity director for the First Liberty Loan Drive. He also was a member of the Interstate Commerce Commission, which position he held until 1921.

1929—From this year until 1934, Mr. Woolley engaged in private law practice, with the firm of Esch, Kerr, Woolley & Shipe.

1934–37—Chairman of the New York Stockholders' Protective Committee of the Missouri-Kansas Pipe Line Co.

1936—Delegate to the Democratic National Convention this year, and again in 1940. Chairman of the National Democratic Council of D.C., 1935–36.

1945—For the next 2 years, Mr. Woolley served on 12 emergency boards of the National Mediation Board.

1958—Mr. Woolley died in Washington, D.C., December 15, and was buried in Fairfax, Va.

RAYMOND THOMAS BAKER

Director of the Mint
March 1917 to March 1922
(No. 313)

OBV. Bust of Raymond T. Baker, Director of the Mint of the United States.

REV. In the center, front view of the Mint at Philadelphia; to either side, a caduceus, symbol of office. An eagle is in the foreground, above the Seal of the Treasury Department. The Latin inscription, Thesauri Americae Septentrionalis Sigillum (The Seal of the Treasury of North America).

By George T. Morgan.

RAYMOND THOMAS BAKER

1877—Born in Eureka, Nev., November 22, the son of George Washington and Mary Agnes (Hall) Baker. Educated at the Oakland High School and Anderson's Academy, Oakland, Calif. Later, was a mining prospector in Nevada.

1910—Managed the campaign by which his brother, Cleveland, was elected attorney general of Nevada.

Held the post of Warden at the State Prison for 18 months, during which time he is credited with effecting many reforms, among which is the inauguration of the honor system in prisons.

1913—Managed the successful campaign of Key Pittman for the U.S. Senate, and was his secretary in Washington.

1914—Secretary to the American Ambassador at Petrograd, Russia, for 2 years.

1917–22—Appointed by President Woodrow Wilson to succeed Mr. von Engelken as Director of the Mint.

The Act of July 9, 1917, was passed, approving a modification of the newly issued quarter dollar design for the purpose of increasing its artistic merit.

Charles E. Barber, Mint Engraver, died January 18, 1917. He had entered the Mint Service in 1869, as assistant to his father, William, and succeeded him as engraver in 1880. Mr. Baker arranged to have Barber's assistant, George T. Morgan, commissioned to succeed him on April 10, 1917.

The demand for coin continued to climb during the whole of Mr. Baker's tenure, necessitating 16- and 24-hour operations. Added to this was the rise in the number of gold and silver deposits at the assay offices, particularly New York. During the fiscal year 1918, over 68 million silver dollars were converted into bullion, under the Act of April 23, 1918, the bullion being used to assist foreign governments at war with the enemies of the United States.

The work of the New York Assay Office had been hampered for many years by inadequate and unsuitable quarters. An event of more than passing importance to the Mint Service was the commencement in the fiscal year 1919 of work on a new building. A bomb explosion in September of 1920, occurring almost directly in front of the entrance, caused damage to the structure which delayed occupancy until March of 1921.

During his term Mr. Baker personally devised and supervised installation of improved methods and appliances for increasing the capacity of the coinage mints. Included were the use of large-capacity electric melting furnaces in lieu of small gas and oil burning furnaces, mechanical conveyors in lieu of hand-propelled, heavily loaded trucks; rearrangement of floor space and of machinery so as to facilitate and expedite operations; and the addition of new machinery. Many of the improvements were designed and built in the machine shop at the Philadelphia Mint.

The Philadelphia Mint constructed complete coining equipment for the newly established Manila Mint. Building of the coining presses marked the first time coining presses had been built in any mint in the United States.

The Peace design on the silver dollar was first minted in 1921.

Mr. Baker was designated in 1918 by the Secretary of the Treasury to serve as a member of the Gold Commission, which body studied the international currency and exchange stiuation and its effect upon economic and financial conditions in the United States.

1922—Mr. Baker had been prominently associated with mining interests in Nevada, and became actively engaged in this and the banking field after leaving the Mint position in March.

1926—Baker made an unsuccessful bid as Democratic candidate for the U.S. Senate.

1935—His death occurred in Washington, D.C., April 28.

FRANK EDGAR SCOBEY

Director of the Mint

March 1922 to September 1923

(No. 314)

OBV. Bust of F. E. Scobey.

REV. A laurel branch. The Treasury Seal, Director of the United States Mint. 1922.

FRANK EDGAR SCOBEY

1866—Born February 27, in Troy, Ohio, the son of William and Martha J. (Vandeveer) Scobey. He was educated in the Troy public schools.

1897—Scobey's political career commenced in 1897, when he became sheriff of Miami County, which position he held for 5 years.

1902—Became Chief Clerk of the Ohio Senate.

1903—Was a member of the Ohio State Republican Executive Committee.

1904—Moved to San Antonio, Tex., where he formed the Scobey Fireproof Storage Co. and became engaged in various real estate ventures. He was a director of the Federal Reserve Bank, a member of the Elks Lodge, Alzafar Temple of the Shrine, and an honorary member of the Rotary Club. He was also active politically.

1922—Mr. Scobey was a longtime friend of Warren G. Harding, their connection reaching back to the years when both served the State of Ohio in various positions of public trust. This friendship continued after Scobey went to Texas. Harding singled him out for appointment to the position of Director of the Mint and he commenced his tenure in March 1922.

The operations of the mints at this time were de-

voted largely to the coinage of standard silver dollars, a total of $110.7 million having been made during the fiscal year 1923. During considerable periods the mints were on an overtime basis, working 16 hours per day in order that the "dead" stock of silver bullion purchased under the terms of the Pittman Act might be reduced to usable cash.

One of the more notable improvements was the installation at the New York Assay Office, of a ventilating system in the operating rooms, together with a Cottrell electrical precipitator for the elimination of the smoke nuisance and recovery of values carried off in the furnace gases. This marked the first time such a precipitator had been used in the Mint Service.

Because of the necessity of providing all practical safeguards for the care of the large values kept in the mints, safety being considered paramount to the educational value and pleasure afforded visitors in witnessing the coinage operations, the mints were closed to visitors. The collection of coins and medals housed at the Philadelphia Mint was sent to the National Museum in Washington, D.C., prior to the close of the fiscal year 1923. Here it remains to this day.

1923—Mr. Scobey resigned in October, following the death of President Harding, and returned to private life.

1931—Scobey died in San Antonio, Tex., February 7, 1931, and is buried in Troy, Ohio.

ROBERT JOHN GRANT

Director of the Mint
November 1923 to May 1933

(No. 315)

OBV. Bust of Robert J. Grant, Director of the Mint, 1932.

REV. South front of the Treasury Building in Washington, D.C., showing statue of Alexander Hamilton, first Treasury Secretary. A stylized shield symbolizing the United States of America. Ribbons and festoon, with tablet carrying the Treasury Seal and the date MCMXXIII.

By John R. Sinnock.

ROBERT JOHN GRANT

1862—Born in Springville, Nova Scotia, November 12, the son of Peter James and Christy (Grant) Grant. Attended public schools in Nova Scotia.

1880—Came to the United States and worked for a Boston printing firm. Attended evening classes at high school.

1889—Was active as a mining engineer for about 20 years, in the pursuit of which his travels took him to Canada, Australia, and Mexico, as well as in the United States.

1892—Leased the Gold Bug Mine in Arizona; 2 years later he leased a mine in Aspen, Colo.

1896–99—Assistant manager of the Portland Gold Mining Co., Cripple Creek, Colo., and in 1898–99, he held the same post at the W. S. Stratton Independent Mine. While assistant manager at the Stratton Independent Mine, it produced over $4 millions in gold.

1904—Manager of the Cosmopolitan Mine in Kookynie, a

British corporation with which Herbert Hoover was associated.

1906–17—Was associated with mines in Mexico, after which he entered the practice of consulting mining engineer, until 1917, with offices in Denver, Colo.

1917–21—Engineer for the Colorado Pure Lead Corporation of New York, in Colorado.

1919—Director of the Colorado State Food Administration; also served during 1919–21 as a member of the Colorado Examining Board of Engineers.

1921—Appointed by President Harding to serve as Superintendent of the U.S. Mint at Denver, Colo.

1923–33—Appointed Director of the Mint by President Calvin Coolidge, and remained in this position, by reappointment, for 10 years.

Mint institutions in operation at the beginning of his tenure were the coinage mints at Philadelphia, San Francisco, and Denver; the assay office at New York; mints at New Orleans and Carson City, being conducted as assay offices; and assay offices at Boise, Helena, Deadwood, Seattle, and Salt Lake City. The seven last-named institutions were, in effect, bullion-purchasing agencies for the large institutions, and also served the public by making, at nominal charge, assays of ores and bullion. Electrolytic refineries were in operation at the New York, Denver, and San Francisco institutions.

George T. Morgan, commissioned engraver in 1917, and connected with the Mint Service since 1876, died January 4, 1925, and was succeeded by Mr. John R. Sinnock.

The Deadwood Assay Office was closed June 30, 1927, due to the lack of deposits sufficient to justify its continued operation.

The Mint prepared the gold medal presented to Col. Charles A. Lindbergh by act of Congress approved May 24, 1928, to commemorate his flight in the SPIRIT OF ST. LOUIS from New York to Paris, May 20–21, 1927.

The Mint also prepared the medal presented to Thomas A. Edison by Joint Resolution of the Congress approved May 29, 1928. The medal commemorated Edison's achievements in illuminating the path of progress through the development and application of inventions that have revolutionized civilization.

The undesirability of the $2.50 gold coins for circulation purposes demonstrated through a series of years, resulted in passage of the Act of April 11, 1930, discontinuing both the coinage and issuance of these pieces after the date of the act.

The New York Assay Office and the Seattle Assay Office both moved into new quarters in 1932. The year prior, the New Orleans Mint staff moved into smaller but adequate quarters in the Customhouse, and the Boise Assay Office occupied quarters specially arranged for it in a new Federal building.

A new design for the quarter dollar was authorized by the Act of March 4, 1931, as an incident of the bicentennial celebration of the birth of George Washington. John Flanagan executed the winning model.

Assay office facilities at Boise, Helena, Salt Lake City, and Carson City were closed down at the end of the fiscal year 1933, since with improved transportation facilities, most bullion deposits reached the Government through the mails and express companies, and the remaining bullion-receiving institutions adequately covered the field and provided for the prompt turning into usable cash of either newly mined bullion or that reclaimed from industry.

By act approved February 28, 1929, the Congress awarded gold medals to Major Walter Reed and his associates in recognition of the high public service rendered and disabilities contracted in the interest of humanity and science as voluntary subjects for experimentation during yellow fever investigations. These medals were prepared by the Mint during Mr. Grant's term of office.

Shortly before Mr. Grant's tenure ended, the President issued the Order of April 20, 1933, prohibiting gold hoarding and establishing Government control of the export of gold as a means of centralizing the Nation's holdings in the hands of the Government.

1933—Grant resigned the Director's post to become financial advisor in charge of the Chinese National Government Mint at Shanghai. When the government moved to Nanking, he remained at Shanghai as government representative to handle financial and monetary affairs.

1941—Returned to America, because of ill health.

1949—Mr. Grant died November 24, at Pasadena, Calif.

NELLIE TAYLOE ROSS

Director of the Mint
May 1933 to April 1953
(No. 316)

OBV. Bust of Governor Nellie Tayloe Ross, Director of the Mint of the United States, 1933.

REV. An allegorical figure, seated before a stand and weighing coins. A scroll is held in her left hand. A shield with the arms of the Treasury Department. A stack of ingots; a modern coining press. Around the edge are the names of the four principal departments of the Mint: Melting and Refining; Coining; Assaying; Engraving.

By John R. Sinnock.

NELLIE TAYLOE ROSS

Born in St. Joseph, Mo., and educated in both public and private schools.

1902—Married William Bradford Ross and went with him to Wyoming. For 20 years after her marriage, Mrs. Ross devoted most of her energies to her home, her husband, and her children. Mr. Ross was elected Governor of Wyoming in 1922, but died before completing his elected term.

1925—Mrs. Ross was elected Governor of Wyoming, to fill out the unexpired term of her husband, and served until January of 1927. Mrs. Ross had the distinction of being the first woman to assume the governorship of any State. She was defeated by a close margin in her bid for reelection. Later, because of her reputation as a fine speaker, she was invited to make many appearances on the lecture platform, and eventually addressed groups in every State of the Union.

1929—Was vice chairman of the Democratic National Committee, with offices in Washington, D.C., from 1929 to 1932, and was instrumental in organizing the Women's Division.

1933–53—President Franklin Delano Roosevelt's appointment of Mrs. Ross to serve as Director of the Mint also marked the first time a woman ever had occupied this office. She was reappointed by President Roosevelt at the expiration of her first and second 5-year terms, and by President Harry Truman at the expiration of her third term, serving in all 20 years, the longest of any Director of the Mint.

When Mrs. Ross came to the Mint in 1933, activities were at low ebb, owing to the depression, and personnel had been reduced to a minimum. Suddenly, however, and coincidental with the enactment of far-reaching new monetary laws governing the use of gold and silver, a magnitude of work was laid upon the Mint under which the force staggered. Gold from all over the world began flowing to our shores, soon to be followed by great deposits of silver.

With the upswing in business starting in 1934, a demand for coin unprecedented in our history began, which was to continue for many years, and necessitated much 24-hour operation, including Saturdays and Sundays. Coin production for 1933 was 358,269,353 pieces. Just 12 years later, the peak production for the World War II period was more than 4 billion pieces. The number of employees on the payroll at the height of the wartime operations was more than 4,000, a number never equalled before or since.

Such drastic and sudden increase in the activities of the Mint Service called for quick and sharp expansion of facilities of manpower, machinery, vault space, and working space. It was Mrs. Ross' responsibility to cope with these problems; upon her devolved the task of building up an adequate force of skilled and trustworthy persons. The force was trebled and equipment expanded in proportion. New machinery was installed, new vaults were provided or old vaults modernized in every field institution.

A new mint was constructed in San Francisco; the capacity of the mint at Denver was doubled; a new depository for gold was built at Fort Knox, Ky., and one for silver at West Point, N.Y. The protection of the greatly expanded metals stocks required the expansion of the small guard force and many stalwart men, trained in the use of arms, were added to the staff.

It was during Mrs. Ross' tenure that the innovation of striking two coins simultaneously was developed by San Francisco Mint technicians. This enabled greatly increased production of both foreign and domestic coinage of pieces five-cent size or smaller.

The largest Treasury holdings of gold, and the largest ever to be held by any country in the world in its monetary reserves before or since, occurred in September of 1949, and amounted to $24.7 billion. All was in physical custody of the Bureau of the Mint. The highest total in Fort Knox also occurred during Mrs. Ross' tenure, and amounted to $15.6 billion.

The medal department of the Mint was greatly expanded during the war because of military orders for combat awards and decorations reaching into several millions of pieces.

Wartime restrictions imposed upon foreign mints also resulted in the placing of large foreign coinage orders with the U.S. Mint.

Coinage of the 5-cent copper and nickel coin was discontinued in May of 1942 so that the large quantities of copper and nickel thus used could be conserved for the war effort; the substitute, used through 1945, contained a copper-silver-manganese alloy. The zinc-coated steel cent was issued in 1943 to conserve coinage metals.

The 5-cent design was changed in 1938 to bear the likeness of Thomas Jefferson. It is the work of Felix Schlag. The Roosevelt dime was prepared by John R. Sinnock, Mint Engraver, and issued in 1946, in response to national sentiment that the late President be so honored. Mr. Sinnock also designed the Franklin half dollar design issued in 1948.

The management improvement program vigorously projected in 1950, and directed toward continuing improvements in operating procedures, produced revolutionary results in the manufacturing processes of coinage. The massive melting and rolling equipment in the Denver Mint was brought out of the experimental stage of operation into a high state of efficiency. It processed a 400-pound bronze ingot in place of the 6-pound ingot formerly processed in the small rolling mills, and eliminated the hand-pouring method. Also, a new type water-cooled mold, invented by mint technicians at Philadelphia, resulted in a 23-percent reduction in silver melting costs during the year, and realignment of the melting operations, and other mechnical changes at Philadelphia resulted in important economies.

More powerful motors on rolling mills at San Francisco allowed processing of longer and wider ingots, with a resultant increase from 100 to 300 percent in the production of coin blanks without increasing personnel.

Proof coinage was resumed in 1950, for the first time since 1936.

Another little-known "first" for Mrs. Ross was the distinction of being the first woman to have her name appear on the cornerstone of a Government building. The depositories at Fort Knox and West Point, and the mint at San Francisco all bear her name.

It is a well-known fact that George Washington was intensely interested in the infant mint, and tradition has it that some of his family silverware went into the manufacture of the 1792 half dimes. Not so widely known, perhaps, is the fact that Mrs. Ross' mother, Elizabeth Blair Green Tayloe, was descended from Samuel Ball Green, whose mother, Patty Ball, was a cousin of the mother of George Washington.

1953—Mrs. Ross retired from the position of Director of the Mint at the end of April, rounding out a full 20 years as the first woman ever to head the factory-type operation which is the Bureau of the Mint.

1969—Mrs. Ross maintains a residence in Washington, near her two sons, George and Bradford Ross. She continues to be active in church and civic affairs, as well as world travel.

335-478 O - 69 - 11

WILLIAM HOWARD BRETT

Director of the Mint
July 1954 to January 1961
(No. 317)

OBV. Bust of William H. Brett.

REV. The kneeling female figure represents the Mint. Allegorical figures surround the central figure, depicting mining, assaying, melting and refining, and coining. A scale above represents weighing. The Seal of the Treasury Department appears below. The inscription, DIRECTOR OF THE MINT.

By Engelhardus von Hebel.

WILLIAM HOWARD BRETT

1893—Born in Cleveland, Ohio, December 31, the son of William Howard and Alice (Allen) Brett.

Mr. Brett's preliminary education was received in the public schools in Ohio. He attended Dartmouth College and spent the last year in the Tuck School of Business Administration, graduating in 1916 with an A.B. degree. While in school, Brett worked as a civil engineer.

1915—Following graduation, Mr. Brett was associated with the Perfection Spring Co. until the outbreak of World War I.

1917—Married Catherine Ruth Connelly; they have two sons.

Attended the first officer's training camp at Fort Myer, Va., and served as first lieutenant in the U.S. Army until 1918.

1919—After the war, Brett joined Scovell, Wellington & Co. as an industrial engineer, and remained until 1921.

1921—He became vice president and director of the Enamel Products Co. of Cleveland, Ohio.

1943—Mr. Brett moved to Alliance, Ohio, to become vice president and director of Alliance Ware, Inc.

1954–61—President Dwight D. Eisenhower appointed Mr. Brett Director of the Mint in July. He was reappointed in 1959 for a second 5-year term.

As a result of the administration's economy programing, all segments of the Mint organization were carefully reviewed, to effect savings wherever possible, without sacrificing operational efficiency. Major attention was given the modernization of melting and rolling equipment at the Philadelphia Mint, in lieu of building new quarters for that plant. Substantial reductions in manufacturing costs were effected in this area as well as in other departments. Furthering the economy measures, coinage operations were discontinued at the San Francisco Mint in March of 1955, gold and silver refinery operations were halted in 1957, and minting facilities there were dismantled. The assay office at Seattle, Wash., also was closed and its functions absorbed by other Mint offices.

During Mr. Brett's tenure, approximately one-half billion ounces of silver loaned to friendly foreign governments during World War II, were returned to the United States. This required the extensive use of Mint facilities for processing these coins into bullion bars, which were later refined and added to Mint stocks as fine silver bars.

1959—The reverse of the Lincoln cent was redesigned. The portrait side remained the same, but the new reverse depicts the Lincoln Memorial in Washington, D.C., in honor of the sesquicentennial observance of Abraham Lincoln's birth. The new design was first issued in February of that year.

1961—Mr. Brett returned to private business after his resignation as Director of the Mint in January, and resides in Washington, D.C.

EVA ADAMS

Director of the Mint
October 1961 to September 1969
(No. 318)

OBV. Bust of Eva Adams. A stylized Seal of the Treasury Department. In the background are mountains, and equipment depicting a mining camp in Nevada.

By Frank Gasparro.

REV. An eagle, poised in flight over a mountain range, behind which the sun is rising. Director of the Mint United States of America. (The small letter P indicates the medal was manufactured at the Philadelphia Mint.)

By Michael Iacocca.

EVA ADAMS

1908—Born at Wonder, Nev., on September 10, the daughter of Verner Lauer and Cora E. (Varble) Adams. She received her early education in the public school system of Nevada and attended the University of Nevada. Upon graduation, she taught high school in her native State.

1936—Studied at Columbia University in New York, where she received a master's degree in English. Returned to the University of Nevada as an English instructor and assistant dean of women.

1940—Went to Washington, D.C., as Administrative Assistant to Senator Pat McCarran. Upon his death in 1954, she continued as head of the staff of the Nevada Senatorial Office under Senator Ernest Brown, and remained as Administrative Assistant to Senator Alan Bible until she became Director of the Mint. In the meantime, Miss Adams received her LL.B. degree from the Washington College of Law of American University in Washington, D.C. She later received a master's degree in law from George Washington University.

1954—Already a member of the Nevada bar, she was admitted to practice before the Supreme Court of the United States, and later, the District of Columbia bar.

1961—President John F. Kennedy appointed Miss Adams as Director of the Mint, and at the expiration of her 5-year term she was reappointed by President Lyndon B. Johnson for a second 5-year term. Miss Adams is only the second woman to have held this distinguished position.

In recognition of her outstanding work, she was awarded the Exceptional Service Award of the Treasury Department in 1966.

At the time Miss Adams assumed office, more coins were being made than at any previous period in U.S. history. However, when a shortage threatened during 1963–65, the mints were placed on a 24-hour schedule to meet the demand, and a crash program was initiated which doubled production by the acquisition by loan and purchase of 100 coinage presses to augment the 60 already in operation; the expansion of mint staffs in all operating divisions to handle the accelerated operations; the transformation of the small assay office facilities at San Francisco into full-scale minting operations for the manufacture of blanks, and later, the coins themselves; additional expansion was made of facilities at the Denver Mint.

The manufacture of proof coins, and the distribution of these and the uncirculated coin sets, were discontinued during the critical period so that manpower and machinery could be diverted to the making of coins for regular circulation. In 1965, when the crisis had eased, special mint sets were issued for collectors, of better quality than the uncirculated sets but not as fine as the proofs. 1968 saw the resumption of the proof and uncirculated coin set service.

Following the assassination of President Kennedy, President Lyndon B. Johnson signed legislation directing that the late President's likeness be placed on the half dollar. The first of these coins was released in March of 1964.

A world shortage of silver made imperative a survey to develop ways and means of conserving the Nation's dwindling supplies. Miss Adams worked with other department officials and a private consulting firm to formulate a plan which would free the large amount of this metal used in coinage. The findings resulted in passage of Public Law 89–81, known as the Coinage Act of 1965, which completely eliminated silver from the dime and quarter dollar and substantially reduced it in the half dollar. Authorized in place of the silver was clad material, new to the coinage processes, utilizing copper and nickel, for the two smaller denominations, and a modified silver-copper cladding for the half dollar, so that the United States might have a prestige coin containing silver.

The Coinage Act of 1965 authorized formation of the Joint Commission on the Coinage. The purpose of this body, composed of public and private members chaired by the Secretary of the Treasury, is to study and review existing monetary problems relating to coinage and the use of silver, and to advise and recommend with respect thereto to the President, the Secretary of the Treasury, and the Congress. Miss Adams has served as a member of this Commission.

One of the unique features of the effort to keep coins in circulation was the date freeze employed during 1965 and 1966. Normal dating procedures resumed January 1, 1967.

The regulations governing the conduct of business at the mints and assay offices were the subject of an intensive study aimed at revising these important guidelines.

A major accomplishment during Miss Adams' tenure was the authorization and construction of new quarters for the outmoded Philadelphia Mint at 16th and Spring Garden Streets. The new structure, located on Independence Mall, houses the world's most modern "brass mill" melting, casting, and rolling facilities for the production of coinage alloys. It also contains unique and revolutionary minting equipment, such as a "coin rolling machine" capable of producing cents at a rate of 10,000 a minute. Ground was broken September 17, 1965; cornerstone ceremonies were held September 18, 1968; and the formal dedication and opening, August 14, 1969.

Miss Adams worked closely with foreign mints in developing and exchanging ideas for improved production of coins and medals. Of special interest to her was a higher relief on our medals to give them added character, and experimentation in various finishes. She made visits to minting institutions in Canada, Mexico, and Europe, and maintained close liaison in working out mutual problems.

United States Army

GENERAL GEORGE WASHINGTON

(No. 401)

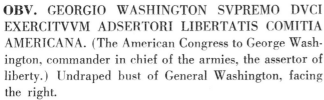

OBV. GEORGIO WASHINGTON SVPREMO DVCI EXERCITVVM ADSERTORI LIBERTATIS COMITIA AMERICANA. (The American Congress to George Washington, commander in chief of the armies, the assertor of liberty.) Undraped bust of General Washington, facing the right.

REV. HOSTIBUS PRIMO FUGATIS. (The enemy put to flight for the first time.) To the left, General Washington on horseback, surrounded by his staff, points toward the British fleet, which is leaving the city of Boston in the background; the American army, in battle array in front of its intrenchments, makes ready to occupy the city. Exergue, BOSTONIUM RECUPERATUM XVII MARTII MDCCLXXVI. (Boston retaken, Mar. 17, 1776.)

By Duvivier.

THE SIEGE AND EVACUATION OF BOSTON

On June 15, 1775, the First Continental Congress, assembled at Philadelphia, made the selection of George Washington as commander in chief of the "forces raised and to be raised in defense of American liberty." The armies of Massachusetts, Connecticut, New Hampshire, and Rhode Island, assembled at Boston, were to become the "Army of the United States."

Two days after Washington's appointment, but before he assumed command of the American Army, the bloody battle of Bunker Hill was fought. The British gained control of Bunker Hill and continued to hold Boston. The American forces retreated to its entrenchments which extended in a 14-mile semicircle around Boston, from Winter and Prospect Hills on its left wing, through the headquar-

ters in Cambridge, to its right wing at Dorchester, southeast of Boston Neck.

Washington arrived in Cambridge on July 3 and assumed the tasks of organizing the army, replacing much of it by another army because of the short-term enlistments which expired by the end of the year. He also concentrated on extending and completing fortifications so as to be better prepared for withstanding a British attack from Boston.

It was Washington's intent to force the British to a conclusive course of action, either to evacuate Boston or to engage in an all-out attack. Preparing for the latter eventuality, and during the winter months, Washington had arranged for ordnance captured from Fort Ticonderoga to be brought into Cambridge. Early in March, Washington seized Dorchester Heights, where he mounted the heaviest of the Ticonderoga guns. This gave the American forces the control of Boston Harbor; it was the first real stroke of military success enjoyed by the American Army in the War for Independence.

When the British entered into a counterattack against Dorchester Heights, from the east, a heavy gale prevented the operation from being carried out and their troops returned to Boston. On March 17, General Howe, the British commander, evacuated Boston and sailed for Halifax.

On March 25, 1776, the Continental Congress resolved: "That the thanks of this Congress, in their own name, and in the name of the thirteen United States colonies, whom they represent, be presented to His Excellency General Washington, and the officers and soldiers under his command, for their wise and spirited conduct in the siege and acquisition of Boston; and that a medal of gold be struck in commemoration of this great event, and presented to His Excellency; and that a committee of three be appointed to prepare a letter of thanks and a proper device for the medal."

GEORGE WASHINGTON, *First President of the United States*

1732—Born at "Wakefield," Westmoreland County, Va.

Self-educated; principal studies were geometry and trigonometry, establishing a foundation for his occupation as a surveyor.

1748—Moved to Mount Vernon, the home of his half-brother, Lawrence; helped survey the lands of Thomas, Lord Fairfax, in the Shenandoah.

1749—Was appointed public surveyor of Culpepper County, Va.; his income from this pursuit enabled him to purchase large tracts of land.

1752—After death of Lawrence Washington, he acquired Mount Vernon by inheritance.

Appointed adjutant general by Governor Robert Dinwiddie, with the rank of major, having the mission of protecting the Southern District of Virginia against French and Indian attacks. This gave Washington experience in the exercise of military strategy and tactics—a field in which he had a particular interest.

1753—Carried ultimatum from Governor Dinwiddie to the French, warning them against encroaching on English lands in the Ohio Valley.

1754—Commissioned lieutenant colonel by Governor Dinwiddie; his regiment sent out to reinforce a British post on the forks of the Ohio River (site of today's modern city of Pittsburgh). This post, occupied and renamed Fort Duquesne by the French, was so firmly established that Washington took up his position at Great Meadows, Pa., naming his new post Fort Necessity. On May 28 he defeated a French scouting party; later Fort Necessity was put under 10 hours of siege by the main French forces and it was necessary to capitulate. Despite this defeat, on July 3, the expedition enhanced Washington's combat experience.

1755—As a colonel, joined the staff of General Braddock for an expedition of regular British troops against Fort Duquesne. The attack met with failure; Braddock was mortally wounded, and the command devolved upon Washington. During this French and Indian onslaught, two horses were shot out from under Washington, and his coat showed four bullet holes.

Was appointed commander in chief of all the Virginia forces with the rank of colonel. For the following 3 years he had the responsibility for the defense of 350 miles of mountainous frontier, with a force of 300 troops, against French and Indian raids. The engagements, which averaged two a month, gave Washington considerable opportunity to develop his skill in conducting warfare over an extensive range of territory.

1758—Resigned his command and withdrew to Mount Vernon, though he had the satisfaction this year of joining the British forces as they moved into the burning ruins of Fort Duquesne, abandoned by the French.

1759—Married Martha (Dandridge) Custis on January 6.

Took his seat in the Virginia House of Burgesses, serving continuously with that body until 1774.

1765—Supported Virginians protesting against the Stamp Act, which made mandatory the use of stamps on commercial and legal documents, newspapers, pamphlets, almanacs, cards and dice; also supported the grievance against the British prohibition of colonial paper money.

1769—Drew up a Nonimportation Act, providing for the imposition of an embargo on various British articles. This act was ratified by the Virginia House of Burgesses.

1774—Met with other Burgesses at the Raleigh Tavern at Williamsburg on May 27, after the Assembly had been dissolved by the Governor, and signed the proceedings of that meeting.

On August 1, at the provincial convention held in Williamsburg, was among the foremost advocates for colonial self-government.

Was elected a Virginia delegate to the First Continental Congress, which met in September 1774.

1775—Was a member of the Second Continental Congress beginning in May; served on the committee for drafting Army regulations and planning the defense of New York City.

Was elected commander in chief of the Continental Army and took command on July 3, at Cambridge, Mass.

Although an American attempt to take Quebec and Montreal was not successful, it revealed Washington to be a brilliant tactician and a great soldier.

1776—On March 17, caused the British to evacuate Boston, for which he was awarded a medal by the Congress.

Was defeated on August 27, at the Battle of Long Island.

On Christmas night, he crossed the Delaware and crushed the Hessians at the Battle of Trenton.

1777—Expelled the British from Princeton, on January 3.

The battles at Trenton and Princeton were decisive; had it not been for them, the impetus to carry on with the Revolutionary War might have died out.

Attempting to prevent British forces from reaching the Chesapeake Bay, Washington intercepted them at Brandywine Creek, Chester County, Pa. on September 11. Although defeated, this engagement prevented British forces from reaching Philadelphia for a period of 2 weeks.

Fought a gallant, but unsuccessful battle at Germantown on October 3–4. This action is believed to have damaged British morale and to have convinced the French of the determination of the Americans to persist in the War for Independence.

1777–78—With his troops, he endured the hardships of winter encampment at Valley Forge.

1778—By authority of the Congress, Washington was given power to build a permanent army, one involving 3-year enlistments, or for the duration of the war; was given assistance by Baron von Steuben who undertook intensive troop training. In March the French entered into an alliance with the Americans.

On June 28, American forces overtook the British at Monmouth and held the field while the British retreated from Philadelphia to New York City.

1781—Though Washington's preliminary plans were for a joint American-French attack against the British held city of New York, he made the decision to utilize the French fleet under Admiral de Grasse, to attack Cornwallis at Yorktown. Bottled up and cut off from a sea escape by the French, Cornwallis surrendered on October 19.

After Yorktown, the American forces drew back to quarters at Newburgh, N.Y.

1783—Held the Army together until November 25, when the British evacuated New York City, and he led the American troops into the city.

On December 4, Washington said farewell to his officers at Fraunces Tavern in New York City; on December 23, at Annapolis, he resigned his commission, and he returned to his home at Mount Vernon.

GENERAL HORATIO GATES

OBV. HORATIO GATES DUCI STRENUO COMITIA AMERICANA. (The American Congress to Horatio Gates, a valiant general.) Bust of General Gates, facing to the left.

REV. SALUS REGIONUM SEPTENTRIONAL. (The safety of the northern regions.) Lieutenant General Burgoyne is surrendering his sword to General Gates. In the background, on the left, the vanquished troops of Great Britain are grounding their arms and standards. On the right is the victorious American Army, in order of battle, with colors flying. By the side of the two generals are a drum and a stand of colors. Exergue: HOSTE AD SARA-TOGAM IN DEDITION ACCEPTO DIE XVII OCT. MDCCLXXVII. (The enemy surrendered at Saratoga on the 17th of October 1777.)

By N. Gatteaux.

THE SURRENDER OF GENERAL BURGOYNE AT SARATOGA

By congressional resolution of November 4, 1777, a gold medal was awarded for presentation to General Horatio Gates, in commemoration of three successful engagements which defeated British plans to isolate New England by occupying the Hudson Valley:—the Battle of Bennington,

163

the Battle of Fort Stanwix (Fort Schuyler), and the Battle of Saratoga.

On October 16, 1777, the British, under General Burgoyne, sent a force of Hessian Dragoons to capture American stores at Bennington, Vt. The American forces, under Gen. John Stark, infiltrated the British ranks from the flanks and rear, disguised as loyalists. At this juncture, Stark is reputed to have cried out: "There, my boys, are your enemies. You must beat them or Molly Stark is a widow tonight." The initial engagement was highly successful for the Americans, as was a second engagement which occurred after British reinforcements arrived. In all, the British suffered casualties of 700 men, as compared with American losses of 30 killed and 40 wounded.

As part of General Burgoyne's plan, Colonel St. Leger was to move his troops from Oswego, down the Mohawk Valley, to join Burgoyne in Albany. Standing in the path of his advance was Fort Stanwix, which St. Leger invested on August 3, 1777.

Commanding Fort Stanwix was Col. Peter Gansevoort, and his assistant, Lt. Col. Marinus Willet. Learning of the siege laid upon Stanwix, American reinforcements were sent from Fort Dayton (now Herkimer, N.Y.). These relief forces were ambushed by a well-planned Indian attack, during which Gen. Nicholas Herkimer was mortally wounded. Propped up against a tree, he lighted his pipe and directed the battle for 8 hours. Although these forces did not get through, replacements were dispatched by General Schuyler, then at Stillwater. When news of their approach reached St. Leger, he lifted the siege of Fort Stanwix and departed for Oswego (August 22) and later to Montreal.

The third success which occasioned the gold medal awarded by congressional resolution of November 4, 1777, involved the engagement of the British and the Americans at a point north of Albany, known as Bemis Heights and Freeman's Farm, close by. The resolution cites: "the main army of six thousand men, under Lieutenant General Burgoyne, after beaten in different actions, and driven from a formidable post and strong intrenchments, (were) reduced to the necessity of surrendering themselves upon terms honourable and advantageous to these States, on the 17th day of October last, to Major General Gates."

The first engagement took place on September 19 at Freeman's Farm, about 1 mile north of the American forces. Proceeding with two columns, the British engaged the Americans in 3 hours of fighting which swayed back and forth over Freeman's Farm. Repeatedly the British regiments had to re-form their lines and charge with fixed bayonets, only to be stopped short by deadly fire of American riflemen, who used natural cover to great advantage. It was European versus frontier tactics; and in this forested, ravine-slashed terrain irregular riflemen

proved superior to the formal line of battle. When American reinforcements were placed where they threatened to outflank the British right, British reinforcements of Hessians arrived, and the Americans were forced to withdraw. The British entrenched in the vicinity of Freeman's Farm for a period of 3 weeks, anxiously awaiting further aid from Sir Henry Clinton in the South.

In the absence of reinforcements which did not arrive, Burgoyne had no recourse but to seek a second engagement or retreat. He chose the former course of action and entered into battle, again, on October 7. Within an hour after the opening clash, Burgoyne lost eight cannon and more than 400 officers and men. Darkness ended the day's fighting and Burgoyne withdrew his troops to their Great Redoubt, which protected the high ground and river flats at the northeast corner of the battlefield. A day later, they took refuge in a fortified camp on the heights at Saratoga. There an American force that had grown to nearly 20,000 men surrounded his exhausted army. In the face of these great odds, Burgoyne was forced to surrender on October 17, 1777.

HORATIO GATES

1728—Born at Maldon, England.

1745—Joined the British military service.

1749—Served under General Cornwallis in Nova Scotia.

1755—Served under General Braddock in the expedition against Fort Duquesne (now Pittsburgh); was shot through the body; during same engagement Braddock was mortally wounded. Gates recuperated on a farm he had purchased in Virginia.

1775—Appointed by the Congress as Adjutant General, with the rank of brigadier general. Accompanied George Washington to Cambridge and served with him during the siege of Boston.

1776—Congress gave him command of the forces of the North, with the rank of major general, serving under General Washington.

Placed Benedict Arnold in charge of an improvised fleet to hold Lake Champlain against British forces emerging from Canada. Though the engagement which followed was not won by the Americans, the fact that the British withdrew to Montreal after the action, known as the Battle of Valcour Island, gave the Americans additional time to prepare for the final showdown in the North the following year.

1777—On October 17, General Burgoyne surrendered his forces to General Gates at Saratoga.

1780—Placed in command of American forces in the South; was defeated by Cornwallis at Camden, S.C., and was relieved by Nathaniel Greene.

1783—Retired to Virginia; later moved to New York after emancipating his slaves.

1806—Died in New York City.

GENERAL DANIEL MORGAN

OBV. DANIELI MORGAN DUCI EXERCITUS. An Indian, a quiver upon her back, emblematic of America, placing a laurel wreath upon the brow of General Morgan; in the background, trophy of arms and flags; below, COMITIA AMERICANA. (The American Congress to General Daniel Morgan.)

REV. VICTORIA LIBERTATIS VINDEX. (Victory, the vindicator of liberty.) General Morgan is leading his troops, who advance with colors flying, and put to flight the British Army; in the foreground, a combat between an Indian and a dismounted cavalry soldier. Exergue: FVGATIS CAPTIS AVT CAESIS AD COWPENS HOSTIBUS XVII. JAN. MDCCLXXXI. (The enemy put to flight, taken, or slain, at the Cowpens, Jan. 17, 1781.)

By Dupre.

THE BATTLE OF COWPENS

The victory of American arms at Cowpens in 1781 over a corps of British regulars, was one of the most brilliant, and heartening in the War for Independence. It came after a 2-year period of defeat and persecution.

After failing to quell the rebellion in the North, the British decided late in 1778 to shift their theater of operations into the southern provinces. They captured Savannah at the end of December and soon all of Georgia was subjugated. In the spring of 1780 they besieged and captured Charleston, opening South Carolina for invasion. Gen. Horatio Gates was defeated in Camden (S.C.) in August that year, and Cornwallis moved on to North Carolina, establishing his headquarters at Charlotte.

On October 7, 1780, the British were set back for the first time. At King's Mountain (Mechlenberg County, S.C.) American riflemen completely destroyed a Tory force, causing Cornwallis to draw back to Winnsboro (S.C.) where he set up his headquarters.

In Philadelphia, the Congress conferred with Gen. Nathaniel Greene, who was appointed on the recommendation of General Washington, to succeed Gates in command of the Southern Army. Greene was given extraordinary powers to carry on the Revolution in the distant South and regain the conquered States.

On December 4, 1780, Greene took command of his forces at Charlotte. He was so inferior in numbers to Cornwallis that direct confrontation was out of the question until he could raise and equip a larger force. For this reason he decided on a program of partisan warfare—harassing the enemy's flanks, breaking up his communications, and intercepting supplies.

Small as his army was, Greene divided his forces and sent Gen. Daniel Morgan with about 900 men to threaten British outposts in the northwestern section of South Carolina. It was a risky movement, for the two detachments were 140 miles apart, with Cornwallis between them.

Fortunately, Cornwallis scattered his forces, rather than attacking either of Greene's detachments, one at a time, with his full strength. He sent Lt. Col. Banastre Tarleton to intercept Morgan.

Learning that the British forces were approaching, Morgan decided to make his stand at a place near the North Carolina border called the Cowpens, because of a nearby winter cattle enclosure. Here on January 16, 1781, Morgan awaited Tarleton's attack.

Morgan formed three lines. In the front line he put his skirmishers, a group of riflemen under Maj. Joseph McDowell and Maj. William Cunningham. They were to begin firing when the enemy was within 50 yards and then fall back to a second line, 150 yards back.

The second line consisted of militia led by Col. Andrew Pickens. This line was to await the approach of the

British, fire twice, and then fall back to the third line, 150 yards back.

The third line, the main line of militia, was commanded by Col. John Eager Howard.

Heading the reserve was Lt. Col. William Washington's cavalry and mounted militiamen.

As the British force of 1,050 men approached in a straight line and penetrated the first two American lines, they thought they had won an easy victory, only to be met by deadly fire and bayonet attack by the American main line of defense, and by Washington's cavalry attack. The battle action went substantially as it was planned, though not without some confusion on the part of dispersed American forces, whose ranks were hastily and effectively reformed under the leadership of Morgan.

Finding themselves surrounded, the British surrendered. Their losses were over 200 killed and 600 taken prisoner. American losses were 72 killed and wounded.

DANIEL MORGAN

1736—Born near Junction, in Hunterdon County, N.J.
1754—Moved to Charles Town, Va. (now West Virginia).
Served with the Colonial forces during the French and Indian wars.

1775—Served under Washington at Cambridge, as captain of a company of Virginia riflemen.
Accompanied General Arnold to Canada and taken prisoner during the ill-fated assault on Quebec.
1776—Served under Washington, again, as colonel of the 11th Virginia Regiment, which incorporated his rifle corps.
Greatly distinguished himself at the Battle of Saratoga, in which Burgoyne was defeated.
1780—Commissioned as brigadier general in the Continental Army.
1781—Commanding the troops in western North Carolina, he won the brilliant victory at Cowpens on January 17, for which the Congress, by resolution of March 9, 1781, gave him a vote of thanks and a gold medal.
Resigned because of ill health and retired to his plantation, "Saratoga" near Winchester, Va.
1794—Commanded the Virginia militia ordered out by President Washington, to suppress the Whiskey Insurrection.
1797-99—Was a member of Congress.
1802—Died in Winchester, Frederick County, Va., on July 6. Interment at Mount Hebron Cemetery.

LIEUTENANT COLONEL JOHN E. HOWARD

(No. 404)

OBV. JOH. EGAR HOWARD LEGIONIS PEDITUM PRAEFECTO COMITIA AMERICANA. (The American Congress to John Eager Howard, commander of a regiment of infantry.) Lieutenant Colonel Howard, on horseback, is in pursuit of a foot soldier of the enemy who is carrying away a standard. A winged Victory hovers over him, holding in her right hand a crown of laurel, and in her left a palm branch.

REV. Within a crown of laurel: QUOD IN NUTANTEM HOSTIUM ACIEM SUBITO IRRUENS PRAECLARUM BELLICAE VIRTUTIS SPECIMEN DEDIT IN PUGNA

AD COWPENS XVII JAN. MDCCLXXXI. (Because by rushing suddenly on the wavering lines of the enemy, he gave a brilliant example of martial courage at the battle of the Cowpens, Jan. 17, 1781.)

By Duvivier.

JOHN E. HOWARD

1752—Born in Baltimore County, Md.
1776—Appointed captain, he served under Gen. Hugh Mercer in the Battle of White Plains, N.Y.

166

1777—Promoted to the rank of major; fought at Germantown, being second in command of the 4th Maryland Regiment.

1778—Fought at the Battle of Monmouth.

1779—Became lieutenant colonel of the 5th Maryland Regiment of infantry; served in the South under Generals Gates, Greene, and Morgan, and taking a brilliant part in every engagement.

1781—Distinguished himself, under General Morgan, by heading the bayonet charge of the main line of defense at the Battle of Cowpens. Held in his hands at one time the swords of seven British officers who had surrendered to him. Awarded a silver medal by act of Congress, March 9, 1781.

Was colonel of the 2d Maryland regiment at Eutaw Springs.

1789–91—Governor of Maryland.

1791–1803—U.S. Senator from Maryland.

1798—When war with France was expected, he was selected by General Washington as one of his brigadier generals.

1814—Organized the defense of Baltimore, at the time the British burned Washington.

1827—Died on October 12; interment in Old St. Paul's Cemetery, Baltimore.

LIEUTENANT COLONEL WILLIAM WASHINGTON

(No. 405)

OBV. GULIELMO WASHINGTON LEGIONIS EQUIT. PRAEFECTO COMITIA AMERICANA. (The American Congress to William Washington, commander of a regiment of cavalry.) Lieutenant Colonel Washington, at the head of his men, is pursuing the enemy's cavalry. A winged Victory hovers above him, holding in her right hand a crown of laurel, and in her left a palm branch.

REV. Within a crown of laurel: QUOD PARVA MILITUM MANU STRENUE PROSECUTUS HOSTES VIRTUTIS INGENITAE PRAECLARUM SPECIMEN DEDIT IN PUGNA AD COWPENS XVII JAN. MDCCLXXI. (Because in vigorously pursuing the enemy with a handful of soldiers he gave a noble example of innate courage at the battle of the Cowpens, Jan. 17, 1781.)

By Duvivier.

WILLIAM AUGUSTINE WASHINGTON

1752—Born in Stafford County, Va.; a distant relation of George Washington.

Educated for the church, but entered the army under Col. Hugh Mercer as a captain of infantry.

1776—Fought in the Battle of Long Island. At the Battle of Trenton, he headed an advance party of the 3d Virginia; was wounded together with his lieutenant, James Monroe, then less than 18 years of age, afterwards, President of the United States.

1777—Served under General Washington at the Battle of Princeton.

1778—Was a major in Colonel Baylor's corps of cavalry and was with that officer when attacked by General Grey at Tappan.

1779—Served under General Lincoln in South Carolina and was active in command of light corps in the neighborhood of Charleston.

1781—Distinguished himself at the victory of the Cowpens, where his cavalry of 80 men came out from a concealed eminence, drove the British forces back, and helped achieve their surrender. Was awarded a silver medal by resolution of the Congress, March 9.

Fought at Guilford Court House and at Hobkirk's Hill near Camden.

Was a cavalry officer under General Greene at the Battle of Eutaw Springs. His dragoons were defeated with a loss of nearly half their strength. Washington, himself, was wounded and taken prisoner. He remained in captivity at Charleston until the close of the war, where he settled.

Served in the South Carolina Legislature; resided on his plantation at Sandy Hill, S.C.

1798—Appointed brigadier general.

1810—Died in Charleston, March 6.

FRANCOIS LOUIS TEISSEIDRE DE FLEURY

(No. 406)

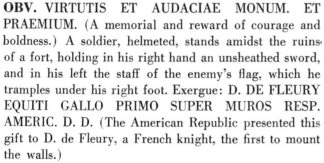

OBV. VIRTUTIS ET AUDACIAE MONUM. ET PRAEMIUM. (A memorial and reward of courage and boldness.) A soldier, helmeted, stands amidst the ruins of a fort, holding in his right hand an unsheathed sword, and in his left the staff of the enemy's flag, which he tramples under his right foot. Exergue: D. DE FLEURY EQUITI GALLO PRIMO SUPER MUROS RESP. AMERIC. D. D. (The American Republic presented this gift to D. de Fleury, a French knight, the first to mount the walls.)

REV. AGGERES PALUDES HOSTES VICTI. (Fortifications, marshes, enemies overcome.) The fortress of Stony Point, with two turrets and a flag flying. At the base of the hill are two water batteries, one of which is being discharged at a vessel on the river. Six vessels on the Hudson River. Exergue: STONY-PT. EXPUGN. XV JUL. MDCCLXXIX. (Stony Point carried by storm. July 15, 1779.)

By Duvivier.

FRANCOIS LOUIS TEISSEIDRE DE FLEURY

1749—Born at St. Hippolyte, Languedoc, France; educated as an engineer.

1768–70—Entered the French Army as a volunteer and served in the Corsican campaigns.

1777—Entered the American Army as a volunteer; received a congressional appointment as captain of engineers; joined Washington's army and was wounded toward the end of the Fort Mifflin campaign on the Delaware.

At Brandywine, the horse he was riding was shot and De Fleury was again wounded. Congress presented him with a horse "as a testimonial of the sense they had of his merits." On November 26 was promoted to lieutenant colonel.

1779—In the assault on Stony Point, July 15, he commanded one of the attacking columns, was the first to enter the main works, and struck the British flag with his own hands.

By resolution of Congress on October 1, De Fleury was awarded a silver medal.

1780—Served under General Count de Rochambeau in several campaigns including the siege and taking of Yorktown.

1790—Returned to France, and after further service with the French Army, he retired.

GENERAL ANTHONY WAYNE

OBV. ANTONIO WAYNE DUCI EXERCITUS COMITIA AMERICANA. (The American Congress to General Anthony Wayne.) America, personified as an Indian queen, wearing a cap and a skirt of feathers, and having at her feet a bow, an alligator, and the American shield, presents to General Wayne a laurel and a mural crown.

REV. STONEY-POINT EXPUGNATUM. (Stony Point carried by storm.) A view of the area of assault, including both sides of the Hudson River; Point Fort in the distance, a battery and troops in the foreground. Six ships on the Hudson River. Exergue: XV JUL. MDCCLXXIX (July 15, 1779).

By Gatteaux.

THE BATTLE AT STONY POINT

The Battle at Stony Point on July 16, 1779, was the last military action of importance in the northern theater in the War for Independence. It was important as a morale builder for the patriots and as a demonstration of the developing skill of the American Army, and it had other significant consequences. The assault paralyzed the British commander, Sir Henry Clinton. When his reinforcements failed to materialize, and with the heavy loss of men in Connecticut and Stony Point, he lost the offensive. The action at Stony Point enabled Washington to tighten his grip on the Hudson and especially on West Point, "the key to the Continent."

Stony Point is located about 35 miles north of New York City, on the west side of the Hudson River. The battle which took place here came after a long period of stalemate in the North that followed the Battle of Monmouth in June 1778.

At the beginning of June 1779, the British took without opposition the unfinished American fort at Stony Point. Verplanck's Point, on the east side of the river opposite

Stony Point, was captured at the same time. Stony Point is a steep promontory jutting half a mile into the river and rising 150 feet above the water, which all but surrounds it. A marsh, under water at high tide, protected the inland side of the post. Having secured this strong position, Clinton pushed the fortifications to completion and manned them with a sizable force.

Washington was greatly concerned over the loss of the two strongpoints on either side of the river and after a thorough reconnaisance ordered Gen. Anthony Wayne to regain Stony Point. Wayne moved in after dark on July 15, and at about midnight his elite corps launched its assault with muskets unloaded and with orders to use the bayonet. Within 20 minutes the fort had been secured and its surprised garrison made prisoners. The American loss was 15 killed and 80 wounded. The British losses were 63 killed, 70 wounded, and 543 captured.

BRIG. GEN. ANTHONY WAYNE

1745—Born at Waynesborough, Chester County, Pa.

   Educated in Philadelphia; became a surveyor.

1774—Elected a member of the Pennsylvania Convention.

1776—Appointed colonel of a regiment; served under General Thomas in Canada, and took part in the engagements at Three Rivers and at Ticonderoga.

1777—Promoted to the rank of brigadier general, under Washington.

   Fought at Brandywine, where he held the center position of defense against the main crossing of the British. Later he suffered defeat from their hands in a bloody massacre at Paoli's Tavern.

   Fought with Washington at Germantown, and wintered at Valley Forge.

1778—Led an advance attack on Monmouth.

1779—At midnight on July 15, he stormed Stony Point on the Hudson River.

Congress gave him a vote of thanks and a gold medal, after receiving the report from General Washington that Wayne's "conduct throughout the whole of this arduous enterprise merits the warmest approbation of Congress. He improved upon the plan recommended by me, and executed it in a manner that does signal honour to his judgment and to his bravery. In a critical moment of the assault, he received a flesh wound in the head with a musket ball, but continued leading on his men with unshaken firmness."

While Washington was explaining his plans for the recapture of Stony Point, Wayne is said to have remarked: "General, if *you* will only plan it, I will storm *Hell!*" It was for willingness to undertake such deeds of daring that Wayne was given the nickname, "Mad Anthony."

1780—Prevented British occupation of West Point, when Benedict Arnold tried to surrender it.

1781—Participated, with great success, in the Yorktown Campaign, under Lafayette.

1782—Occupied Savannah (July 11) and Charleston, S.C. (December 14).

1792—Appointed major general and commander in chief of the Western Army in the war against the Indians.

1794—In the Battle of Fallen Timbers (near Toledo, Ohio), Wayne gained an important victory over the Miami Tribe of Indians.

1795—Negotiated a treaty with the Indians at Greenville, which resulted in opening the Northwest for settlement.

1796—Died at Presque Isle, now Erie, Pa., on December 14. His remains were later placed in a monument in the cemetery of Radnor Church, near Waynesborough.

GENERAL NATHANIEL GREENE

(No. 408)

OBV. NATHANIELI GREEN EGREGIO DUCI COMITIA AMERICANA. (The American Congress to Nathaniel Greene, a distinguished general.) Bust of General Greene, in uniform, facing the left.

REV. SALUS REGIONUM AUSTRALIUM. (The safety of the southern regions.) A winged Victory holds a crown of laurel in her right hand, and a palm branch in her left; one foot is resting on a trophy of arms and flags of conquered enemies. Exergue: HOSTIBUS AD EUTAW DEBALLATIS DIE VIII SEPT MDCCLXXXI. The enemy vanquished at Eutaw on the 8th of September 1781.)

By Dupre.

NATHANIEL GREENE

1742—Born at Potowomut, Warwick Township, R.I. Worked at his father's iron foundry. Studied law.

1771–72—Member of the Rhode Island Legislature.

1774—Helped organize the Kentish Guards, a militia company, in which he served as a private.

1775—Served as a deputy to the General Assembly; made a brigadier general by the Rhode Island General Assembly, heading three volunteer regiments; served with Washington at the siege of Boston and commissioned a brigadier general in the Continental Army.

1776—Given command of the city of Boston, after its evacuation by the British. Commanded the troops on Long Island; fell ill of malarial fever.

While convalescing, recommended that Washington evacuate New York and burn it, to prevent its use as a headquarters and depot of supplies for the British.

On December 25, after crossing the Delaware and while in command of the left wing of the Army, surprised the British at Trenton, seized their artillery, and prevented their retreat to Princeton.

1777—Served with Washington at the Battle of Princeton and was given command of a new division.

Fought at the Battles of Brandywine and Germantown.

1778—With reluctance, and without relinquishing his authority to lead troops in action, he accepted the assignment as quartermaster general, a post he filled so eminently as to merit General Washington's comment: "by extraordinary exertions you so arranged it as to enable the army to take to the field the moment it was necessary, and to move with rapidity against the enemy."

Headed a division of the army at Valley Forge; participated in the Battles of Monmouth and Rhode Island.

1780—Fought at the Battle of Springfield; resigned his post as quartermaster general and resumed duties in the line, now being second in command to Washington.

Given command of West Point after Arnold's treason; was president of the court-martial at the trial of Major Andre, condemned to die as a spy.

Selected by Washington and approved by Congress, Greene was made commander in chief of the southern department. He succeeded Gen. Horatio Gates at a time when the British had practically completed their conquest of the South.

1781—General Greene divided his army, to retain the initiative, advancing with one part against the British right flank at Camden, S.C., and sending Gen. Daniel Morgan toward the British left at Ninety Six, a British fortified post in western South Carolina.

Cornwallis divided his own army three ways, sending Tarleton after Morgan and reinforcing Camden, while with his main body he marched northward to cut the American supply line.

Tarleton pushed forward and came upon Morgan's men at the Cowpens on January 17. Morgan wiped out the attackers and though Tarleton escaped, the latter's major usefulness had ended.

Morgan quickly rejoined Greene and the American Army began retreating northward.

Cornwallis was determined that Greene should not escape. Stripping his army of everything not essential, his army marched swiftly in pursuit. Greene stayed just ahead of him, meanwhile encouraging the guerilla leaders to harass the British rear and disrupt the supply lines.

Greene barely won the race for Virginia, crossing the swollen Dan River a few hours ahead of his pursuers. Having failed to catch Greene, Cornwallis withdrew to Hillsboro and sought to rebuild his depleted army.

Greene received reinforcements and advanced on the British. At Guilford Courthouse, on March 15, the armies collided. Although the British retained possession of the field, Cornwallis was so badly shattered that he moved his army to Wilmington, on the coast, where the British Navy could support and supply it.

With Cornwallis out of the way, Greene returned to South Carolina. His ensuing operations involved the Battle of Hobkirk's Hill on April 25, a 4-week siege of Ninety Six, and the Battle of Eutaw Springs on September 8, the last major engagement in South Carolina. From a tactical standpoint, Greene lost these battles. Yet, he won the campaign in the long run. The tireless marches he skillfully planned and directed so exhausted the enemy as to cause them to withdraw from the interior of South Carolina.

After the Battle of Eutaw Springs, the British forces in the south remained bottled up at Charleston and at Savannah where they remained until the end of the War of Independence.

On October 29, 1781, the Congress extended its thanks to Major General Greene "for his wise, decisive, and magnanimous conduct in the action of the 8th of September last, near the Eutaw Springs, in South Carolina, in which, with a force inferior in numbers to that of the enemy, he obtained a most signal victory." The same resolution provided that a captured British battle standard be presented to Greene "as an honorable testimony of his merit" and that a golden medal emblematical of the battle and victory also be bestowed on him.

1785—Greene moved to a plantation on the Savannah River which the State of Georgia presented to him.

1786—Died on June 19.

335-478 O - 69 - 12

OBV. HENRICO LEE LEGIONIS EQUIT. PRAEFEC-TO. COMITIA AMERICANA. (The American Congress to Henry Lee, major of cavalry.) The bust of Major Lee, facing the right.

REV. Within a crown of laurel: NON OBSTANTIB FLUMINIBUS VALLIS ASTUTIA & VIRTUTE BELLI-CA PARVA MANU HOSTES VICIT VICTOSQ. ARMIS HUMANITATE DEVINXIT. IN MEM PUGN AD PAULUS HOOK DIE XIX AUG. 1779. (Notwithstanding rivers and ramparts, he conquered, with a handful of men, the enemy by skill and valor, and attached by his humanity those vanquished by his arms. In commemoration of the Battle of Paulus Hook, Aug. 19, 1779.)

By Joseph Wright.

HENRY ("*Light Horse Harry*") LEE

1756—Born at "Leesylvania" in Prince William County, Va.

1773—Graduated from Princeton College.

1776—Commissioned a captain, heading a company of Virginia cavalry, June 18. (During the campaigns of 1775 and 1776 there was not a single troop horse attached to the Continental Army.)

1777—Became attached to and a part of the First Continental Dragoons.

1778—Attacked by British cavalry of 200 men, Lee and a small band of 10 men made such a resolute and determined defense that the enemy retreated. By a special act of Congress, April 7, in recognition of his brave and distinguished services, was promoted to a major commandant and authorized to augment his corps by the enlistment of two troops of horse.

1779—Having been in the supporting party at the successful storming of Stony Point, Lee wanted to undertake a similar undertaking on his own at Paulus

Hook, a British occupied fort in what is now Jersey City, N.J. In giving his consent, Washington limited the number of men to be assigned, and directed that though no attempt should be made to keep the fort, the main purpose of the mission would be to surprise the garrison and bring off as many prisoners as could be secured.

Just before daybreak on August 19, as the tide was rising, with a force of 200 men, Lee's forces rushed forward—as at Stony Point—without firing a shot. They cleared the abatis, crossed the ditch around the fort, and entered the works. Capturing 158 prisoners, Lee immediately began his retreat and arrived safely back at the Hackensack Bridge, after 27 hours of continuous marching and more than a little fighting. American losses were two killed and three wounded.

By act of September 24, Lee was given the thanks of Congress "for remarkable prudence, address, and bravery displayed in the attack on the enemy's fort and works at Paulus Hook" and in terms approved his humanity, and granted him a gold medal. [The medal was made under the personal supervision of Thomas Jefferson.]

1780—By act of October 21, his battalion was designated "Lee's partisan corps."

Commissioned lieutenant colonel.

1785–88—Served as a member of the Continental Congress; advocated the adoption of the Federal Constitution in the Virginia Convention of 1788.

1791–94—Governor of Virginia.

1794—Commanded the U.S. forces in the Whiskey Insurrection in Pennsylvania.

1799–1801—Served as a Federalist to the Sixth Congress; honorably discharged from the Army. At the request of Congress, pronounced the eulogy upon

President Washington before both branches of Congress, in which Washington is characterized as the man "first in war, first in peace, and first in the hearts of his countrymen."

1818—Died on Cumberland Island, Georgia; buried at Dungeness, Ga.
1913—Reinterment in the Lee Mausoleum at Lexington, Va.

LIEUTENANT GENERAL WINFIELD SCOTT

(No. 410)

(No. 424)

No. 410. The Niagara Campaign.

OBV. MAJOR GENERAL WINFIELD SCOTT. Bust of General Scott, facing the right.

REV. A serpent, entwined in a wreath of laurel and palm, is swallowing its tail—emblem of immortality through glory and victory. RESOLUTION OF CONGRESS NOVEMBER 3, 1814. BATTLES OF CHIPPEWA JULY 5, 1814. NIAGARA JULY 25, 1814.

By Furst.

No. 424. The Mexican Campaign.

OBV. In a pendant: MAJOR GENERAL WINFIELD SCOTT. Undraped bust of General Scott, facing the left. Fifteen stars on each side. Exergue: RESOLUTION OF CONGRESS MARCH 9, 1848.

By Ellis and Wright.

REV. Six crowns of laurel and oak intertwined; in each the name of one of the Mexican victories of General Scott: VERA VRUZ. CERRO GORDO. CONTRERAS. SAN ANTONIO & CHURUBUSCO. MOLINO DEL REY. CHAPULTEPEC. In the center is the taking of the capital, CITY OF MEXICO, which General Scott is observing on horseback.

By Humphries and Wright.

No. 427. The Mexican Campaign (presented by Commonwealth of Virginia).

OBV. A bust of General Scott, resting upon a branch of laurel and of oak, is placed upon a pedestal, supported upon each side by an eagle, behind which, projecting at either side, are several colors and various other military emblems. The pedestal bears the inscription: THE COMMONWEALTH OF VIRGINIA PRESENTS THIS MEDAL TO MAJOR-GENERAL WINFIELD SCOTT, AS A MEMORIAL OF HER ADMIRATION FOR THE GREAT AND DISTINGUISHED SERVICES OF HER SON WHILST COMMANDER-IN-CHIEF OF THE AMERICAN ARMIES IN THE WAR WITH MEXICO, 1847.

REV. A column upon two stands of colors, entwined by a branch of laurel. A wreath formed of oak branches encloses the designs and inscriptions, and is held at the bottom by a shield bearing the coat of arms of the State of Virginia. Upon the top of the column an eagle, with outstretched wings and carrying a branch of laurel in its beak, has alighted. The cap of the column bears the date 1848, and just below is the word MEXICO. The leaves of the laurel branch surrounding the column bear the names of the several battles during the campaign which the recipient commanded, viz.: CHAPULTEPEC, DEL REY, CHURUBUSCO, CONTRERAS, CERRO GORDO, VERA CRUZ; and upon the base of the column is the date 1812. On the right background a party is bombarding before the walls of the City of Mexico, another party is storming a fort upon the brow of a hill; on the left background troops are advancing upon a fort, and to their left a besieging party is opening fire upon the city before them. Legend: FECIT QUOD COGITAVIT. Exergue: FROM VIRGINA.

By C. C. Wright.

WINFIELD SCOTT

1786—Born in Dinwiddie County, near Petersburg, Va.

1805–06—Attended William and Mary College, Williamsburg, Va.

Studied law and for some time engaged in practice.

1808—Appointed captain of light artillery, U.S. Army.

Served in Louisiana under Gen. James Wilkinson, but resigned on account of differences with him.

1811–12—Staff duties, under Brig. Gen. Wade Hampton, in New Orleans.

1812—Lieutenant colonel of the 2d Artillery Regiment; taken prisoner at Queenstown, N.Y., by the British; exchanged as a prisoner of war.

1813—Promoted to colonel; leading the 2d Artillery he captured Fort George and defeated the British at Upholds Creek.

Became adjutant general under Major General Dearborn.

1814—Promoted to brigadier general and joined General Brown at Niagara. Initiated vigorous drill training and military discipline. Distinguished himself at Chippewa. In his official battle report, General Brown stated:

"Brigadier General Scott is entitled to the highest praise our country can bestow: to him, more than any other man, I am indebted for the victory of the 5th of July."

On July 25 at Lundy's Lane (Niagara), with a small force under him at that time, he faced the entire British-Canadian Army; had two horses shot out from under him; was wounded in the side and then was disabled by a shot which shattered his left shoulder.

By resolution of November 3, 1814, for his service at Chippewa and Niagara, the Congress gave him a vote of thanks and a gold medal. Breveted a major general September 14.

1815—Sent on mission to France to study military methods.

1816—Formulated the first basic U.S. drill regulations for field exercises and maneuvers of infantry.

1818, 1821, 1824, 1826—Headed Board of Tactics for the U.S. Army.

1832—Commanded in the Black Hawk War.

1835—Campaigned against the Creek and Seminole Indians.

Sent to settle a boundary dispute between Maine and Canada.

1841—Promoted to major general and Commander in Chief of the Army.

1847—In the war with Mexico, he led an expedition which captured the fortress at Vera Cruz on March 26; won the battles at the mountain pass of Cerro Gordo, April 18, Contreras, August 19; Churubusco, August 20; Molino del Rey, September 8; Chapultepec, September 13; and captured Mexico City, September 14, raising the American flag over the palace there and paving the way for negotiation of a peace treaty. For these brilliant campaigns by resolution of March 9, 1848, the Congress gave him a vote of thanks and a gold medal.

1850—Honorary degree of LL.D. from Columbia College, New York.

1852—Whig candidate for President; was defeated by Franklin Pierce.

1855—Was made lieutenant general by brevet, February 28.

1861—Honorary degree from Harvard College, Cambridge; retired from the Army.

1866—Died at West Point, N.Y., May 29; interment in the National Cemetery, West Point.

MAJOR GENERAL EDMUND PENDLETON GAINES

OBV. MAJOR GENERAL EDMUND P. GAINES. Bust of General Gaines, facing the right.

REV. RESOLUTION OF CONGRESS NOVEMBER 3. 1814. A winged Victory, standing on a British shield, holds a palm branch in her left hand, and places with her right a crown of laurel upon a cannon standing upright in the ground, and forming the center of a trophy of the enemy's arms; on the cannon is the inscription ERIE. Exergue: BATTLE OF ERIE AUG. 15. 1814.

By Furst.

EDMUND PENDLETON GAINES

1777—Born in Culpeper County, Va.

1799—Appointed 2d lieutenant, 6th Infantry, U.S. Army.

1802—1st lieutenant.

1804—Military Collector of Customs at Mobile, Ala.

1807—Captain. Arrested Aaron Burr and served as a witness against him, when he was tried in Richmond, Va., for conspiracy.

1812—Promoted to major, and then to lieutenant colonel.

1813—As a colonel, he covered the retreat at Chrysler's Field; adjutant general in command of Fort Erie.

1814—Serving as a brigadier general, he greatly distinguished himself by defending Fort Erie against the British on August 15; was badly wounded on the 28th of the same month.

Breveted major general, September 14.

For his gallantry and good conduct, and for "repelling with great slaughter the attack of a British veteran army, superior in numbers (at Fort Erie)," the Congress gave him a vote of thanks and a gold medal, by resolution of November 3, 1814.

Was commander of the Southern Military District.

1817—Served as a commissioner to deal with the Creek Indians in the South. Fought in the Creek and Seminole Indian Wars, under Gen. Andrew Jackson.

1832—Was successful in engagement against the Black Hawk Indians, while serving as commander of the Eastern Department of the U.S. Army.

1835—Commanded an expedition in the Florida War.

1846—Was in command of the Western Department of the Army; later reassigned to the Eastern Department.

1849—Died in New Orleans, June 6.

MAJOR GENERAL PETER B. PORTER

OBV. MAJOR GENERAL PETER B. PORTER. Bust of General Porter, in uniform, facing the right.

REV. RESOLUTION OF CONGRESS NOVEMBER 3. 1814. A winged Victory, holding in her right hand a palm branch and a wreath of laurel, and in her left three standards, upon which are written: ERIE CHIPPEWA NIAGARA. She dictates to the muse of History, who is seated on the ground, writing. Exergue: BATTLES OF CHIPPEWA JULY 5. 1814. NIAGARA JULY 25. 1814. ERIE SEP. 17. 1814.

By Furst.

PETER BUEL PORTER

1773 —Born in Salisbury, Conn.

1791—Graduated from Yale College.

1793—Attended Litchfield (Connecticut) Law School; was admitted to the bar; and commenced practice in Canandaigua, N.Y.

1797–1804—Clerk of Ontario County; member of the New York State Legislature.

1809–13—Moved to Buffalo, N.Y.; elected to the House of Representatives, 11th and 12th Congresses; served as Chairman of the Committee of Foreign Relations.

1813–14—Raised and commanded a Pennsylvania and New York volunteers militia which was incorporated with Indians of the Six Nations.

1814—Was commissioned a major general, in command of New York militia.

Presented a gold medal under joint resolution of Congress dated November 3, 1814, for gallantry and good conduct in the several conflicts of Chippewa, Lundy's Lane (Niagara), and Erie.

1815–16—Served in the House of Representatives, 14th Congress; resigned; appointed Secretary of State of New York.

1816–22—Served as International Boundary Commissioner under the Treaty of Ghent to determine the boundary between the United States and Canada.

1817—Unsuccessful candidate for Governor of New York State.

1824–30—Regent of the University of the State of New York.

1828–29—Appointed Secretary of War in the Cabinet of President John Quincy Adams.

1840—Served as a Whig presidential elector.

1844—Died at Niagara Falls, N.Y., March 20; interment in Oakwood Cemetery, Niagara Falls.

MAJOR GENERAL JACOB BROWN

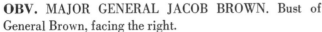

OBV. MAJOR GENERAL JACOB BROWN. Bust of General Brown, facing the right.

REV. RESOLUTION OF CONGRESS NOVEMBER 3, 1814. In the center of a trophy, composed of the enemy's arms and flags, are the Roman fasces, emblem of the strength and of the union of America. The fasces are surrounded by a crown of laurel, from which hang three shields, each bearing the name of one of the three victories: NIAGARA ERIE CHIPPEWA. At the foot of the trophy the American eagle, with outspread wings, holds in its talons a British standard. Exergue: BATTLES OF CHIPPEWA. JULY 5. 1814. NIAGARA. JULY 25. 1814. ERIE. SEP. 17. 1814.
By Furst.

THE NIAGARA CAMPAIGNS

Following a series of unsuccessful campaigns against the British in Canada, a group of relatively young generals was selected to spearhead a new invasion of Canada in 1814. Heading the American Northern Army was Maj. Gen. Jacob Brown, with his brigade commanders: Winfield Scott, Eleazer Wheelock Ripley, Peter Buel Porter, James Miller, and Edmund Pendleton Gaines. The American forces numbered about 3,500 men. The British forces, approximately equal in number, were under the command of Lt. Gen. Sir Gordon Drummond; 1,000 of them were stationed at York and about 2,600 were strung out along the Niagara under Maj. Gen. Phineas Riall.

The action in the Niagara campaigns centered about York (now Toronto) and Burlington Heights on the north and western shores of Lake Ontario, and along Lake Niagara. On the west bank of the Niagara (proceeding south) is Fort George, Queenstown, Lundy's Lane, Chippewa, and

Fort Erie; on its east bank (also proceeding south) is Fort Niagara, Fort Schlosser, Black Rose, and Buffalo.

Brown commenced his campaign on July 3, 1813, by moving his troops across the Niagara to invest Fort Erie, which surrendered on the afternoon of that day. Brown then proceeded north, up the Niagara. Riall, gathering his forces, proceeded south, along the west coast of the Niagara and halted, 14 miles above Fort Erie, at Chippewa. Here, on July 4, the British and American forces engaged in battle. The effectiveness of artillery and superior maneuvering of the Americans compelled Riall to withdraw in confusion; his forces retreated to Fort George and Burlington Heights. British losses were 500 men; the Americans, 300.

Three weeks following their defeat at Chippewa, the British forces were reformed under the personal direction and command of General Drummond. He sent troops across the Niagara to Fort Schlosser to seize the American ammunition and supply depot. Hoping to draw the British away from Fort Schlosser, Brown ordered an attack on Riall who had moved his forces to Lundy's Lane, a few miles north of Chippewa. On the 25th of July, 1814, Riall's and Brown's forces met and engaged in a savage combat which extended into the night and continued the next day. Brown and Scott were both severely wounded and had to be evacuated from the field; the American command passed to Ripley. Riall, himself wounded, was captured. Both sides claimed victory; losses on both sides were almost 30 percent. On July 26, the Americans withdrew to Fort Erie.

Placed under the command of Gen. Edmund P. Gaines, the fortifications of Fort Erie had been greatly improved by the U.S. Army Corps of Engineers after its capture by the

Americans on July 3. The British, under General Drummond, laid siege to the fort on August 13, a siege that continued on for over a month, with heavy casualties on both sides. In one attack, alone, the Fort Erie blockhouse was blown up, with a loss of 900 British soldiers and 100 Americans. Wounded in combat, General Gaines turned the command back to General Brown who had convalesced sufficiently to take command of his troops. After secret preparations, Brown made a sortie on September 17, 1814, using 1,600 men, to rush two British positions from their entrenchments. The British works were destroyed or rendered unserviceable. The loss to the British was 500 men; American losses were equally as heavy. On September 21, Drummond retreated beyond the Chippewa. This was the last major action on the Niagara; operations moved east. The next major land engagement was at Plattsburg, N.Y.

JACOB BROWN

1775—Born in Bucks County, Pa.

Schoolteacher.

1796–98—Land surveyor in Ohio. Studied law.

1799—Moved to Jefferson County, N.Y., where he became a judge; established village now known as Brownville.

1809—Commissioned colonel and given command of a New York militia regiment.

1810—Brigadier general, New York Militia.

1812—Given command of a 200-mile frontier extending from Oswego to Lake Francis, he repelled an attack by a superior British force at Ogdensburg, where his headquarters were located.

1813—Commissioned brigadier general, U.S. Army.

1814—Commissioned major general; same year was appointed Commander in Chief of the U.S. Army on the Canadian frontier. For his outstanding service in the Battles of Chippewa (July 5), Lundy's Lane (Niagara) July 25, and Erie (September 17), the Congress by resolution of November 3, 1814, gave him a vote of thanks and a gold medal.

Retained command of the Northern Division of the U.S. Army.

1821—Became Commander in Chief of the U.S. Army.

1828—Died in Washington, D.C., February 24; interment at Congressional Cemetery.

BRIGADIER GENERAL JAMES MILLER

(No. 414)

OBV. BRIGADIER GENL JAMES MILLER. Bust of General Miller, in uniform, facing the right. Exergue: I'LL TRY. His answer when he received the order to attack the enemy's batteries on the hill at Niagara.

REV. RESOLUTION OF CONGRESS NOVEMBER 3. 1814. Colonel Miller, at the head of his troops, is carrying the British batteries on the hill at Lundy's Lane (Niagara).

Exergue: BATTLES OF CHIPPEWA, JULY 5. 1814. NIAGARA. JULY 25. 1814. ERIE SEP. 17. 1814.

By Furst.

JAMES MILLER

1776—Born in Peterborough, Hillsborough County, N.H.

1803–08—Practiced law at Peterborough.

1808—Entered the Army with the rank of major, 4th Regiment of the U.S. Infantry. Was stationed at Fort Independence at Boston Harbor.

1810—Commissioned lieutenant colonel.

1812—Distinguished himself in the West, under General Harrison. Served under General Hull in the invasion of Canada.

1814—Became a colonel of the 21st Infantry.

Greatly distinguished himself at Chippewa, Lundy's Lane (Niagara), and Erie, for which he was breveted a brigadier general. He received the thanks of Congress and a gold medal, by resolution of November 3, 1814.

At Lundy's Lane, when asked to assault and capture the British batteries on the heights, he made the celebrated reply, "I'll try, Sir." His efforts met with eminent success.

1819—Resigned from the Army.

1819–25—Governor of Arkansas Territory.

1825–49—U.S. Collector of Customs at Salem, Mass.

1851—Died at Temple, N.H., July 7.

BRIGADIER GENERAL ELEAZER W. RIPLEY

(No. 415)

OBV. BRIG. GENERAL ELEAZER W. RIPLEY. Bust of General Ripley, in uniform, facing the right.

REV. RESOLUTION OF CONGRESS NOVEMB. 3. 1814. A winged Victory, standing, holds in her right hand a trumpet and a crown of laurel, and with her left is hanging upon a palm tree a shield on which are the words: CHIPPEWA NIAGARA ERIE. Exergue: BATTLES OF CHIPPEWA JULY 5. 1814. NIAGARA JULY 25. 1814. ERIE. AUG. 15 SEP. 17. 1814.

By Furst.

ELEAZER WHEELOCK RIPLEY

1782—Born in Hanover, N.H.

1800—Graduated from Dartmouth College, Hanover. Studied law; admitted to the bar and commenced practice in Waterville, Maine (a district of Massachusetts).

1807–12—Became a member and speaker of the Massachusetts House of Representatives; member of the Massachusetts Senate.

1812—Commissioned lieutenant colonel and given command of the 21st (present 5th) Infantry Regiment, to be enlisted in Massachusetts.

1813—Served under General Wilkinson in the Canadian Campaign; was wounded in the attack on York (now Toronto); commissioned colonel; took part in the battle at Chrysler's Field.

1814—Commissioned brigadier general; sent to Niagara; given a 1,400-man brigade; fought at Chippewa, Lundy's Lane (Niagara), and Fort Erie where he was severely wounded. Awarded a gold medal by resolution of the Congress on November 3, 1814, for gallantry and good conduct.

1820—Resigned from the Army and resumed private practice of law in New Orleans.

1832—Served in the Louisiana Senate.

1835–39—Served in the U.S. House of Representatives, in the 24th and 25th Congresses.

1839—Died in West Feliciana Parish, La., on March 2; interment at Francisville, La.

MAJOR GENERAL ALEXANDER MACOMB

(No. 416)

OBV. MAJOR GENERAL ALEXANDER MACOMB. Bust of General Macomb, in uniform, facing the right.

REV. RESOLUTION OF CONGRESS NOVEMBER 3. 1814. The American Army repulsing the British troops, who are striving to cross the Saranac River. To the left, Plattsburgh in flames; to the right, naval battle on Lake Champlain; in the distance, Cumberland Head. Exergue: BATTLE OF PLATTSBURGH SEPT. 11, 1814.

By Furst.

ALEXANDER MACOMB

1782—Born in Detroit, Mich.

1798–99—Entered a corps called the "New York Rangers;" obtained a cornetcy in the calvary.

1802—Graduated from the U.S. Military Academy. Commissioned 1st lieutenant, Corps of Engineers, U.S. Army.

1805–12—Promoted to captain (1805); major (1808); lieutenant colonel (1810) and Adjutant General (1812); during which time he had responsibility for the coastal fortifications in the Carolinas and Georgia. Authored a treatise on "Martial Law and Court Martials;" transferred to the artillery; colonel 3d Artillery (1812).

1814—As brigadier general, he raised a New York regiment and was given command of the northern portion of the frontier bordering on Lake Champlain; he defeated the British at the Battle of Plattsburgh.

Congress gave him a vote of thanks and a gold medal by resolution of November 3, 1814, for "gallantry and good conduct in defeating the enemy at Plattsburg on the eleventh of September, repelling with one thousand five hundred men, aided by a body of militia and volunteers from New York and Vermont, a British veteran army greatly superior in numbers." On the day of the Battle of Plattsburg, Captain Macdonough defeated the British fleet on Lake Champlain. These two actions caused a British retreat to Canada.

1819—Breveted major general.

1821—Appointed chief of the Corps of Engineers.

1828—Promoted to major general and Commanding General of the Army, succeeding Gen. Jacob Brown.

1840—Author of "The Practice of Court Martial".

1841—Died at the headquarters of the Army in Washington, June 25.

MAJOR GENERAL ANDREW JACKSON

OBV. MAJOR GENERAL ANDREW JACKSON. Bust of General Jackson, in uniform, facing the right.

REV. RESOLUTION OF CONGRESS FEBRUARY 27. 1815. A winged Victory, holding in her left hand a crown of laurel, and a tablet upon which she has written, at the dictation of Peace, the word ORLEANS. Exergue: BATTLE OF NEW ORLEANS JANUARY 8. 1815.

By Furst.

ANDREW JACKSON ("*Old Hickory*")

1767—Born in Waxhaw Settlement, S.C.

Attended the "old field" school and academy of Doctor Humphries. Served in the Battle of Hanging Rock during the Revolution; was captured by the British and confined in the stockade at Camden, S.C.; refusing to shine the boots of one of his captors, he received a saber slash which he bore the remainder of his life.

Left an orphan at 14 years of age; worked for a time in a saddler's shop and afterwards taught school.

Studied law in Salisbury, N.C.

1787—Was admitted to the bar and commenced practice of law in Guilford County, N.C.

1788—Moved to Nashville, Tenn.

1791—Appointed prosecuting attorney for South West Territory under General Blount.

1796—Delegate to the Tennessee Constitutional Convention. Was Tennessee's first representative of the State to the Fourth Congress.

1797–98—Elected to the U.S. Senate.

1798–1804—Served as judge of the Tennessee Supreme Court; moved to the "Hermitage" near Nashville; appointed major general of the Tennessee Militia (1802).

1813—During a march from Natchez, Miss., to Nashville, Tenn., Jackson displayed such endurance and strength and he displayed such concern for the welfare and privations of his militia, that his troops gave him the nickname of "Old Hickory."

1814—Commanding the Tennessee Militia, he defeated the Creek Indians on March 27, at Horseshoe Bend, Ga.; this was in retaliation for their massacre at Fort Mims in the Mississippi Territory.

Commissioned major general, U.S. Army, with command of the 7th Southwestern Military District.

1815—Led the U.S. Army to New Orleans where he defeated the British on January 8, 1815. His victory was so overwhelming as to make him an outstanding hero of the War of 1812.

On February 27, 1815, the Congress awarded a gold medal to Jackson and resolved that: "the thanks of Congress be, and they are hereby given, to Major General Jackson, and, through him, to the officers and soldiers of the regular army, of the militia and of the volunteers under his immediate command, and to the officers and soldiers charged with the defence of Fort St. Philip, for their uniform gallantry and good conduct, conspicuously displayed against the enemy, from the time of his landing before New Orleans until his final expulsion from the State of Louisiana, and particularly for the valour, skill, and good conduct on the eighth of January last, in repulsing, with great slaughter, a numerous British army of chosen veteran troops, when attempting by a bold and daring attack to carry by storm the works hastily thrown up for the protection of New Orleans, and thereby obtaining a most signal victory over the enemy with a disparity of loss, on his part, unexampled in military annals."

British losses in the Battle of New Orleans were over 2,000 men; American losses were less than 100.

1817—Because of Indian and outlaw harassment of U.S. citizens on the Florida frontier, Jackson headed an expedition which was so successful that it virtually captured Florida.

1821—Declined the position of Minister to Mexico.

1823–25—Served in the U.S. Senate; unsuccessful Democratic candidate for President in 1824.

1828—Elected President of the United States; reelected in 1832.

1837—Retired to his country home near Nashville, Tenn.

1845—Died; interment at "The Hermitage."

MAJOR GENERAL WILLIAM HENRY HARRISON

(No. 418)

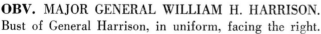

OBV. MAJOR GENERAL WILLIAM H. HARRISON. Bust of General Harrison, in uniform, facing the right.

REV. RESOLUTION OF CONGRESS APRIL 4, 1818. America, personified as a maiden, with a spear in her right hand and resting on the American shield, places with her left a crown of laurel on a trophy formed of the arms of the enemy, on which hangs a buckler, with the inscription FORT MEIGS BATTLE OF THE THAMES. Exergue: BATTLE OF THE THAMES OCTOBER 5. 1813.

By Furst.

THE BATTLE OF THE THAMES

Perry's famous dispatch: "We have met the enemy and they are ours," concluding the Battle of Lake Erie, was received by Gen. William Harrison on September 12, 1813. This meant that it was now the Army's turn to act, for the purpose of regaining Detroit and the Michigan Territory which had been surrendered to the British a year earlier.

One wing of Harrison's forces, garrisoned at Fort Meigs, consisted of about 2,500 regulars. This was augmented by 3,000 Kentucky volunteer infantry led by Governor Isaac Shelby, and by a Kentucky mounted regiment organized by Congressman Richard M. Johnson. The latter received a commission as colonel of Kentucky Volunteers.

On September 24, 1813, Harrison transferred his main forces into Canada, to a point about 3 miles below the British Fort Malden. The British commander, Col. Henry Proctor, had evacuated Malden because he realized he could not hold it with Lake Erie in the possession of the American Navy. Proctor fell back by the road up the Thames River.

Harrison's forces followed, and on the 5th of October they engaged the enemy at a point near Moravian Village in what is now known as the Battle of the Thames. The British were routed, losing 12 killed, 22 wounded, and 600 captured. American losses were seven killed and 22 wounded, five of whom soon died. Tecumseh, the famous Indian leader serving with Proctor, was among the slain; his northwestern confederacy was broken up; and as a result of the battle, the Indians abandoned their dependence on England.

The victory of Harrison on the Thames, coupled with that of Perry on Lake Erie, ended the British power on the Great Lakes, crushed the Indians, and regained the Territory of Michigan, with the exception of Fort Mackinac, for the United States.

WILLIAM HENRY HARRISON
(*"Old Tippecanoe"*)

1773—Born in Berkeley, Charles City County, Va.

Pursued classical studies; attended Hampden-Sidney College, Virginia; studied medicine.

1791—Commissioned by President Washington ensign in the First Infantry; served in the Indian wars under General St. Clair and afterward under General Wayne as an aide-de-camp.

1797—Was made captain and given command of Fort Washington.

1798—Resigned his Army commission; appointed Secretary of the Northwest Territory.

1799—Served as a delegate from the Territory Northwest of the Ohio River, to the Sixth Congress.

1801—Territorial Governor of Indiana and also Indian Commissioner.

1811—Defeated the Indians on November 7, at Tippecanoe.

1812—Brigadier General in the U.S. Army; then promoted to major general.

1813—October 5, again defeated the British and Indians in the Battle of the Thames; was awarded a gold medal for this action by congressional resolution of April 4, 1818.

1814—Resigned from the Army.

Head commissioner to treat with the Indians.

1815–19—Elected representative as a Whig to the 14th Congress; reelected to the 15th Congress.

1819–21—Member of the State Senate.

1825–28—Served in the U.S. Senate.

1828–29—Minister to Colombia.

1836—Unsuccessful Whig candidate for President.

1841—Served as President until his death, April 4, which occurred 1 month after his inauguration.

Interment in the Harrison Tomb, opposite Congress Green Cemetery, North Bend, Ohio.

GOVERNOR ISAAC SHELBY

(No. 419)

OBV. GOVERNOR ISAAC SHELBY. Bust of Governor Shelby in a general's uniform, facing the right.

REV. BATTLE OF THE THAMES. OCTO. 5, 1813. The battle of the Thames; in the background, a forest; in the foreground, the mounted riflemen are charging the enemy. Exergue: RESOLUTION OF CONGRESS APRIL 4, 1818.

By Furst.

ISAAC SHELBY

1750—Born in Hagerstown, Md.

Became a surveyor.

1771—Moved to Bristol, Tenn.

1774—Appointed lieutenant; served at the Battle of Point Pleasant.

1777—Distinguished himself at the Battle of Long Island.

Appointed captain by Governor Patrick Henry and made commissary general of the Virginia forces.

1779—Commissioned a major by Governor Thomas Jefferson; because of a change in the State lines, his residence became part of North Carolina. Resigned his Virginia commission and was appointed a colonel in the North Carolina Militia.

1780—Displayed great gallantry in the Battle of King's Mountain, for which he received a sword of honor and thanks from the Virginia Legislature.

1781–82—Served under Gen. Francis Marion in the South; elected to the South Carolina Legislature; recalled to active duty and served under General Greene in the vicinity of Charleston.

1791—Member of the Constitutional Convention.

1792—Upon the admission of the State of Kentucky into the Union, an almost unanimous vote elected Shelby as its first Governor.

1813—At the age of 63, he recruited and led several thousand men to fight with General Harrison at the Battle of the Thames on October 5. Congress gave him a vote of thanks and a gold medal.

1817—Declined to serve as Secretary of War under President Madison because of ill health.

1818—Acted as a commissioner with General Jackson in negotiating a treaty with the Chickasaw Indians.

1826—Died in Lincoln County, Ky., July 18.

COLONEL GEORGE CROGHAN

(No. 420)

OBV. PRESENTED BY CONGRESS TO COLONEL GEORGE CROGHAN 1835. Bust of Colonel Croghan, in uniform, facing the right.

REV. In a pendant: PARS MAGNA FUIT (His share was great). Major Croghan and his small force defending Fort Stephenson against the attack of the British Army. In the background, three gunboats on Lake Erie. Exergue: SANDUSKY 2: AUGUST 1813.

By Furst.

THE DEFENSE OF FORT STEPHENSON

The Congress declared war against Great Britain on June 18, 1812. Although occupied on the continent with the French, the British maintained armed forces in Canada under Sir George Provost. Heading the 41st Regiment under Provost was a Col. Henry Proctor who led his forces in July 1813, against Fort Meigs, an American post in northern Ohio. Accompanying him were several hundred British regulars and about 1,000 Indians. A joint British-Indian attack on Fort Meigs was a failure, as the fort was too well defended, and a plan to lure the Americans from the fort by a feigned attack was not successful.

Leaving a force to continue the siege at Fort Meigs, Proctor withdrew his forces and led them down the Maumee, along Lake Erie, and up to the small American post at Fort Stephenson. This fort, orginally established as a trading post as early as 1745, was garrisoned by less than 200 American troops under the command of Maj. George Croghan.

Proctor hoped that Fort Stephenson would be surrendered without a struggle and he argued with Croghan that if it were necessary to take the fort by storm, the Indians could not be restrained. Croghan would not yield; he had told his commanding officer, Gen. William Henry Harrison that "We have determined to maintain this place, and by Heaven we will."

On August 2, 1813, the British began their assault. The fort was bombarded by gunboats in the river, and from shore batteries of three 6-pounders. Not being able to make a breach, the British 41st Regiment marched to the pickets of the fort. They were mowed down by Croghan's Kentucky sharpshooters. The fort had only one piece of artillery, affectionately known as "Old Betsy," which was uncovered and brought to bear on the enemy. With great and effective force, Old Betsy emitted nails and grape. After 2 hours and with a loss of all of his officers, Proctor withdrew, leaving casualties of 26 dead, 38 wounded, and about 30 missing. American casualties were one killed and seven wounded. After the disaster at Fort Stephenson,

Proctor raised the siege at Fort Meigs and fell back to Canada.

GEORGE CROGHAN

1791—Born near Louisville, Ky.

1810—Graduated from William and Mary College, Va.

1811—Was a volunteer aide-de-camp to Colonel Boyd, second in command at the Battle of Tippecanoe.

1812—Appointed captain in the regular army. Marched with a Kentucky detachment, under General Winchester, to relieve General Hull in Canada.

1813—Commissioned major; made an excellent record in the defense of Fort Meigs, where he served as an aide to General Harrison.

Distinguished himself at Fort Stephenson, for which he was later brevetted a lieutenant colonel, and awarded a gold medal by resolution of the Congress on February 13, 1855.

1817—Resigned his commission.

1824—Served as a postmaster; reentered the Army.

1825—Promoted to rank of Inspector General and colonel.

1846—Served under Gen. Zachary Taylor in Mexico, taking part in the Battle of Monterey.

1849—Died in New Orleans, January 8.

MAJOR GENERAL ZACHARY TAYLOR

(No. 421)

No. 421. For Palo Alto and Resaca de la Palma.

OBV. MAJOR GENERAL ZACHARY TAYLOR. Bust of General Taylor, in uniform, facing the right.

Portrait by William Garl Brown, model by John T. Battin, dies by Franklin Peale.

REV. Within a wreath of laurel and palm inclosing a serpent biting its tail—emblem of immortality through glory and victory: RESOLUTION OF CONGRESS JULY 16th 1846. PALO ALTO MAY 8th 1846 RESACA DE LA PALMA MAY 9th 1846.

No. 422. For Monterey.

OBV. MAJOR GENERAL ZACHARY TAYLOR. Bust of General Taylor, in uniform, facing the right.

REV. Within a wreath of oak: RESOLUTION OF CONGRESS MARCH 2nd 1847 MONTEREY SEPTEMBER 1846.

By J. B. Longacre.

No. 423. For Buena Vista.

OBV. MAJOR GENERAL ZACHARY TAYLOR. RESOLUTION OF CONGRESS: MAY 9, 1848. Undraped bust

187

of General Taylor, facing the right; underneath, branches of oak and laurel.

By S. Ellis and C. C. Wright.

REV. BUENA VISTA FEB. 22. & 23. 1847. Within a circle formed by two serpents, one of which is a rattlesnake, the American Army, commanded by General Taylor, is repulsing the attack of the Mexicans. Beneath are branches of cactus and oak.

By F. A. Smith and C. C. Wright.

ZACHARY TAYLOR ("*Old Rough and Ready*")

1784—Born in Orange County, Va.

Moved to a plantation near Louisville, Ky.

1808—Entered the Army as first lieutenant, 7th Infantry.

1810—Captain, assigned to duty at Fort Knox, Ky.

1812—Distinguished himself on September 5 by his defense of Fort Harrison in Indiana against the Indians, led by Tecumseh. Was breveted major.

1814—Full major; was given command of Fort Knox.

1819—Lieutenant colonel, 4th Infantry, New Orleans.

1822—Built Fort Jesup on the Louisiana frontier.

1829–32—Indian superintendent at Fort Snelling, Minn.

1832—Colonel in charge of 1st Infantry Regiment, Fort Crawford.

Served as a regimental commander under Gen. Henry Atkinson during the Black Hawk War. This campaign was waged mainly in Illinois and Wisconsin with a faction of Sac and Fox Indians led by Chief Black Hawk.

1837—Won the Battle of Lake Okeechobee against the Seminoles, December 25, for which he won promotion to brigadier general and was made commander in chief in Florida, 1838. It was because of this campaign he was given the nickname "Old Rough and Ready."

1840—Commander of the first division in the Southwest; moved from Kentucky to Louisiana, where he bought a plantation near Baton Rouge.

1845—Appointed commander of the Army of Occupation in Texas.

1846—In January 1846, following a break in diplomatic relations with Mexico, President Polk ordered General Taylor to positions on or near the Rio Grande. Taylor promptly established a supply depot at Point Isabel (Fort Polk) and erected fortifications at a point opposite the river from Matamoros (Mexico), which he later called Fort Brown (Brownsville).

Mexican forces crossed the Rio Grande in April; they ambushed 63 Americans, killing 11 of them and capturing or wounding the others. Following this, President Polk sent a message to the Congress, telling them that American blood had been shed on American soil. The Congress authorized a declaration of war, and on May 13 the war bill was signed into law.

Even before a formal declaration, Taylor had already made the war with Mexico a fact. On May 8 he met a force of 6,000 Mexican troops at Palo Alto, a few miles north of the present town of Brownsville. With American forces a third the size of the Mexican unit, Taylor and his troops engaged in combat which started in midafternoon and continued for 5 hours. The superior artillery equipment, its skillful use and precise deployment by American troops inflicted heavy casualties on the Mexicans, causing them to withdraw the following morning.

Taylor threw advance parties forward to cover the Mexican retreat, and on the afternoon of May 9 he marched the main body of his troops in pursuit. Writing from his camp at Resaca de la Palma, 3 miles from Matamoros, Taylor gave the following account of the battle:

"When near the spot where I am now encamped, my advance discovered that a ravine crossing the road had been occupied by the enemy with artillery. I immediately ordered a battery of field artillery to sweep the position, flanking and sustaining it by the 3d, 4th, and 5th Regiments, deployed as skirmishers to the right and left. A heavy fire of artillery and of musketry was kept up for some time, until finally the enemy's batteries were carried in succession by a squadron of dragoons and the regiments of infantry that were on the ground. He was soon driven from his position, and pursued by a squadron of dragoons, battalion of artillery, 3d Infantry, and a light battery, to the river. Our victory has been complete. Eight pieces of artillery, with a great quantity of ammunition, three standards, and some one hundred prisoners have been taken; among the latter, General La Vega and several other officers. One general is understood to have been killed. The enemy has recrossed the river (Rio Grande), and I am sure will not again molest us on this bank."

On July 16, 1846, the Congress awarded a gold medal to General Taylor and resolved that: "the thanks of Congress are due, and are hereby tendered to Major General Zachary Taylor, commanding the army of occupation, his officers and men, for the fortitude, skill, enterprise, and courage which have distinguished the recent brilliant operations on the Rio Grande."

Taylor's next major campaign was directed to Monterey, a heavily fortified city in northeastern Mexico. The Mexican commander, Gen. Pedro de Ampudia, had occupied the town with his forces, constructed defenses commanding the northern approaches, and installed artillery and troops in the heights commanding the city. Taylor hurled divisions at the fortress from all directions, with particular emphasis on the fortified hills. On September 23, after house-to-house fighting, the Americans completed their conquest, securing an armistice from Ampudia.

In his report on the victory, General Taylor stated:

"Upon occupying the city, it was discovered to be of great strength in itself, and to have its approaches carefully and strongly fortified. The town and works were armed with forty-two pieces of cannon, well supplied with ammunition, and manned with a force of at least 7,000 troops of the line, and from 2,000 to 3,000 irregulars. The force under my orders before Monterey, was 425 officers and 6,220 men. Our artillery consisted of one ten-inch mortar, two twenty-four-pounder howitzers, and four light field batteries of four guns each; the mortar being the only piece suitable to the operations of a siege.

By resolution of March 2, 1847, the Congress awarded a second gold medal and its thanks to General Taylor "for the fortitude, skill, enterprise, and courage which distinguished the late brilliant military operations at Monterey."

A third gold medal was presented to General Taylor by resolution of the Congress on May 9, 1848. The resolution commended him for "valor, skill, and good conduct, conspicuously displayed, on the twenty-second and twenty-third days of February last (1847), in the battle of Buena Vista, in defeating a Mexican army of more than four times their number, consisting of chosen troops, under their favorite commander, General Santa Anna."

After Buena Vista, the Mexican War shifted to Vera Cruz, where Gen. Winfield Scott won a splendid victory, on March 29, 1847.

1849—Became President of the United States.
1850—Died in the White House, July 9.

MAJOR GENERAL ULYSSES S. GRANT

(No. 425)

OBV. MAJOR GENERAL ULYSSES S. (Simpson) GRANT. JOINT RESOLUTION OF CONGRESS DECEMBER 17. 1863. Bust of General Grant, in uniform, facing the left. In the upper part of a circle, branches of laurel and oak; in the lower part, sugarcane, the cotton plant, tobacco leaves and wheat, united by the national flag; in a second circle, 13 stars, emblematical of the 13 original States of the Union.

By Antrobus and Paquet.

REV. America, personified as a maiden, is seated on a rainbow, with the eagle at her side. She holds in her left hand a cornucopia of flowers, and in her right a crown of laurel and the American shield, on which, in bend, is the word DONELSON. Below, dividing the medal into two parts, is a trophy of arms, surmounted by the cap of liberty, and protected by two sentinels kneeling; to the left is the city of Vicksburg, at the foot of which flows the Mississippi River, bearing two steamboats; VICKSBURG: to the right are Lookout Mountain and Missionary Ridge; the Federal army encamped on the banks of the Tennessee River; CHATTANOOGA. In a first circle the Mississippi River, on which are four steamers, two of which are gunboats; MISSISSIPPI RIVER; in a second, 13 stars—emblematical of the 13 original States of the Union.

ULYSSES SIMPSON GRANT

1822—Born at Point Pleasant, Clermont County, Ohio.

1843—Graduated from the U.S. Military Academy; commissioned brevet lieutenant in the 4th Infantry.

1845–47—Promoted to full second lieutenant; fought under Gen. Zachary Taylor in the battles of Palo Alto, Resaca de la Palma, and Monterey.

1847—Served under Gen. Winfield Scott in the battles leading to the surrender of Mexico City; promoted to first lieutenant, for bravery.

1848—Was breveted captain at Chapultepec.

Service in the Mexican campaigns gave him an opportunity to know many of the men who, later, held commands in the Confederate Army.

1848–52—Assigned garrison duty in New York and Michigan.

1854–60—Resigned his commission, after service on the west coast, farmed in Missouri, and went into real estate in St. Louis.

1860—Moved to Galena, Ill., to work in his father's leather shop.

1861—With the outbreak of the Civil War, he reentered service, with the Union forces, as a colonel of the 21st Illinois Volunteers.

Promoted to brigadier general, with headquarters at Cairo, Ill., he occupied Paducah, Ky. (a strategic point at the junction of the Tennessee and Ohio Rivers).

Fought at Belmont, Mo., where the Confederates forced him to retreat.

1862—Was ordered to take Confederate positions in northwestern Tennessee: Fort Henry on the east side of the Tennessee River and, 12 miles away, Fort Donelson on the west side of the Cumberland River. These two forts were constructed by the Confederates in 1861 to defend the Mississippi valley; they were manned by garrisons which totaled about 2,500 men.

On February 6, 1862, a fleet of Union gunboats attacked Fort Henry. Realizing the vulnerability of his forces, the Confederate commander ordered a retreat. Retaining a small force to man the guns, he covered the withdrawal of his men to Fort Donelson and then surrendered the fort. Confederate losses were 16 men; Union losses were 29 killed and wounded.

While Grant was moving his body of 16,000 troops overland to Fort Donelson, the Confederates moved 12,000 additional men into the garrison. They did this to protect their line of communications with Confederate forces north around Bowling Green, and to deny access to the Cumberland River which, if opened, would enable Union forces to reach Nashville.

The attack on Fort Donelson began on February 13. It was renewed the following day when an additional force of 11,000 Union troops arrived. By a surprise attack on the 15th, the Confederates succeeded in opening a road to Nashville, but failed to take advantage of it. During the night some of the Confederate troops escaped by steamer. On the 16th, realizing that he was greatly outnumbered, the Confederate commander asked for an armistice. Grant made the now famous reply: "No terms except unconditional and immediate surrender can be accepted. I propose to move immediately upon your works." The Confederate garrison, with its 11,500 men, 40 guns, and great quantities of ammunition, surrendered. Confederate losses at Donelson were 2,000 killed and wounded; Union losses, 2,700.

Grant's next major engagement was at Shiloh, in western Tennessee. After 2 days of bloody battle, and greatly outnumbered, the Confederates were forced to retreat. Confederate casualties were over 10,000; the Union more than 13,000.

On October 25, 1862, Grant was ordered to take Vicksburg, Miss., the principal Confederate stronghold on the Mississippi River.

1863—In January, Grant moved his troops down from Memphis and took a position at Young's Point, which is about 20 miles above Vicksburg, off the west bank of the Mississippi River. Situated on a steep bluff, 235 feet above the east bank of the river, Vicksburg held a strategic location and almost impregnable position. As early as 1791 it had been developed by the Spanish for use as a fortress.

After futile attempts to cross the river in the vicinity of Vicksburg, Grant moved his forces south to a a point where Bruinsburg lay, across the river. Here he waited for the Union fleet which sailed downstream and withstood the fire of Vicksburg's guns on the night of April 16. Within 2 weeks, the Union forces were carried across the river and promptly moved northeast and dispersed a Confederate force at Fort Gibson.

Augmenting Grant's forces, Sherman arrived by crossing the river at Grand Gulf, above Bruinsburg, and proceeded to the east of Vicksburg, where they captured the main supply base at Jackson. The Confederates moved some forces out from Vicksburg and engaged Union troops at Champion's Hill, which lies midway between Jackson and Vicksburg; but they were driven back to Vicksburg. After two heavy, unsuccessful assaults on Vicksburg, Grant settled down to siege warfare. On July 4, unable to obtain reinforcements or supplies, Vicksburg finally surrendered. Confederate losses were 10,000 dead, 31,000 prisoners, including 15 generals; the Union losses were almost as staggering—9,400 dead.

The climax to Grant's achievements in the year 1863 took place when he moved on to Chattanooga in October, to relieve a beleaguered Union Army which had been held in a state of siege by Confederate forces. As a major general and commanding the Army of the West (as the Vicksburg army was henceforth called), Grant was joined by the armies of his three generals, Sheridan, Sherman, and Thomas. After a month of preparation, the Union forces engaged the Confederates in a battle. Union forces cleared the top of Lookout Mountain of Confederate troops on the 24th. On the 25th, Union troops were ordered to seize the Confederate rifle pits at the foot of Missionary Ridge. They seized the pits and then, without waiting for further orders, they stormed up the steep and crumbling sides of the mountain in the face of a deadly fire from 30 cannons trained on every path and drove the Confederate commander and his troops from the crest of the hill. After the latter action, the Confederate force of 35,000 men withdrew southward into Georgia.

On December 17, 1863, Congress gave Grant a gold medal for Fort Donelson, Vicksburg, and Chattanooga.

1864—Appointed Commander in Chief of the U.S. Army, March 17, with the rank of lieutenant general.

1864–65—Heading the Army of the Potomac, he fought the Battles of the Wilderness and besieged Richmond.

1865—Suffered great losses at Battles of Spotsylvania and Cold Harbor. Received Lee's surrender at Appomatox Court House, April 9.

1866—Was made full general, the first since George Washington to hold that rank.

1867–68—Served as Secretary of War ad interim, but resigned when the Senate refused to replace E. M. Stanton, and the office was turned back to him.

1869—Started first term as President of the United States.

1872—Reelected to the Presidency.

1885—Died at Mount McGregor, N.Y.; interment Riverside Drive, New York City.

United States Navy

CAPTAIN JOHN PAUL JONES

(No. 501)

OBV. JOANNI PAVLO JONES CLASSIS PRAE-FECTO. COMITIA AMERICANA. (The American Congress. To John Paul Jones, Commander of the fleet.)

REV. HOSTIVM NAVIBVS CAPTIS AVT FVGATIS. (The Enemy's Ships Captured or Put to Flight.) Naval action between the U.S. frigate BONHOMME RICHARD, 42 guns, Capt. John Paul Jones (sailing to the right), and the British frigate SERAPIS, 50 guns, Capt. Richard Pearson. Both vessels are grappled, lying head and stern. The BONHOMME RICHARD is on fire, and her crew are boarding the SERAPIS which is, itself, severely damaged. To the left a third vessel, the ALLIANCE, 32 guns, the consort of the BONHOMME RICHARD which did not support Jones during the action. Two sailors in the sea at the left, clinging to a spar. Exergue: AD ORAM SCOTIAE XXIII. SEPT. M.DCCLXXVIIII. (At Scotland's shore 23 Sept. 1779. Dupre fecit.)

JOHN PAUL JONES, *U.S. Navy*

1747—Born in Kirkcudbright County, Kirkbean Parish, Scotland, on July 6.

1759—Made his first trip to America, as an apprentice in a merchant ship, to visit his brother William, a tailor in Fredericksburg, Va.

1766—Later served on board merchant ships as third mate, chief mate, and master.

1775—After coming to America, he received a commission as lieutenant in the new Continental Navy. Assigned as first lieutenant on board the flagship ALFRED in the Delaware, he raised the first flag to fly over a Continental naval vessel. This was in early December and the flag was the "Grand Union", combining the Union Jack of Great Britain and 13 red and white stripes for the Colonies. He stated later, "I hoisted with my own Hands the Flag of Freedom the First time * * * and I have Attended it ever since with Veneration on the Ocean."

1776—Participated in the first expedition of the new Continental Navy, an amphibious operation against the British at New Providence in the Bahamas; received a promotion to captain and given command of the 12-gun sloop PROVIDENCE, which outwitted two British frigates, captured 16 prizes and destroyed two fishing fleets. Later transferred to command of the ALFRED, Jones continued his mission of seeking out and destroying British shipping with great success.

1777—Was appointed to the newly built 18-gun sloop RANGER and sailed to France to report to the American commissioners. Upon arriving in Quiberon Bay on February 15 the RANGER exchanged gun salutes with the French fleet. This was the first official salute to the "Stars and Stripes" by a foreign government, and was a recognition of the new nation's independence.

With characteristic boldness Jones sailed into British home waters, landed raiding parties on the coast, engaged and took H.M. sloop DRAKE in a bitter engagement.

1779—In one of the most celebrated battles of naval history, John Paul Jones cradled some of the finest fighting traditions of the U.S. Navy. The action took place off the eastern coast of England near the chalk cliffs at Flamborough Head. Jones had been given command of an old 42-gun East Indianman with rotten timber which he renamed the BONHOMME RICHARD in honor of Benjamin Franklin, U.S. envoy to France. Although Jones commanded a small squadron at the same time, it was the BONHOMME RICHARD alone which was destined to fight a bitter close battle with the new, powerful British frigate SERAPIS, 44 guns.

Though the ships sighted each other shortly after noon on September 23, 1799, action did not open until evening at which time both ships fired broadsides into each other. Two of the heavy guns on the BONHOMME RICHARD burst and the third was abandoned for fear of the same horrifying result. The crew concentrated on the lighter cannons and small arms to clear the decks of the SERAPIS. The SERAPIS attempted to cross RICHARD's bow to attain a deadly raking position, but lacked the headway to complete the maneuver. Then Jones, following the SERAPIS' movements, ran RICHARD's bow into the enemy's stern. It was at this point that Captain Pearson of the SERAPIS hailed to ask if the RICHARD had asked for quarter. John Paul Jones bellowed back his immortal words: "I have not yet begun to fight."

For some 2½ hours the ships pounded each other at point-blank range. The SERAPIS critically hulled the BONHOMME RICHARD, setting her afire from stem to stern and putting her in a sinking condition. When the British attempted to board, Jones and his indominable men sent them reeling back. Then, with her remaining cannons and Marine small arms fire and hand grenades from her tops, the shattered BONHOMME RICHARD continued to pour a devastating fire into the SERAPIS. Finally, the British captain struck his colors. Jones had won a glorious victory.

In describing the condition of his ship after the battle ended, Jones reported:

> The rudder Was Cut entirely off, the stern frame, and transoms Were almost Entirely Cut away, the timbers, by the lower Deck especially, from the mainmast to the Stern, being greatly decayed with age, were mangled beyond my power of description, and a person must have been an Eye-Witness to form a just idea of the tremendous scene of Carnage wreck and ruin, that Every Where appeared. Humanity Cannot but recoil from the prospect of Such finished horror, and Lament that War Should produce Such fatal consequences.

Fatally stricken, 2 days after the battle, the BONHOMME RICHARD slipped below the waves; Jones had already transferred his command to the captured SERAPIS and sailed her triumphantly to Holland.

1780—Granted the cross of the Institution of Military Merit by the King of France which entitled him to be addressed as "Chevalier."

1781—Arrived in Philadelphia and was given command of the ship-of-the-line AMERICA then under construction. When the ship was finished, however, Congress presented her to the King of France to replace a French ship wrecked in Boston harbor.

1783—Was sent to France as a prize agent and effected a partial settlement on the collection of prize monies.

1787—On October 16, during John Paul Jones' final return to America, a resolution was passed by Congress "unanimously that a medal of gold be struck and presented to the Chevalier John Paul Jones in commemoration of valorous and brilliant services of that officer in the command of a squadron of French and American ships under the flag off the coast of Great Britain * * *"

1792—After service for Catherine the Great in the Russian Navy as a rear admiral, Jones died and was buried in the St. Louis cemetery for foreign protestants in Paris. After more than a century his grave was located and his body was returned to the United States escorted by a fleet of warships. One of the first and most celebrated naval heroes in American history came to rest in 1906 at the U.S. Naval Academy, Annapolis. Those who today view the remains of John Paul Jones in the crypt below the beautiful Academy chapel cannot fail to recall his prophetic words—"Without a Respectable Navy—Alas America."

CAPTAIN THOMAS TRUXTUN

(No. 502)

OBV. PATRIAE PATRES FILIO DIGNO. THOMAS TRUXTUN. (The fathers of the country to their worthy son. Thomas Truxtun.) Bust of Captain Truxtun, in uniform, facing the left.

REV. UNITED STATES FRIGATE CONSTELLATION of 38 GUNS pursues, attacks and vanquishes the FRENCH ship LA VENGEANCE of 54 GUNS 1 FEBY 1800. Naval action between the U.S. frigate CONSTELLATION, Captain Truxtun, and the French frigate LA VENGEANCE, Captain Pitot. The CONSTELLATION has lost her main mast. Exergue: BY VOTE OF CONGRESS, TO THOMAS TRUXTUN 29 MARCH 1800.

Design attributed to Archibald Robinson of New York City, and engraving to Robert Scot, Mint Engraver.

THOMAS TRUXTUN, *U.S. Navy*

1755—Born near Hempstead, Long Island, N.Y.

1767—Shipped out on a merchant vessel, the PITT; later impressed into Britain's Royal Navy and served with distinction on board H.M.S. PRUDENT, 64 guns.

1775—Served as a lieutenant on board the privateer CONGRESS. Later commanded two privateers which were highly successful in capturing British cargoes which helped to keep the struggle for independence alive.

1782—While in command of ST. JAMES and carrying Mr. Thomas Barclay, U.S. Consul General to France, he successfully withstood an attack by British frigate GOODRICH, 32 guns.

1794—Received a commission as captain in the new U.S. Navy and given command of the frigate CONSTELLATION building in Baltimore. Wrote one of the earliest American books on navigation:

Remarks, Instructions, and Examples Relating to the Latitude and Longitude.

1797—Published *Instructions, Signals, and Explanations Offered for the U.S. Fleet.* Truxtun is often called the "father of naval communications."

1798—With the CONSTELLATION, 38 guns; led a squadron to Havana to escort home a group of American merchant ships threatened by French privateers.

1799—On February 9 engaged and captured L'INSURGENTE, a French frigate of 40 guns near the island of Nevis south of St. Kitts in the Caribbean. French casualties were 70 killed or wounded. American were three men killed or wounded. Truxtun's insistence on training and discipline paid handsome dividends in the U.S. Navy's baptism of fire.

1800—On February 1 the CONSTELLATION had a 5-hour night engagement with LA VENGEANCE, 54 guns, off Guadeloupe. Although the French ship was able to slip away in the night she was a totally shattered vessel. One hundred and sixty men had been killed or wounded on the French man of war at the cost of 39 Americans killed or wounded. Speaking of this powerful foe, Captain F. M. Pitot of LA VENGEANCE reported that, "he must have been an American; for no other people on earth could load so rapidly, fire so accurately, and fight so desperately." A month following the battle with LA VENGEANCE Congress awarded Truxtun a gold medal for his gallantry and good conduct in the engagement. "Wherein an example was exhibited by the Captain, officers, sailors and marines, honorable to the American name, and instructive to its rising navy."

1822—Died in Philadelphia.

COMMODORE EDWARD PREBLE

OBV. EDWARDO PREBLE DUCI STRENUO. Exergue: COMITIA AMERICANA. (The American Congress to Edward Preble, a valiant officer.) Bust of Commodore Preble, in uniform, facing the left.

REV. VINDICI COMMERCII AMERICANI. (To the vindicator of American commerce.) The U.S. fleet, commanded by Commodore Preble, is bombarding Tripoli. The American vessels are in line and several boats manned are seen in the water, casting off to attack the enemy's shipping and batteries. Exergue: ANTE TRIPOLI MDCCCIV. (Off Tripoli 1804.)

By Reich.

EDWARD PREBLE, *U.S. Navy*

1761—Born at Falmouth (Portland), Maine.

1778—Served as midshipman in the Massachusetts State Navy.

1779—While on the Massachusetts ship PROTECTOR, 26 guns, Captain Williams, participated in an action in which a British frigate of 36 guns blew up off Newfoundland. Later the PROTECTOR was captured by the enemy and Preble was held on board a prison ship in New York Harbor.

1782—Served as a lieutenant under Captain Little on the Massachusetts cruiser WINTHROP which, on a short cruise took five prizes.

1783—After the American Revolution ended Preble spent the next 15 years in the merchant service and was once captured by pirates.

1798—Commissioned lieutenant in the U.S. Navy and commanded the brig PICKERING in Commodore John Barry's squadron in the West Indies.

1799—Commissioned captain and given command of the ESSEX, 36 guns.

1800—Preble in the ESSEX, first U.S. warship to round the Cape of Good Hope, protected American trade from French privateers and convoyed a merchant fleet from the West Indies.

1803—Given command of the CONSTITUTION, he led the Mediterranean squadron against the pirates of Tripoli. (American commerce, unprotected by naval strength, had fallen easy prey to the marauding Barbary corsairs. Unless ransom was paid, ships were captured and crews sold).

1804—Since the spring of 1803 Preble's force had effectively blockaded Tripoli. When he began his general attacks against the fortifications and water defenses at Tripoli, his squadron, in addition to flagship CONSTITUTION, consisted of three brigs, three schooners, six gunboats and two bomb vessels loaned to him by the King of the Two Sicilies. Opposing Preble was a walled city protected by batteries mounting 115 pieces of heavy cannon and defended by some 25,000 troops. The harbor was protected by 19 gunboats, two galleys, two schooners of eight guns each, and a brig mounting 10 guns. As he laid his plans he wrote to Captain W. Bainbridge who was imprisoned in Tripoli after the enemy captured the frigate PHILADELPHIA. "* * * may the almighty disposer of all events aid me in my plans and operations for the good of my country * * *"

While Preble lacked the supporting troops to actively capture Tripoli the force of his attacks and the potency of the U.S. Navy threat led the Pasha to sue for peace the following spring. The American seamen, Preble trained and led, defeated the Tripolitans in their own favorite hand-to-hand combat. Throughout the operations Preble's squadron afforded outstanding combat training for numerous young officers who later distinguished themselves in the War of 1812. Preble's splendid leadership imbued his subordinates with the readiness and keen fighting spirit which have always characterized men of the U.S. Navy.

1805—In his report to the Congress on February 20, 1805, President Jefferson stated: "The energy and judgment displayed by this excellent officer [Commodore Preble] through the whole course of service lately confided to him, and the zeal and bravery of his officers and men in the several enterprises executed by them, cannot fail to give high satisfaction to Congress and their country, of whom they have deserved well." On March 3, 1805, by resolution of Congress, a gold medal was awarded to Commodore Preble.

1807—Died in Portland, Maine.

CAPTAIN ISAAC HULL

(No. 504)

OBV. ISAACUS HULL PERITOS ARTE SUPERAT JUL. MDCCCXII AUG. CERTAMINE FORTES. (Isaac Hull conquers in July 1812, the skilled by strategem, and in August, the strong in battle.) Bust of Captain Hull, in uniform, facing the left.

REV. HORAE MOMENTO VICTORIA. (Victory in the space of an hour.) Naval action between the U.S. frigate CONSTITUTION, 44 guns, Captain Hull, and the British frigate GUERRIERE, 49 guns, Capt. J. R. Dacres. The CONSTITUTION, firing her starboard battery, carries away the GUERRIERE'S mizzenmast, which, in falling, takes with it the mainmast; the GUERRIERE, having already lost her foremast, is completely dismasted; the CONSTITUTION, on the contrary, is but slightly injured in her rigging. Exergue: INTER CONST. NAV. AMER. ET GUER. ANGL. (Between the American vessel CONSTITUTION and the English vessel GUERRIERE.)

By Reich.

ISAAC HULL, *U.S. Navy*

1773—Born at Derby, Conn.

1787—Began sea service as a cabin boy on board a merchant ship.

1794—Named master of a merchantman.

1798—Entered the U.S. Navy as a lieutenant.

1800—First lieutenant of the frigate CONSTITUTION under Commodore Silas Talbot. Showed great ingenuity in this assignment when he captured the French privateer SANDWICH. Commodore Talbot's report of this incident to the Navy Department stated: "No enterprise of like moment was ever better accomplished."

1803—Assigned to command the schooner ENTERPRISE and later the same year the brig ARGUS, then serving with Commodore Edward Preble's Mediterranean squadron.

1804—ARGUS sailed for Alexandria, Egypt, carrying William Eaton, Navy Agent to the Barbary States and formerly the American Consul at Tunis. Eaton and the claimant to the throne of Tripoli then led a force, which included men from ARGUS, overland across the Lybian desert to the Tripolitan town of Derne. Supported by the ARGUS and other ships, the American expedition captured Derne. Hull was soon promoted to Master Commandant.

1806—Commissioned captain.

1810—Assumed command of the CONSTITUTION.

1812—Hull distinguished himself twice in the War of 1812. Both incidents are memorialized in a gold medal awarded him by the Congress the following year, January 29, 1813.

On July 17, 1812, while cruising off Egg Harbor, N.J., Hull fell in with a British squadron of five men-of-war. Resourcefully, the American captain resorted to kedging anchors—brought out by small boat crews, dropped, and the CONSTITUTION laboriously hauled up to them. The operation was repeated over and over. The British resorted to the same tactics. Hull pumped more than 2,000 gallons of fresh water over the side to lighten the ship and when a slight breeze sprang up CONSTITUTION made good her escape.

On August 19, 1812 about 750 miles east of Boston, the CONSTITUTION sighted and prepared for an engagement with the British frigate GUERRIERE. In a fierce closely fought battle the GUERRIERE was forced to surrender. The British frigate was so badly shattered that she could not be saved. Hull burned her at sea. It was during her action with GUERRIERE that the CONSTITUTION is said to have won the sobriquet "Old Ironsides."

Reporting to the Secretary of the Navy on the action Hull wrote that "* * * it gives me great pleasure to say that from the Smallest Boy in the ship to the oldest Seaman not a look of fear was seen. They all went into action, giving three cheers, and requesting to be laid close alongside the Enemy."

1813—Commanded the Navy Yard at Boston and later at Portsmouth.

1815—Appointed to the Board of Navy Commissioners.

1824—Sailed in the frigate UNITED STATES as Commodore on the Pacific Station.

1829—Named Commandant of the Washington Navy Yard.

1839—Commodore of the Mediterranean Squadron in flagship OHIO.

1843—Died in Philadelphia.

CAPTAIN JACOB JONES

(No. 505)

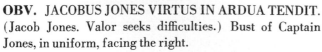

OBV. JACOBUS JONES VIRTUS IN ARDUA TENDIT. (Jacob Jones. Valor seeks difficulties.) Bust of Captain Jones, in uniform, facing the right.

REV. VICTORIAM HOSTI MAJORI CELERRIME RAPUIT. (He quickly snatched victory from a superior enemy.) Naval action between the U.S. sloop-of-war

WASP, 18 guns, Captain Jones, and the British brig FROLIC, 22 guns, Captain Thomas Whinyates. The WASP has lost her maintopmast, and is raking the FROLIC as she lays her on board. The Americans are in possession of the enemy's forecastle. Exergue: INTER WASP NAV. AMERI. ET FROLIC NAV. ANG. DIE

XVIII OCT. MDCCCXII. (Between the American vessel WASP and the English vessel FROLIC, Oct. 18, 1812.)

By Furst.

1768—Born near Smyrna, Kent County, Del.

1786-98—Studied medicine at Dover, Del., and after further study at the University of Pennsylvania, he practiced his profession; later changed to a clerkship in the Supreme Court of Delaware.

1799—Entered the U.S. Navy as a midshipman, and joined the frigate UNITED STATES under Commodore John Barry.

1801—Commissioned a Lieutenant.

1803—Was taken prisoner in Tripoli when the PHILADELPHIA went aground; held captive for 20 months.

1810—Promoted to Master Commandant.

1812—On October 18, while commanding the sloop-of-war WASP he fell in with the British brig FROLIC. A bitter broadside battle, which took place in heavy seas, resulted in the surrender of the FROLIC. The British brig suffered some 90 casualties among a crew of about 110; the WASP had five killed and five wounded. (Soon after this engagement, the WASP was captured by the British ship-of-the-line, POICTIERS, 74 guns).

1813—On January 29, Congress passed a resolution awarding a gold medal to Jones. He consistently demonstrated a dedication to duty which is an essential ingredient of naval leadership.

Received his commission as a captain and was given command of the 38-gun frigate MACEDONIAN.

1821—Named Commodore of the Mediterranean Squadron.

1823—Appointed to the Board of Navy Commissioners.

1826—Served as Commodore of the Pacific Squadron.

1829-50—Commanded ashore at Baltimore and New York, and as Governor of the Naval Asylum in Philadelphia.

1850—Died in Philadelphia.

CAPTAIN STEPHEN DECATUR, JR.

(No. 506)

OBV. STEPHANUS DECATUR NAVARCHUS, PUGNIS PLURIBUS, VICTOR. (Stephen Decatur, a naval captain, conqueror in many battles.) Bust of Captain Decatur, in uniform, facing the right.

REV. OCCIDIT SIGNUM HOSTILE SIDERA SURGUNT. (The enemy's standard falls, the stars rise.) Naval action between the U.S. frigate UNITED STATES, 44 guns, Captain Decatur, and the British frigate MACEDONIAN, 49 guns, Captain Carden; the UNITED STATES to leeward, is firing her port broadside; the MACEDONIAN has lost her mizzenmast, her fore and maintopmasts, and her mainyard; the UNITED STATES has but a few shots in her sails. Exergue: INTER STA. UNI. NAV. AMERI. ET. MACEDO. NAV. ANG. DIE XXV OCTOBRIS MDCCCXII (Between the American warship UNITED STATES and the English warship MACEDONIAN, Oct. 25, 1812.)

By Furst.

STEPHEN DECATUR, JR., *U.S. Navy*

1779—Born in Sinepuxent, Worcester County, Md.

1798—Appointed a midshipman in the U.S. Navy; served in the frigate UNITED STATES, commanded by Commodore John Barry.

1799—Appointed acting lieutenant. Sailed in the UNITED STATES with the peace commissioners for France.

1801—Promoted to lieutenant of the frigate ESSEX, he served in the Mediterranean in Commodore Dale's squadron. Prior to departure Decatur told his men: "We are now about to embark upon an expedition which may terminate in our sudden death, our perpetual slavery, or our immortal glory. * * * The first quality of a good seaman, is, personal courage, —the second, obedience to orders, —third, fortitude under sufferings; to these may be added, an ardent love of country."

1804—While serving under Commodore Preble in the Mediterranean, he captured a ketch which was renamed the INTREPID. With a volunteer crew, Decatur bravely sailed into Tripoli harbor to destroy the frigate PHILADELPHIA which had been captured by the enemy. The Americans sprang to the frigate's deck, quickly put the defending Tripolitans to route, scattered combustibles about the ship, and tumbled back on board the INTREPID. Soon PHILADELPHIA was wrapped in flames and completely destroyed. Admiral Nelson called this "the most bold and daring act of the age;" it won for Decatur promotion to Captain.

1812—On October 25, while commanding the UNITED STATES, he captured the British frigate MACEDONIAN, off the Canary Islands. The long range gunnery of the UNITED STATES was accurate and devastating in its effectiveness. The Britisher's effort to close and board was thwarted by Decatur while the UNITED STATES cannonade cut the MACEDONIAN to ribbons. For this victory, the Congress awarded a gold medal to Decatur by resolution of January 29, the following year.

1815—Sailed for the Mediterranean in command of a squadron of nine ships, and through a resolute show of force and diplomatic skill brought the pirates of Algiers to honorable terms. Upon his return to Norfolk, Decatur at an honorary dinner gave his famous toast: "Our country! * * * may she always be in the right; but our country, right or wrong."

Later the same year was appointed a member of the Board of Naval Commissioners.

1819—Completed his home on the square across from the White House, Washington. Decatur House stands today, and its carriage house holds the Naval Historical Foundation's excellent Truxton-Decatur Museum.

1820—Died as a result of a duel with Commodore James Barron of Bladensburg, Md. Decatur's untimely death was universally mourned.

CAPTAIN WILLIAM BAINBRIDGE

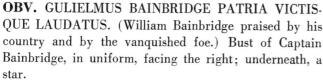

OBV. GULIELMUS BAINBRIDGE PATRIA VICTIS-QUE LAUDATUS. (William Bainbridge praised by his country and by the vanquished foe.) Bust of Captain Bainbridge, in uniform, facing the right; underneath, a star.

REV. PUGNANDO (In fighting.) The naval action is over. The British frigate JAVA, 49 guns, Captain Lambert, is completely dismasted; while the U.S. frigate CONSTITUTION ("Old Ironsides"), 44 guns, Captain Bainbridge, is but slightly damaged in her rigging. Exergue: INTER CONST. NAV. AMERI. ET JAV. NAV. ANGL. DIE XXIX DECEM. MDCCCXII (Between the American warship CONSTITUTION and the English warship, JAVA, Dec. 29, 1812.)

By Furst.

WILLIAM BAINBRIDGE, *U.S. Navy*

1774—Born in Princeton, N.J.

1789—Entered the Merchant service as an apprentice on board the ship HOPE for a voyage to Holland, during which he saved the life of the captain who was about to be thrown overboard by a mutinous crew; later commanded the same vessel.

1798—Entered the Navy as a lieutenant; was captured by the French frigate VOLONTIER while on his first cruise and taken to Guadeloupe.

1799—Promoted to Master Commandant, sailed in the brig NORFOLK to the West Indies; captured and destroyed a number of vessels; also protected U.S. merchant ships.

1800—Promoted to captain and sailed as commanding officer of the frigate GEORGE WASHINGTON, to carry tribute to the Dey of Algiers—the price the young American Republic had to pay because of weakness at sea. Bainbridge was also compelled to carry, under the Turkish flag, the Dey's emissary to Constantinople. With a deep sense of mortification, Bainbridge wrote: "I hope that I may never again be sent to Algiers with tribute unless I am authorized to deliver it from the mouth of our cannon."

1803—The frigate PHILADELPHIA, Capt. William Bainbridge, while chasing a pirate ship off Tripoli, grounded on uncharted rocks. After sustaining a heavy attack by swarms of Tripolitans, Bainbridge was finally forced to surrender his ship. The enemy refloated PHILADELPHIA, and she was a powerful menace to Commodore Preble's squadron until destroyed by Lt. Stephen Decatur, Jr. Bainbridge and his officers and men remained captives until the end of the war.

1812—Was commanding the CONSTITUTION when she fell in with the British frigate JAVA off the coast of Brazil. The ensuing battle at close range lasted over 2 hours. A shot carried away the CONSTITUTION's wheel and drove a copper bolt into Bainbridge's thigh but he bravely kept the deck. In an attempt to board the CONSTITUTION, the captain of the JAVA was mortally wounded. After suffering heavy casualties and being completely dismasted by the American gunners, JAVA struck her colors. Bainbridge burned his prize at sea.

1813—Awarded a gold medal by congressional resolution of March 3, and a special award of $50,000 was made by the Congress to the officers and crew.

1821—After serving as Commodore of the Mediterranean Squadron in the INDEPENDENCE and COLUMBUS, Bainbridge served on shore, commanding navy yards and as a member of the Board of Naval Commissioners.

1833—Died in Philadelphia.

335-478 O - 69 - 14

LIEUTENANTS WILLIAM BURROWS
AND EDWARD R. McCALL

OBV. VICTORIAM TIBI CLARAM. PATRIAE MAE-STAM. (A victory brilliant for thee, sorrowful for thy country.) A funeral urn upon a tomb is surrounded with naval emblems; a crown of laurel is hanging from a trident. Inscribed on the tomb: W. BURROWS.

OBV. EDWARD R. McCALL NAVIS ENTERPRISE PRAEFECTUS. SIC ITUR AD ASTRA. (Edward Rutledge McCall, Commander of the vessel ENTER-PRISE. Thus one attains glory.) Bust of Lieutenant Mc-Call, in uniform facing the right.

REV. VIVERE SAT VINCERE. (To conquer is to live enough.) Naval engagement between the U.S. brig-of-war ENTERPRISE, 14 guns, Lieutenant Burrows, and the British brig-of-war BOXER, 14 guns, Capt. Samuel

Blythe. The ENTERPRISE is raking the BOXER, fore and aft. The latter has lost her maintopmast. Exergue: INTER ENTERPRIZE NAV. AMERI, ET BOXER NAV. BRIT. DIE IV SEPT. MDCCCXII. (Between the American vessel ENTERPRISE, and the British vessel BOXER, Sept. 4, 1813.)

By Furst.

Off the coast of Maine on September 5, 1813, Lieutenant Burrows commanding the brig ENTERPRISE captured the British brig BOXER after a fierce and gallant action which claimed the lives of both commanding officers. After Lieutenant Burrows was struck down, Lieutenant McCall handled the ENTERPRISE with great courage and skill.

WILLIAM BURROWS, *U.S. Navy*

1785—Born near Philadelphia, Pa. His father later became Commandant of the Marine Corps.

1799—Entered the U.S. Navy as a midshipman; his first cruise was in the PORTSMOUTH, Captain McNeil.

1803—Assigned to the CONSTITUTION under Commodore Preble as an acting lieutenant during the Tripolitan War.

1808—Commanded a gunboat on the Delaware, enforcing the embargo.

1809—Assigned to the PRESIDENT, Captain Bainbridge, and then, as first lieutenant on board the HORNET, Captain Hunt.

1812—While on furlough, he served on the merchant ship THOMAS PENROSE bound for Canton; later captured by the British and carried into Barbados.

1813—Mortally wounded during the victorious engagement between his ship, the brig ENTERPRISE, and the British brig BOXER. Burrows bravely pleaded: "* * * the colors must never be struck."

1814—Awarded a gold medal posthumously by Congress on January 6, 1814.

EDWARD R. McCALL, *U.S. Navy*

1790—Born in Beaufort, S.C.

1808—Entered the Navy as a midshipman and joined the sloop-of-war HORNET, Capt. John H. Dent.

1811—Assigned to the ENTERPRISE, under the command of Lt. Johnston Blakeley and later under Lt. William Burrows. Promoted to acting lieutenant.

1813—Commissioned lieutenant, assumed command of the ENTERPRISE, after Lieutenant Burrows was wounded in the engagement with the BOXER.

1814–17—Awarded a gold medal by resolution of January 6, 1814. Was transferred to the sloop-of-war ONTARIO and later to the JAVA, Commodore O. H. Perry, for Mediterranean duty.

1825—Promoted to the rank of Master Commandant, and subsequently to the rank of captain (1835).

1853—Died in Bordentown, N.J.

CAPTURE OF THE BRITISH FLEET ON LAKE ERIE
10 SEPTEMBER 1813

(No. 510)　　　　　　　　　　　　　　　(No. 511)

OBV. OLIVERUS H. PERRY. PRINCEPS STAGNO ERIENSE. CLASSIM TOTAM CONTUDIT. (Oliver H. Perry, commander in chief, destroyed on Lake Erie an entire fleet.) Bust of Captain Perry, in uniform, facing the right.

OBV. JESSE D. ELLIOTT. NIL ACTUM REPUTANS SI QUID SUPERESSET AGENDUM. (Jesse D. Elliott. Considering nothing done, if aught remained to be done.) Bust of Captain Elliott, in uniform, facing the right.

REV. VIAM INVENIT VIRTUS AUT FACIT. (Valor finds or makes a way.) The U.S. fleet on Lake Erie, carrying 54 guns and commanded by Captain Perry, stands out to meet the British fleet with 63 guns, under Captain Bar-

clay. Exergue: INTER CLASS. AMERI. ET BRIT. DIE X SEPT. MDCCCXIII. (Between the American and British fleets, Sept. 10, 1813.)

By Furst.

The decisive victory of Master Commandant Oliver Hazard Perry at Lake Erie secured the vital Great Lakes and the vast Northwest Territory for the United States. He had carried into battle a flag with the immortal words of Capt. James Lawrence who was mortally wounded only a few months earlier: "Don't give up the ship." Perry, after his stunning triumph, sent his famous dispatch: "We have met the enemy and they are ours."

OLIVER HAZARD PERRY, *U.S. Navy*

1785—Born in South Kingston, R.I.; later attended private schools of Kingston, Tower Hill, and Newport, specializing in mathematics and navigation.

1799—Entered the Navy as a midshipman, served in his father's ship the GENERAL GREENE in the West Indies during the Quasi War with France.

1802–6—Served in the Mediterranean during the Tripolitan War on board the ADAMS, CONSTELLATION and others; promoted to acting lieutenant (1803).

1807–9—Promoted to lieutenant; employed building gunboats in Rhode Island and Connecticut; later commanded a flotilla of gunboats to enforce the embargo.

1809—Given command of the schooner REVENGE.

1812—As Master Commandant, he was given a division of gunboats at Newport, R.I.

1813—Transferred to build and command a fleet on strategic Lake Erie. On September 10, Perry, demonstrating great personal bravery and brilliant seamanship, met and defeated the British squadron under Captain Barclay. On that day he notified the Secretary of the Navy: "It has pleased the Almighty to give to the arms of the United States a signal victory over their enemies on this lake (Erie). The British squadron, consisting of two ships, two brigs, one schooner, and one sloop, have this moment (4 p.m.) surrendered to the force under my command, after a sharp conflict." The Battle of Lake Erie secured the vital northern water arteries for the American cause.

1814—Received a gold medal by resolution of the Congress on January 6, for the decisive and glorious victory gained. Perry was also promoted to the rank of captain.

1816—Commanded the NAVA in the Mediterranean.

1819—Sailed for the coast of South America and died of yellow fever at Port of Spain, Trinidad, August 23. His remains were later carried on board a U.S. naval vessel to a final resting place in Newport, R.I. (1826).

JESSE DUNCAN ELLIOTT, *U.S. Navy*

1782—Born in Hagerstown, Md.; later studied at Carlisle, Pa.

1804—Appointed midshipman, cruised in ESSEX under Commodore James Barron and later (1807) was on board the CHESAPEAKE when it was fired upon and boarded by the British frigate LEOPARD.

1810—Promoted to lieutenant.

1812—Served under Commodore Isaac Chauncey on the Great Lakes, and on October 8, commanding an expedition, he captured the British brigs DETROIT and CALEDONIA, at anchor below the British guns at Fort Erie. Congress voted him a sword in recognition of his success.

1813—Promoted to Master Commandant, placed in command of the NIAGARA, and second in command to Perry in the Battle of Lake Erie on September 10. For his part in Perry's great victory, and by resolution of the Congress of February 19, 1814, Elliott was awarded a gold medal.

1818–45—Promoted to captain, he commanded the West Indian and the Mediterranean squadrons, and the Navy yards at Boston and Philadelphia.

1845—Died in Philadelphia.

CAPTAIN OLIVER HAZARD PERRY

(Medals Authorized by the State of Pennsylvania)

(No. 522)

(No. 522A)

OBV. OLIVERUS HAZARD PERRY. PRO PATRIA VICIT. Bust of Perry, to right; below, PRESENTED BY THE GOVERNMENT OF PENNSYLVANIA.

REV. WE HAVE MET THE ENEMY AND THEY ARE OURS. Scene of the battle, with Perry standing in a small boat as he is being transferred from the LAWRENCE to the NIAGARA; in exergue, BRITISH FLEET ON LAKE ERIE CAPTURED SEPTEMBER 10, 1813.

By Furst.

Another medal commemorative of the victory on Lake Erie was struck by order of the State of Pennsylvania, for presentation to such of her citizens who had volunteered to serve on board the American squadron on that occasion. These medals bear the same obverse as that awarded by the State to Capt. Oliver Perry in this action.

REV. Around top border WE HAVE MET THE ENEMY AND THEY ARE OURS.—Perry. Within a wreath of laurel TO _____ (blank left for insertion of name of recipient). Below: IN TESTIMONY OF HIS PATRIOTISM AND BRAVERY IN THE NAVAL ACTION ON LAKE ERIE SEPTEMBER 10, 1813.

By Furst.

CAPTAIN JAMES LAWRENCE

OBV. JAC. LAWRENCE DULCE ET DECORUM EST PRO PATRIA MORI (James Lawrence. It is sweet and becoming to die for one's country.) Bust of Captain Lawrence in uniform, facing the right.

REV. MANSUETUD. MAJ. QUAM VICTORIA. (Clemency greater than victory.) The action is over. The U.S. sloop-of-war HORNET, 18 guns, Captain Lawrence, is lying to and sending her boats to the rescue of the crew of the British brig-of-war PEACOCK, 18 guns, Capt. William Peake, which has lost her mainmast, and is going down by the head. Exergue: INTER HORNET NAV AMERI ET PEACOCK NAV ANG DIE XXIV FEB MDCCCXIII. (Between the American vessel HORNET and the English vessel PEACOCK, Feb. 24, 1813.)

By Furst.

JAMES LAWRENCE, U.S. Navy

1781—Born in Burlington, N.J.; later attended law school but changed his studies to navigation.

1798—Entered the U.S. Navy as a midshipman; his first cruise was to the West Indies in the GANGES, Captain Tingey.

1801—Received his commission as acting lieutenant on board the ADAMS, Captain Robinson; later was second in command, under Capt. Stephen Decatur, Jr., in the INTREPID when the captured PHILADELPHIA was destroyed in Tripoli Harbor to prevent her use by the enemy. Decatur later said of Lawrence: "He always stood with his conscience; his conscience told him his duty and he had no more dodge in him than the mainmast."

1802—Promoted to lieutenant.

1808–11—Served as first lieutenant of the CONSTITUTION and later as commanding officer of the VIXEN, WASP, and ARGUS.

1811—Became Master Commandant.

1812—Assumed command of the HORNET.

1813—While cruising in the West Indies on February 24, Lawrence found the PEACOCK off Demerara under a tropical twilight. As they passed in opposite directions, the guns of each were brought to bear on the other. The HORNET came about and fired so rapidly and accurately that the PEACOCK surrendered 20 minutes after the fight began and sank before Lawrence could rescue all her crew.

In his message to Congress, President James Madison stated:

> "In continuance of the brilliant achievements of our infant Navy, a signal triumph has been gained by Captain Lawrence and his companions in the HORNET sloop-of-war, with a celerity so unexampled and a slaughter of the enemy so disproportionate to the loss of the HORNET as to claim for the conquerors the highest praise and the full recompense provided by Congress * * *"

Given command of the CHESAPEAKE in May 1813, Lawrence fell mortally wounded in an engagement with the British ship SHANNON. Four days later, he died.

Buried with military honors at Halifax, Nova Scotia, his remains were afterward taken to Trinity churchyard in New York City. His tombstone reads: "The heroic commander of the frigate CHESAPEAKE. Whose remains are here deposited, With his expiring breath, Expressed his devotion to his country; Neither the fury of battle, the anguish of a mortal wound, Nor the horrors of approaching death, Could subdue his gallant spirit. His dying words were, "DON'T GIVE UP THE SHIP."

DEFEAT OF THE BRITISH FLEET ON LAKE CHAMPLAIN SEPTEMBER 11, 1814

(No. 513)

(No. 514)

(No. 515)

OBV. THO. MACDONOUGH. STAGNO CHAMPLAIN CLAS. REG. BRIT. SUPERAVIT. (Thomas Macdonough defeated the Royal British fleet on Lake Champlain.) Bust of Captain Macdonough, in uniform, facing the right.

OBV. ROB. HENLEY EAGLE PRAEFECT. PALMA VIRTU. PER AETERNIT. FLOREBIT. (Robert Henley, commander of the EAGLE. The palm of bravery will flourish forever.) Bust of Captain Henley, in uniform, facing the right.

OBV. STEP. CASSIN TICONDEROGA PRAEFECT. QUAE REGIO IN TERRIS NOS. NON PLENA LAB. (Stephen Cassin, commander of the TICONDEROGA. What region of the earth is not full of our works.) Bust of Lieutenant Cassin, in uniform, facing the right.

REV. UNO LATERE PERCUSSO. ALTERUM IMPA-VIDE VERTIT. (Beaten on one side, he fearlessly turns the other.) Naval action on Lake Champlain, between the U.S. fleet, carrying 86 guns, under Captain Macdonough, and the British fleet, with 95 guns, commanded by Commodore Downie. To the right, the city of Plattsburgh in flames. Exergue: INTER CLASS. AMERI. ET BRIT. DIE XI SEPT. MDCCCXIII. (Between the American and British fleets, Sept. 11, 1814.)

The naval engagement on Lake Champlain, on the morning of September 11, 1814, was one phase of the land-sea assault planned by the British to gain control of the lake, invade from Canada, and bring the war to a rapid and successful end. On land, General Macomb was left to man Plattsburgh's forts with a force much smaller than that of Gen. Sir George Prevost who opposed him. Macdonough flew his flag in the SARATOGA, 26 guns. Realizing the long-range gunnery superiority of the British fleet headed by Commodore George Downie, whose flag was the CON-FIANCE, Macdonough decided to meet the British challenge by having his fleet strung out at anchor in Plattsburgh Bay and to there engage the enemy. In rigging his ships for battle at anchor, Macdonough skillfully used kedges and hawsers in such a way as to be able to "wind" his ships around, bringing fresh broadsides to fire on the British at the critical moment in the battle. This maneuver of almost doubling his firepower resulted in the capitulation of the British fleet and, later, the flight of General Prevost back to Canada. The invasion threat was ended.

THOMAS MACDONOUGH, *U.S. Navy*

1783—Born in Newcastle County, Del.
1800—Entered the U.S. Navy as a midshipman; later served in the Tripolitan campaign; was with Decatur on the INTREPID when the latter blew up the PHILADELPHIA, then in possession of the enemy at Tripoli.
1807—Promoted lieutenant and, in 1813, a Master Commandant.
1814—On September 11, defeated the British squadron commanded by Commodore George Downie (killed in action) on Lake Champlain. Macdonough was promoted to captain and on October 20, 1814, he was awarded a gold medal by Congress for the decisive and outstanding victory gained over a

British squadron of superior strength. Macdonough said of his victory: "The Almighty has been pleased to grant us a signal victory on Lake Champlain, in the capture of one frigate, one brig, and two sloops of war of the enemy."
1825—He died at sea while on his way home after commanding the Mediterranean Squadron.

ROBERT HENLEY, *U.S. Navy*

1783—Born in Williamsburg, Va.; later educated at the College of William and Mary.
1799—Entered the U.S. Navy as a midshipman.
1800—Under Commodore Thomas Truxtun, while on the CONSTELLATION, he participated in the engagement with the French frigate LA VENGEANCE: later was granted leave to continue a course of lectures in navigation and naval science at Williamsburg.
1807—Assumed command of a gunboat at Norfolk and promoted to lieutenant.
1814—Was second in command to Commodore Macdonough in the engagement on Lake Champlain, as commander of the brig EAGLE, meriting a gold medal by resolution of Congress on October 26.
1821—In command of the HORNET.
1825—Promoted to captain.
1829—Died in Charleston, S.C.

STEPHEN CASSIN, *U.S. Navy*

1782—Born in Philadelphia, Pa.
1800—Entered the U.S. Navy as a midshipman and served with distinction in the war with Tripoli.
1807—Appointed lieutenant.
1814—Commanded the TICONDEROGA in Macdonough's victory on Lake Champlain, meriting the comment of his commanding officer that his ship had gallantly sustained her full share of the action. For his conduct, he was promoted Master Commandant and awarded a gold medal by resolution of Congress on October 26.
1822–23—Commanded the sloop PEACOCK in the capturing of several pirate vessels in the West Indies.
1825—Promoted to captain.
1857—After commands at Newport, R.I., and the Washington Navy Yard, he died in Washington, D.C.

OBV. LUDOVICUS WARRINGTON DUX NAVALIS AMERI. (Lewis Warrington, American Naval commander.) Bust of Captain Warrington, in uniform, facing the right.

REV. PRO PATRIA PARATUS AUT VINCERE AUT MORI. (Prepared to conquer or die for his country.) Naval action between the U.S. sloop-of-war PEACOCK, 18 guns, Capt. Lewis Warrington, and the British sloop-of-war EPERVIER, 18 guns, Captain Wales; the PEACOCK, to leeward, is firing her port broadside. The EPERVIER has lost her maintopmast. Exergue: INTER PEACOCK NAV. AMERI ET EPERVIE NAV. ANG. DIE XXIX MAR. MDCCCXIV. (Between the American vessel PEACOCK and the English vessel EPERVIER, March 29 [sic. April] 1814.)

By Furst.

LEWIS WARRINGTON, *U.S. Navy*

1782—Born in Williamsburg, Va.; later educated at the College of William and Mary.

1800—Entered the Navy as a midshipman; later served under Commodore Preble in the Tripolitan campaign.

1805—Promoted to lieutenant, commanded a gunboat at Norfolk.

1809—Named first lieutenant of the brig SIREN bearing dispatches to France.

1813—As Master Commandant, was given command of the sloop-of-war PEACOCK.

1814—On April 29, while cruising off the coast of Florida, encountered the British sloop EPERVIER, a vessel of the same armament. After an engagement of 42 minutes, the British surrendered. The gold medal awarded by Congress on October 21, 1814, was in testimony of the gallantry and conduct of the officers and crew in an action which displayed the decisive effect and great superiority of American gunnery. Warrington was promoted to captain the same year.

1816–51—Served with distinction, both ashore and afloat, in senior billets which included service as commandant of the Navy Yard at Norfolk, the West Indian Squadron, a member of the Board of Navy Commissioners, Chief of the Navy Bureau of Ordnance and Yards and Docks, and as *ad interim* Secretary of the Navy.

1851—Died in Washington, D.C.

CAPTAIN JOHNSTON BLAKELEY

(No. 517)

OBV. JOHNSTON BLAKELEY REIP. FAED. AM. NAV. WASP DUX. (Johnston Blakeley, Captain of the American Federal Republic's vessel WASP.) Bust of Captain Blakeley, in uniform, facing right.

REV. EHEU! BIS VICTOR PATRIA TUA TE LUGET PLAUDITO. (Alas! twice conqueror, thy country laments and applauds thee). Naval action between the U.S. sloop-of-war WASP, 18 guns, Capt. Johnston Blakeley, and the British brig REINDEER, 18 guns, Capt. William Manners; the WASP, to windward, is firing her port broadside. The British vessel is striking her colors. Exergue: INTER WASP NAV. AMERI. ET REINDEER NAV. ANG. DIE XXVIII JUNIUS MDCCCXIV. (Between the American vessel WASP and the English vessel REINDEER, June 28, 1814.)

By Furst.

JOHNSTON BLAKELEY, *U. S. Navy*

1781—Born at Seaford, County Down, Ireland; brought to North Carolina as an infant by his parents, both of whom died when he was a youth.

1797—Attended the University of North Carolina at Chapel Hill.

1800—Entered the Navy and later served under Commodore Preble in the Tripolitan Campaign.

1813—As a lieutenant, commanded the ENTERPRISE protecting coastal trade. The same year made a Master Commandant and transferred to the WASP.

1814—On June 28, engaged the British brig REINDEER in the English Channel. After a violent gunnery duel, side by side, Captain Manners endeavored to board the WASP and was killed; the British boarders were cut down, and the WASP's men swept across the REINDEER from stem to stern. The British brig was so badly damaged that Blakeley burned her.

Continuing his cruise, Blakeley took the British brig AVON and the brig ATALANTA. The following month the WASP was lost at sea without trace.

The determined bravery, the cool intrepidity, and the sad fate of Captain Blakeley are memorialized in the gold medal which was awarded by the Congress November 3, 1814.

CAPTAIN JAMES BIDDLE

OBV. THE CONGRESS OF THE U.S. TO CAPT. JAMES BIDDLE. FOR HIS GALLANTRY GOOD CONDUCT AND SERVICES. Bust of Captain Biddle, in uniform, facing the right.

REV. CAPTURE OF THE BRITISH SHIP PENGUIN BY THE U.S. SHIP HORNET. Naval action between the U.S. sloop-of-war HORNET, 18 guns, Captain Biddle, and the British sloop-of-war PENGUIN, 19 guns, Captain Dickinson. The HORNET, to windward, is raking the PENGUIN. The British vessel has lost her main-top-gallant-mast. In the distance the peak of Tristan d'Acunha. Exergue: OFF TRISTAN D'ACUNHA MARCH XXIII MDCCCXV.

By Furst.

JAMES BIDDLE, *U.S. Navy*

1783—Born in Philadelphia, Pa.

1800—Entered U.S. Navy as a midshipman.

1802—Sailed to the Mediterranean on the frigate CONSTELLATION to protect commerce against Tripolitan cruisers.

1803—Taken prisoner in the ill-fated frigate PHILADELPHIA by the Tripolitans. Held captive during balance of war with Barbary pirates.

1805—Liberated, promoted to lieutenant, given command of a gunboat.

1811—Served as a courier between the United States and American minister in Paris.

1812—Assigned to sloop-of-war WASP and participated in the capture of the British sloop FROLIC. Later, FROLIC was recaptured and Biddle was taken by the British.

1813—Exchanged as a prisoner, promoted to Master Commandant, and given command of the sloop-of-war HORNET, 18 guns; escaped British blockade off New Haven, Conn.

1815—On March 23, off Tristan d'Acunha in the South Atlantic, the HORNET met and captured the British sloop-of-war PENGUIN in the last warship action in the War of 1812. The cannonade was furious, and when the British attempt to board failed and the PENGUIN lost a mast and bowsprit, the Union Jack was struck. Biddle was severely wounded in the battle.

1816—Awarded a gold medal by Resolution of Congress, February 22.

1817—Sent in the sloop-of-war ONTARIO to the Columbia River to take possession of the Oregon Territory for the United States.

1826—Represented the United States in a commercial treaty with Turkey.

1845—Served as Flag Officer in East India Squadron and negotiated first treaty with China.

1848—Died in Philadelphia.

CAPTAIN CHARLES STEWART

(No. 519)

OBV. CAROLUS STEWART NAVIS AMER. CONSTITUTION DUX. (Charles Stewart, captain of the American vessel CONSTITUTION.) Bust of Captain Stewart, in uniform, facing the right.

REV. UNA VICTORIAM ERIPUIT RATIBUS BINIS. (He snatched victory from two vessels with one.) Naval action between the United States frigate CONSTITUTION, carrying about 50 guns (in the center), Capt. Charles Stewart, and the British frigate CYANE, 34 guns (on the right), Capt. Gordon Falcon, and the sloop-of-war LEVANT, 21 guns (on the left), Captain the Honorable George Douglass. The CONSTITUTION, to windward, is opening with her port battery on the LEVANT: both British vessels are returning the fire from their starboard batteries. Exergue: INTER CONSTITU. NAV. AMERI. ET LEVANT ET CYANE NAV. ANG. DIE XX. FEBR. MDCCCXV. (Between the American vessel CONSTITUTION and the English vessels LEVANT and CYANE, on the 20th of February 1815).

By Furst.

CAPTAIN CHARLES STEWART, *United States Navy*

1778—Born in Philadelphia, Pa., of Irish parents.
1791—Entered the maritime service, rising from cabin boy to command of a merchant vessel.
1798—Appointed a lieutenant in the U.S. Navy, on board the frigate UNITED STATES in the squadron of Commodore John Barry.

1806—Promoted to captain; later supervised the construction of gunboats in New York and in commercial enterprises in the East Indies and Mediterranean.
1812—Assigned to a number of commands, each with increasing responsibilities and signal success: the EXPERIMENT, the SIREN, the ARGUS, the HORNET, and the CONSTELLATION, capturing a number of enemy vessels.
1815—While in command of the CONSTITUTION, battled and took warships CYANE and LEVANT. The engagement opened with the CONSTITUTION to windward and abreast of CYANE which was leading LEVANT. Using the cannons' smoke and approaching darkness as cover, LEVANT attempted to rake CONSTITUTION by luffing under her stern, but Captain Stewart, detecting the enemy maneuver, turned CONSTITUTION's broadside on LEVANT while CYANE surged ahead out of the action. Continuing his brilliant maneuvers, Stewart raked the enemy with devastating effectiveness. CYANE struck and, after a chase of several hours, LEVANT was also captured.
1816—Voted a gold medal by the Congress on February 22 for his gallantry, good conduct and service in the 1815 action, after a brave and skillful combat.
1856—Retired as a Commodore after holding a succession of senior posts ashore and afloat.
1862—Promoted to rear admiral on retired list.
1869—Died in Bordentown, Pa.

LOSS OF THE UNITED STATES BRIG-OF-WAR SOMERS

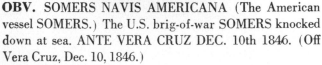

OBV. SOMERS NAVIS AMERICANA (The American vessel SOMERS.) The U.S. brig-of-war SOMERS knocked down at sea. ANTE VERA CRUZ DEC. 10th 1846. (Off Vera Cruz, Dec. 10, 1846.)

REV. PRO VITIS AMERICANORUM CONSERVATIS. (For having saved the lives of Americans.) Three men-of-war's boats, English, Spanish, and French, pulling for the SOMERS. A vacant space on the medal for the name of the recipient.

By C. C. Wright.

By resolution of Congress, March 3, 1847, this medal was prepared for presentation to the officers and men belonging to or attached to the French, British, and Spanish ships of war in the harbor of Vera Cruz, who so gallantly and at the imminent peril of their lives, aided in rescuing many of the officers and crew of the U.S. brig SOMERS which went down in a sudden squall. Thirty-nine men were lost. Capt. Raphael Semmes, later the celebrated commander of the Confederate raider ALABAMA, was absolved of all blame in the loss of his ship.

CAPTAIN DUNCAN N. INGRAHAM

(No. 521)

OBV. The U.S. sloop-of-war ST. LOUIS, and the Austrian brig-of-war HUSSAR, are at anchor in the roads of Smyrna; while a second Austrian war vessel and three mail steamers are at a little distance. The city of Smyrna and the ruins of the Acropolis, on Mount Pagus, are in the background. Exergue: SMYRNA. AMERICAN SLOOP OF WAR ST. LOUIS. AUSTRIAN BRIG OF WAR HUSSAR.

REV. Within a wreath of laurel and oak: PRESENTED BY THE PRESIDENT OF THE UNITED STATES TO COMMANDER DUNCAN N. INGRAHAM AS A TESTIMONIAL OF THE HIGH SENSE ENTERTAINED BY CONGRESS OF HIS GALLANT AND JUDICIOUS CONDUCT ON THE 2d OF JULY 1853. JOINT RESOLUTION OF CONGRESS AUGUST 4th 1854. Exergue: The American eagle, with outspread wings, holds an anchor in its talons; above are 31 stars, the whole lighted by the rays of the sun.

By Eastman and Longacre.

DUNCAN N. INGRAHAM, *U.S. Navy*

1802—Born in Concord, Mass.

1812—Became a midshipman at age of 9, served in the War of 1812 on board the frigate CONGRESS and on Lake Ontario in the MADISON.

1825—Promoted to lieutenant.

1838—Promoted to Master Commandant.

1846—Member of Commodore Conner's staff at the capture of Tampico in the Mexican War.

1853—Martin Koszta, a Hungarian refugee, was seized by Austrian authorities in June 1853 and placed on board the Austrian brig-of-war HUSSAR. Learning that Koszta had taken preliminary steps to secure U.S. naturalization, and being advised by appropriate authority that Koszta was entitled to American protection, Captain Ingraham boarded the Austrian ship and demanded his release. It appeared that the matter could only be decided by a naval engagement. However, by mutual agreement, Koszta was turned over to the French Consul. He was later released and returned to the United States.

1856—Appointed Chief of the Bureau of Ordnance.

1860—Given command of the RICHMOND in Mediterranean Squadron.

1861—Resigned from U.S. Navy and entered Confederate States Navy, Chief of Ordnance at Richmond, later commander of naval forces on the South Carolina coast.

1863—Commanded ironclads PALMETTO STATE and CHICORA in a successful attack against Union blockaders.

1891—Died in Charleston, S.C.

COMMODORE MATTHEW CALBRAITH PERRY
FOR TREATY OF PEACE WITH JAPAN, 1854

OBV. Head of Commodore Perry, to left, with the legend COMMODORE M. C. PERRY.

REV. Within a wreath composed of oak and laurel branches, the stems of which pierce an heraldic naval crown—a circlet heightened with the sterns and hosted sails of ancient ships alternating, with a ring inscribed MISSISSIPPI, appears the legend: PRESENTED TO COM. M. C. PERRY, SPECIAL MINISTER FROM THE U.S.A., BY MERCHANTS OF BOSTON, IN TOKEN OF THEIR APPRECIATION OF HIS SERVICES IN NEGO-TIATING THE TREATY WITH JAPAN SIGNED AT YOKUHAMA MARCH 31 AND WITH LEW CHEW AT NAPA, JULY 11, 1854.

By F. N. Mitchell.

The Boston merchants were particularly interested in this treaty. For many years they had been most actively engaged in trade with China and the neighboring areas.

MATTHEW CALBRAITH PERRY, *U.S. Navy*

1794—Born at Newport, R.I.

1809—Entered Navy as a midshipman, served in the REVENGE, commanded by his brother, Oliver Hazard Perry.

1810—Transferred to PRESIDENT under Commodore John Rogers, participated in battle with LITTLE BELT (1811).

1812—Promoted to lieutenant. Served on board the UNITED STATES.

1816—On leave from the Navy, made a voyage to Holland as master of a merchant vessel.

1820—Named executive officer of the CYANE, aided in establishing a colony of American negroes on the west coast of Africa.

1821—Appointed commanding officer of SHARK, conveyed first American agent to Liberia. Later cruised against West Indian pirates (1822), served as executive officer of NORTH CAROLINA in Mediterranean Squadron (1825).

1826—Promoted to Master Commandant.

1830—Carried John Randolph on board the CONCORD to his ambassadorial post in Russia.

1833—Appointed second in command of the New York Navy Yard and worked to establish a Navy apprentice system. Later helped prepare the first course of instruction for the U.S. Naval Academy and led the movement to organize the U.S. Naval Lyceum (to promote the diffusion of knowledge among naval officers). Perry served as the first curator of the Lyceum (1836), and later the first president.

1837–41—Promoted to captain, ordered to command the FULTON, one of the first steam warships. Perry showed intense interest in steam engineering and its application to naval warfare. He has been called the "Father of the Steam Navy." Perry conducted a survey of lighthouses, and formed the first U.S. naval school of gunnery practice on board the FULTON (1839–40).

1841—Appointed Commandant of the New York Navy Yard.

1843—Placed in command of the African Squadron formed to suppress the slave trade.

1846—Commanding officer of the MISSISSIPPI, later commanded an expeditionary force up the Tabasco River to seize San Juan Bautista, Mexico. The Tabasco operation exemplified the use of versatile seapower in restricted and dangerous waters to carry out a specific mission.

1847—Commanded naval forces in the joint Army-Navy operation that captured Vera Cruz.

1848—Assigned to special duty in New York, including superintending construction of ocean mail steamships.

1853–54—Negotiated historic first commercial treaty between the United States and the hermit kingdom of Japan. The treaty opened certain Japanese ports to American commerce, and provided for the humane treatment for our shipwrecked seamen cast ashore on the coast of Japan. Throughout the difficult negotiations, Commodore Perry combined a show of naval strength with masterful diplomacy and a deep knowledge of the Japanese people and their culture.

1855—Ordered to Washington as a member of the Naval Efficiency Board.

1858—Died in New York City.

LIEUTENANT VICTOR BLUE

(No. 529)

OBV. EXPLORATOR FORTISSIMUS IN PONTO SYLVISQUE FLORUIT. (A scout of great courage he acquitted himself both at sea and in the woods.) Thirteen six-pointed stars (denoting that South Carolina was one of the Thirteen Original States in the Union) on a raised rim, encircling an old-fashioned three-masted ship-of-war, sailing left, with sails spread; the ship and water underneath charged with a large anchor; on the respective blades of the anchor rest the feet of the displayed American eagle.

REV. On an oval shield SOUTH CAROLINA ANIMIS OPIBUSQUE PARATI. (South Carolina ready with its spirit and resources.) On a raised rim enclosing a palmetto tree charged with two crossed staves; two antique cannon, crossed, at the base of the tree. The shield standing to the left of another shield inscribed DUM SPIRO SPERO SPES (While I am breathing I have hope), on a raised rim enclosing a female standing facing; in her right hand extended, is a sprig of palm or olive; behind her appears

the sun on the horizon. The two shields rest on the ground, and respectively have a supporter; that to the left has the Goddess of Liberty, a staff in her right hand, the pole resting on the ground, and surmounted by the traditional Liberty cap; in her right is a laurel wreath. That on the right has a soldier in Continental uniform; in his left hand is a drawn sword with its point on the ground. Above and between the shields is the winged figure of Fame flying to right and blowing a long trumpet. Below this design: THE WOMEN OF SOUTH CAROLINA TO LIEUT. VICTOR BLUE U.S.N. IN HIGH APPRECIATION OF HIS COURAGE ENTERPRISE AND DISTINGUISHED SERVICES IN THE SANTIAGO DE CUBA CAMPAIGN 1898, in eight horizontal lines.

By George T. Morgan.

VICTOR BLUE, *U.S. Navy*

1865—Born in Richmond County, N.C.

1887—Graduated from U.S. Naval Academy.

335–478 O – 69 – 15

1898—Lieutenant in converted yacht SUWANEE. In the war with Spain in 1898, Lieutenant Blue, having had previous experience ashore in Cuba, entered the enemy's country near Santiago de Cuba, and was the first to locate and accurately identify each of Admiral Pasquale Cervera's ships in Santiago Harbor.

1903—Served on the staff of Commander, Asiatic Fleet.

1909—Executive officer of the NORTH CAROLINA, and commanding officer of the YORKTOWN.

1910—Chief of Staff, Pacific Fleet.

1913—Appointed Chief of the Bureau of Navigation (while still a Commander) with temporary rank of rear admiral.

1916—Given command of the battleship TEXAS, which was part of Admiral Rodman's squadron operating with Britain's Grand Fleet in the North Sea during World War I.

1918—Appointed Chief of the Bureau of Navigation.

1919—Promoted to permanent rank of rear admiral.

1928—Died on train enroute from Florida to Washington, D.C.

WORLD CRUISE OF ATLANTIC SQUADRON, 1907

(No. 532)

OBV. THEODORE ROOSEVELT PRESIDENT OF THE UNITED STATES.

Bust, to left.

REV. Columbia standing beneath a flag which is hoisted by a cupid, her right hand resting on an atlas, waves farewell to the departing fleet; on wall, HAMPTON ROADS DEC. 16, 1907 DEPARTURE OF UNITED STATES ATLANTIC FLEET ON CRUISE AROUND THE WORLD.

By Barber and Morgan.

The celebrated round-the-world cruise of the Great White Fleet got underway on December 16, 1907, when 16 battleships departed Hampton Roads, Va., under Rear Adm. Robley D. ("Fighting Bob") Evans, President Theodore Roosevelt had ordered the cruise of good will and diplomacy to test the battleship endurance efficiency, but more particularly to ease tensions between the United States and Japan by a peaceful fleet visit.

The fleet sailed south, rounded Cape Horn, making courtesy calls on both coasts of South America before arriving at San Francisco. Here illness forced Admiral

Evans to relinquish command to Rear Adm. Charles S. Sperry before the powerful armada headed across the vast Pacific.

The ships were met by enthusiastic throngs and genuine friendliness wherever they called—Honolulu, New Zealand, Australia. The warm and tumultous reception received by the U.S. battlewagons and sailors in Japan marked the cruise as a diplomatic success of the first magnitude. Good will replaced the dangerous friction between the two nations.

The Great White Fleet returned home via the Indian Ocean, Suez Canal, and Mediterranean Sea. While the American Squadron was in the Mediterranean, one of the most devastating earthquakes in history struck Messina, Italy. Immediately ships of the fleet steamed at flank speed to the stricken area with medical aid and supplies for the thousands of victims.

After a voyage of 46,000 miles and 14 months, the Great White Fleet returned triumphantly on February 22, 1909, to Hampton Roads to be greeted by President Roosevelt with a much deserved, "Well Done."

VICE ADMIRAL HYMAN GEORGE RICKOVER

(No. 533)

OBV. VICE ADMIRAL HYMAN G. RICKOVER, above portrait, around border. Three quarter view of Vice Admiral Rickover in full uniform with insignia and decorations.

By Frank Gasparro.

REV. To VICE ADMIRAL HYMAN GEORGE RICK-OVER USN By ACT OF THE CONGRESS UNITED STATES OF AMERICA August 19 – 1958, below figure. IN APPRECIATION of his Signal Achievement in the Practical Use of Atomic Energy, around border. Center design, a powerful male figure on bended knee surrounded by eliptical lines representing electrons in orbit—an allegory symbolizing the controlled release of atomic energy. Medal 3 inches in diameter.

By Gilroy Roberts.

HYMAN GEORGE RICKOVER, *U.S. Navy*

1900—Born in Russia, parents immigrated to United States and settled in Chicago, Ill.

1922—Graduated from U.S. Naval Academy, served on board the U.S.S. LA VALLETTE and U.S.S. NEVADA.

1929—Received master of science degree in electrical engineering from Columbia University.

1930—Trained for submarine duty at New London; later served in *S–9* and *S–48*.

1933—Duty in office of the Inspector of Naval Material, Philadelphia, Pa.

1935—Returned to sea duty on board U.S.S. NEW MEXICO.

1937—Command of the minesweeper FINCH, later reported to Cavite Navy Yard, Philippine Islands.

1939—Assigned to Bureau of Ships in Washington, D.C.

1946—Assigned to Atomic Energy Commission's Manhattan project at Oak Ridge, Tenn.

1953—Promoted to rear admiral.

1958—Promoted to vice admiral; medal of appreciation presented by the U.S. Congress to Vice Admiral Rickover.

1961—Received Distinguished Service Medal "For exceptionally meritorious service * * * from January 17, 1955, to January 17, 1960." In presenting the medal Secretary of the Navy William B. Franke said: "* * * as a result of his untiring and relentless efforts, nuclear propulsion has provided us with the foundation of the new Navy—nuclear-powered submarines * * * Nuclear propulsion, developed under his astute leadership, will take its place in history as one of the key developments profoundly affecting all the navies of the world."

1964—Presented with the highly prized Fermi Award "For engineering and administrative leadership in the development of safe and reliable nuclear power and its successful application to our national security and economic needs."

On February 1, 1964, transferred to the retired list but continued on active duty as Assistant Chief of the Bureau of Ships for Nuclear Propulsion.

1966—Appointed Deputy Commander for Nuclear Propulsion, Naval Ship Systems Command.

Miscellaneous

TIME INCREASES HIS FAME

(No. 601)

OBV. GEORGE WASHINGTON PRESIDENT OF THE UNITED STATES, 1789. Engraving attributed to William Kneass, modeled by Du Vivier after Houdon likeness.

REV. TIME INCREASES HIS FAME, within a laurel wreath.

CABINET MEDAL

(No. 602)

OBV. Bust of Washington in civilian dress. Legend: PATER PATRIAE.

REV. A MEMORIAL OF THE WASHINGTON CABINET MAY 1859, within a wreath of olive branches.

Engraved by Anthony Paquet from portrait attributed to Gilbert Stuart.

WASHINGTON AND JACKSON

(No. 603)

OBV. Bust of Washington.

REV. Bust of Jackson.

By Anthony C. Paquet.

COMMENCEMENT OF COIN CABINET

(No. 604)

OBV. Bust of Washington. BORN FEB. 22, 1732. DIED DEC. 14, 1799.

REV. A representation of the Washington Medallic Collection, consisting of 138 specimens, surmounted by a bust

of Washington. Legend: WASHINGTON CABINET OF MEDALS, U.S. MINT. INAUGURATED FEB. 22, 1860.

By Anthony C. Paquet, after Houdon bust and DuVivier's "Washington before Boston" medal.

PRESIDENCY RELINQUISHED

(No. 605)

OBV. Bust of Washington. Legend: G. WASHINGTON PRES. UNIT. STA.

REV. COMMIS. RESIGNED: PRESIDENCY RELING. 1797. Sword and faces (emblems of military authority)

laid down on a pedestal bearing the shield of the United States.

By Holliday, an English die engraver.

OATH OF ALLEGIANCE BY MINT PERSONNEL 1861

(No. 606)

OBV. THE CONSTITUTION IS SACREDLY OBLIG-
ATORY ON ALL. Bust of Washington.

REV. Within an olive wreath: U.S. MINT OATH OF
ALLEGIANCE TAKEN BY THE OFFICERS AND

WORKMEN SEPT. 9, 1861. JAS. POLLOCK, DIREC-
TOR.

By Anthony C. Paquet.

WASHINGTON AND LINCOLN

(No. 607)

OBV. Bust of Washington.

REV. Bust of Lincoln.

By Anthony C. Paquet.

WASHINGTON AND GRANT

(No. 608)

OBV. Bust of Washington.

REV. Bust of Grant.

By Anthony C. Paquet.

WASHINGTON WREATH

OBV. Bust of Washington.

REV. Within a laurel wreath: BORN 1732 DIED 1799. By Anthony C. Paquet.

(Authorized by the Act of February 23, 1931)

WASHINGTON BICENTENNIAL

(No. 610)

OBV. Portrait bust of George Washington in military uniform; above, the legend WASHINGTON; below, a shield bearing his coat of arms separates the years 1732–1932.

REV. Liberty, standing on the prow of the Ship of State, with arms outstretched; in her right hand is a torch and in the left a sword. Above, an eagle with wings spread and 13 stars in the field. *Legend:* PROCLAIM LIBERTY THROUGHOUT THE LAND.

By Laura Gardin Fraser.

JAMES A. GARFIELD

(No. 611)

OBV. Bust of Garfield.

REV. Within a wreath: J. A. GARFIELD BORN NOV 19 1831 DIED SEP 19 1881.

By Charles E. Barber.

LINCOLN AND GARFIELD

(No. 612)

OBV. Bust of Lincoln.

REV. Bust of Garfield.

By Charles E. Barber.

PENNSYLVANIA BICENTENNIAL

(No. 613)

OBV. PENN, 1882. Bust of William Penn.

REV. Pennsylvania State Seal. DISTRIBUTED BY EMPLOYEES OF U.S. MINT DURING THE CELEBRATION OF PENNSYLVANIA'S BICENTENNIAL OCT. 24, 1882.

By George T. Morgan.

VALLEY FORGE CENTENNIAL

OBV. GEORGE WASHINGTON * COMMANDER IN CHIEF * Bust of Washington, to right.

REV. VALLEY FORGE CENTENNIAL 1778–1878. Within a wreath: IN COMMEMORATION OF THE DEPARTURE OF THE CONTINENTAL ARMY JUNE 19.

By W. Barber.

No name in American history conveys more of suffering, sacrifice, and triumph than Valley Forge. Washington's ragged, hungry troops staggered into the camp on December 19, 1777, the wreckage of a defeated army. They endured a bitterly cold and uncomfortable winter, but emerged as a trained army. The military training and discipline imposed at Valley Forge created a force that would meet the enemy on equal terms from then on, and at last defeat him.

Washington's 11,000 troops were mostly unfit for service when he took them into winter quarters at Valley Forge. They had experienced a series of fruitless marches and costly skirmishes, capped by defeat at Brandywine and failure at Germantown. From this camp, named for a small iron mill on Valley Creek, which the British had destroyed, the Army could defend itself and also observe the approaches to Philadelphia. Approximately 900 log huts were raised, and fortifications were thrown up to protect the camp and command nearby roads and rivers. The soldiers were not permitted to huddle in their cabins, but were rigorously drilled and disciplined by "Baron" Frederick von Steuben who, even if he magnified his European rank and title, was nevertheless a drillmaster of surpassing skill. When spring came, the Army was ready for the field as never before, and at Monmouth on June 28, 1778, it made its debut as a skilled force able to meet and defeat British regulars in open combat.

LINCOLN AND GRANT

OBV. Bust of Lincoln.

REV. Bust of Grant.
By Charles E. Barber.

LINCOLN, BROKEN COLUMN

(No. 616)

OBV. Bust of Lincoln.

REV. Broken column, flags and scroll.

By Charles E. Barber.

JAPANESE EMBASSY

(No. 617)

OBV. JAMES BUCHANAN, PRESIDENT OF THE UNITED STATES. Bust of the President.

REV. Within an oak wreath: IN COMMEMORATION OF THE FIRST EMBASSY OF JAPAN TO THE UNITED STATES, 1860.

By Anthony C. Paquet.

This medal was struck to commemorate the formal visit of Japanese envoys with President Buchanan on May 17, 1860, at which time the Embassy of Japan was established in the United States. Following this accreditation ceremony, the principal envoys visited the U.S. Mint at Philadelphia, at which time and in their presence, assays were made of Japanese coins, for the purpose of determining the interchangeable commercial value of their coins with those of the United States.

FREDERICK HENRY ROSE

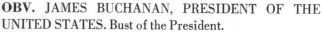

OBV. JAMES BUCHANAN, PRESIDENT OF THE UNITED STATES. Bust of the President.

REV. TO DR. FREDERICK ROSE, ASSISTANT SURGEON, ROYAL NAVY, G.B. Asclepius (legendary Greek physician and god of medicine) standing and shielding a man and woman from death. Exergue: FOR KINDNESS AND HUMANITY TO OFFICERS AND CREW OF THE U.S. STEAMER SUSQUEHANNA.

By Anthony C. Paquet.

Resolution of Congress, May 11, 1858, Voting a Medal to Doctor Rose:

"That the President be, and he is hereby, authorized and requested to cause suitable acknowledgments to be made on the part of this government to Admiral Sir Hewston Stewart, of Her Britannic Majesty's Navy, and officers under his command, for their prompt and efficient aid, and generous hospitality, extended to the dis-abled officers and crew of the United States ship Susquehanna on her late arrival at Port Royal, Island of Jamaica, with the yellow fever on board; on which occasion, besides placing the naval hospital, with an adequate corps of medical officers, nurses and attendants, at their service, eighty-five of the officers and crew of the Susquehanna were safely and promptly conveyed on shore with the aid of the boats of the British squadron, and the lives of the greater portion of them thereby probably saved. And that the President be further requested to cause a gold medal, with appropriate devices, to be presented, on behalf of this government, to Assistant-Surgeon Frederick H. Rose, of the British Navy, who volunteered, with the permission of his commanding officer, to join the Susquehanna, and, at imminent personal risk, devoted himself, on the voyage from Jamaica to New York, to the care of the sick remaining on board."

PROFESSOR LOUIS AGASSIZ

(No. 619)

OBV. AGASSIZ. Bust of the Professor.

REV. TERRA MARIQUE DUCTOR INDAGATIONE NATURAE. Within a laurel wreath: NA 1807 OB 1873

By William Barber.

Born in Switzerland, Jean Louis Rodolphe Agassiz became a naturalized citizen of the United States. He studied medicine at the Universities of Zurich and Heidelberg and at the University of Munich. Agassiz was a world authority on natural history; a prolific writer; an exponent of original research, and an outstanding educator.

INDIAN PEACE MEDAL—GEORGE II

(No. 620)

OBV. GEORGIVS II DEI GRATIA (George II by the Grace of God). Draped and laureated bust, in armor.

REV. LET US LOOK TO THE MOST HIGH WHO BLESSED OUR FATHERS WITH PEACE. A Friend, pointing to the sun, offers a pipe of peace to an Indian before him. Between them is a council fire. Exergue: 1757

A Society of Friends known as the "Friendly Association for Regaining and Preserving Peace with the Indians by Pacific Means" commissioned Edward Duffield, a Philadelphia watch and clock worker, to engrave and strike this medal. Dated 1757, it is believed to be one of the first medals made in the Province of Pennsylvania.

DAVID HOSACK

(No. 621)

OBV. DAVID HOSACK M.D. Head of Dr. Hosack.

REV. Inside top border, the inscription ARTS AND SCIENCE. Depicted are implements of his professional interests: Globe, palette, gavel, book, square, compass, shovel, caduceus, pedestal surmounted by a lyre.

By M. Furst.

Dr. David Hosack was born in New York City in 1769; he attended Columbia University in 1786 and was graduated from Princeton University in 1789. He received his medical degree from the College of Philadelphia in 1791 and commenced the practice of medicine in Alexandria, Va. In 1795 he went to Columbia College as professor of natural history and, later also held the chair of professor of materia medica. He was the attending surgeon at the Burr-Hamilton duel in 1804. In 1807 he became professor of midwifery and surgery in the College of Physicians and Surgeons. Afterwards, he occupied the chairs of the theory and practice of medicine and obstetrics, and the diseases of women and children until 1826, when he was one of the organizers of the Medical Department of Rutgers College. He was the first American surgeon to tie the artery at the upper third of the thigh to correct an aneurysm. He was an incorporator of the American Academy of Fine Arts and also the New York Historical Society, serving as the latter's president from 1820 to 1828. He died in New York City December 22, 1835.

FIRST STEAM COINAGE

(No. 622)

OBV. A Liberty Cap.

REV. UNITED STATES MINT; within a circle: FIRST STEAM COINAGE March 26, 1836.

By Anthony C. Paquet.

On January 23, 1837, Mint Director R. M. Patterson reported from Philadelphia to President Andrew Jackson: "On the 23rd of March last (1836), the first steam coinage in America was executed at this Mint; and the performance of the press, in which the power of the lever is substituted for that of the screw, has answered all our expectations. Since that time, all the copper coins have been struck by this press, and it has been lately used with success for coining half dollars. The workmen are now engaged in making other steam presses; and as these are completed, the coining by human labor will be abandoned, and the work that can be executed in * * * the Mint will be greatly increased." The medal commemorates this epoch in U.S. coinage methods.

UNION PACIFIC RAILROAD

(No. 623)

OBV. PRESIDENCY OF U. S. GRANT. Bust of the President. THE OCEANS UNITED BY RAILWAY MAY 10, 1869.

REV. A landscape with mountains in the background, and bordered to the right and left by the Atlantic and Pacific Oceans respectively. *Legend:* EVERY MOUNTAIN SHALL BE MADE LOW. *Exergue:* MEDAL SERIES OF THE UNITED STATES MINT.

By William Barber.

The Union Pacific Railroad was chartered by Act of July 1, 1862, to build a rail transportation system westward from the Missouri River to meet the Central Pacific of California building eastward.

At Promontory, Utah, on May 10, 1869, the Central Pacific's (now Southern Pacific) Jupiter engine and the Union Pacific's No. 119 stood a scant two rails apart. A golden spike and another of silver were driven into a tie of polished California laurel. The Jupiter and No. 119 inched toward each other, almost touching noses. "The last rail is laid. The last spike is driven. The Pacific railroad is completed," were the words that crackled along telegraph lines to an anxiously waiting Nation. President Grant made the official announcement from the White House.

EMANCIPATION PROCLAMATION

(No. 624)

OBV. ABRAHAM LINCOLN PRESIDENT UNITED STATES. Bust of the President.

REV. MARCH 4, 1861 TO APRIL 15, 1865 (the term of Lincoln's presidency). EMANCIPATION PROCLAIMED JAN. 1, 1863. *Exergue:* MEDAL SERIES OF THE U.S. MINT.

By William Barber.

335-478 O - 69 - 16

Early in the Civil War, President Lincoln withstood pressure to free all the slaves, lest he lose the support of loyal border States and because he recognized the lack of constitutional authority to take such a sweeping action. After the successful Antietam campaign, however, Lincoln issued a preliminary edict on slavery and on January 1, 1863, for the ostensible purpose of depleting southern manpower, he promulgated the formal Emancipation Proclamation. This did not mean that all slaves in the United States were to be free, but only those in rebellion. This action was taken "as a fit and necessary war measure for repressing said rebellion." Ultimate emancipation as a national measure was completed by the Antislavery Amendment to the Constitution.

CYRUS WEST FIELD

(No. 625)

OBV. Within a circle formed by a telegraphic cable: HONOR AND FAME ARE THE REWARD. On clouds in the midst of sunbeams, the bust of Cyrus West Field. A hand from above places a crown on his head; below is the Atlantic Ocean; two ships going in opposite directions are paying out the cable; to the left, the western hemisphere, AMERICA; to the right, the eastern hemisphere, EUROPE; beneath, in a band formed by the Atlantic cable and a chain uniting the two worlds, INDOMITABLE PERSEVERANCE AND ENDURING FAITH ACHIEVED THE SUCCESS.

REV. Within an endless chain: BY RESOLUTION OF THE CONGRESS OF THE UNITED STATES, MARCH 2, 1867. TO CYRUS W. FIELD, OF NEW YORK FOR HIS FORESIGHT, FAITH, AND PERSISTENCY, IN ESTABLISHING TELEGRAPHIC COMMUNICATION, BY MEANS OF THE ATLANTIC TELEGRAPH CONNECTING THE OLD WITH THE NEW WORLD. To the left, the American shield; to the right, a star formed of 31 smaller stars; below, the terrestrial globe, showing AMERICA and EUROPE, surrounded with electric sparks, surmounted by a torch and a caduceus crossed, and resting on branches of laurel and of oak.

Designed by J. G. Bruff; sculpted by W. Barber.

Born in Stockbridge, Mass., on November 30, 1819, Cyrus West Field moved to New York at the age of 15. By 1853 he had retired from a successful paper business and became interested in constructing a telegraph route from the United States to Newfoundland, and from there to England. The enterprise was organized under the title New York, Newfoundland and London Telegraph. Initial telegraphic contact was made between these three points for a brief period in 1858. Notwithstanding mechanical failures which seemed to doom the project, it was placed on a permanent footing after new cable had been successfully laid in 1866. The thanks of the Nation were expressed by the Congress of the United States which voted unanimously to award Mr. Field a gold medal.

DR. JOSEPH PANCOAST

(No. 626)

OBV. PANCOAST. Bust of Dr. Pancoast.

REV. Within a wreath of oak and laurel: JOSEPH PANCOAST M.D. PROF. OF ANATOMY JEFFERSON MEDICAL COLLEGE BORN 1805

By W. Barber.

Born in Burlington County, N.J. in 1805, Joseph Pancoast became an emient surgeon after his graduation from the University of Pennsylvania Medical School. In 1838 he was elected professor of surgery at Jefferson Medical College (Philadelphia) and later transferred to the chair of anatomy which he held until 1874. He developed a number of new and effective operating techniques, particularly in the field of plastic surgery. He died in Philadelphia, at the age of 77.

INDIAN PEACE (GRANT)

(No. 627)

OBV. Within a wreath of laurel and shields of the United States of America: UNITED STATES OF AMERICA. LIBERTY JUSTICE AND EQUALITY—"LET US HAVE PEACE." Bust of the President; under it, a calumet of peace and an olive branch.

REV. Within a circle composed of 36 stars: ON EARTH PEACE GOOD WILL TOWARD MEN 1871. The Western Hemisphere of the globe resting on implements of agriculture, surmounted by a Bible.

By Anthony C. Paquet.

INDIAN PEACE (HAYES)

(No. 628)

OBV. RUTHERFORD B. HAYES. PRESIDENT OF THE UNITED STATES. Bust of the President.

REV. A pioneer and an Indian chief; above, PEACE; below, olive wreath over calumet and tomahawk in saltire.

By George T. Morgan.

238

INDIAN PEACE (GARFIELD)

(No. 629)

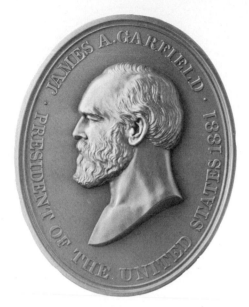 

OBV. JAMES A. GARFIELD. PRESIDENT OF THE UNITED STATES 1881. Bust of the President.

By C. E. Barber.

REV. A pioneer and an Indian chief; above, PEACE; below, olive wreath over calumet and tomahawk in saltire.

By George T. Morgan.

INDIAN PEACE (ARTHUR)

(No. 630)

OBV. CHESTER A. ARTHUR. PRESIDENT OF THE UNITED STATES 1881. Bust of the President.

By C. E. Barber.

REV. A pioneer and an Indian chief; above, PEACE; below, olive wreath over calumet and tomahawk in saltire.

By George T. Morgan.

INDIAN PEACE (CLEVELAND)

(No. 631)

OBV. GROVER CLEVELAND. PRESIDENT U.S.A. 1885. Bust of the President.

By C. E. Barber.

REV. A pioneer with ax in hand, standing and talking to an Indian chief, before a cottage; above, PEACE: below, olive wreath over calumet and tomahawk in saltire.

By George T. Morgan.

INDIAN PEACE (HARRISON)

(No. 632)

OBV. BENJAMIN HARRISON. PRESIDENT U.S.A. 1889. Bust of the President.

By C. E. Barber.

REV. A pioneer and an Indian chief; above, PEACE; below, olive wreath over calumet and tomahawk in saltire.

By George T. Morgan.

LET US HAVE PEACE (GRANT)

(No. 633)

OBV. U. S. GRANT PRESIDENT OF THE UNITED STATES. Bust of the President.

REV. LIBERTY THE TRUE FOUNDATION OF HUMAN GOVERNMENT. LET US HAVE PEACE. Medal Series of the U.S. Mint.

By William Barber.

This medal derives its name from the famous phrase used by Grant in his letter of May 29, 1868, accepting the Republican nomination for the Presidency.

GEORGE F. ROBINSON

(For Protection of Secretary Seward)

(No. 634)

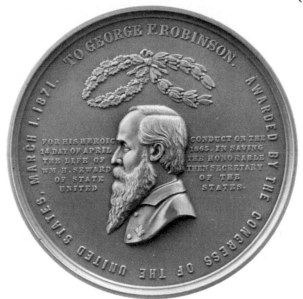

OBV. AWARDED BY THE CONGRESS OF THE UNITED STATES MARCH 1, 1871. — TO GEORGE F. ROBINSON. Bust of Robinson; above his head, wreaths, oak leaves and laurel. — FOR HIS HEROIC CONDUCT ON THE 14 DAY OF APRIL 1865, IN SAVING THE LIFE OF THE HONORABLE WM. H. SEWARD —

THEN SECRETARY OF STATE OF THE UNITED STATES.

REV. Mr. Robinson grappling with the assailant of Secretary Seward, who reclines to right behind partly opened curtain in background.

Designed by C. Y. Coffin; sculpted by Anthony C. Paquet.

241

By resolution of Congress approved March 1, 1871, George Robinson was awarded the thanks of Congress and a gold medal for his heroic actions in protecting, at imminent peril to his own life, the injured and ailing Wm. H. Seward, Secretary of State, from the savage attack of a murderous assassin. He single-handedly fought off the attacker, who was armed with a knife and pistol, receiving serious wounds in the encounter. After the attacker had fled, disregarding his own condition he assisted the Secretary's daughter to tend to the Secretary until arrival of the Surgeon General. After the Secretary's wounds were dressed, his own were attended to and he was hospitalized. He recovered and later left the army for civilian life where he obtained employment as a clerk with the Government.

(July 4, 1776)

U.S. DIPLOMATIC MEDAL

(No. 635)

OBV. TO PEACE AND COMMERCE. America, personified as an Indian queen, holds in her left hand the cornucopia of abundance (Peace) and welcomes Mercury (Commerce) to her shores. Her right hand directs attention to American products, packed ready for export. *Exergue:* IV JUL. MDCCLXXVI.

REV. THE UNITED STATES OF AMERICA. The Great Seal of the United States.

By Augustin Dupre.

This medal was ordered in 1790 by Thomas Jefferson, then Secretary of State during the presidency of George Washington, as "a present proper to be given to diplomatic characters on their taking leave of us." The design itself was conceived by Jefferson and was executed in Paris by the famous sculptor Augustin Dupre. Gold medals, suspended by a chain, were presented to Marquis de la Luzerne, the French Minister to the United States from 1779 to 1784 and to Count de Monstier, French Minister to the United States from 1787 to 1791. Thereafter, the use of this medal as an official diplomatic presentation, was discontinued.

GREAT SEAL CENTENNIAL

(No. 636)

OBV. An American eagle, bearing on its breast the shield of the United States, grasping in its talons an olive branch and arrows. Thirteen stars and a ribbon bearing the motto "E Pluribus Unum" (One Out of Many).

REV. An unfinished pyramid, surmounted by an eye in a triangular glory. At the base of the pyramid, in Roman numerals, the year of the Declaration of American Independence, 1776. From Virgil's "Aenid" came the mottoes: "Annuit Coeptis"—He (God) favored our undertakings, and "Novus Ordo Seclorum"—a new order of the ages. The pyramid, symbol of strength, is in unfinished condition to denote the belief of the designers of the Great Seal that there was still work to be done. The dates 1782 and 1882 represent the year of the Seal's adoption and its commemoration a hundred years later.

By C. E. Barber.

JOSEPH FRANCIS

(No. 637)

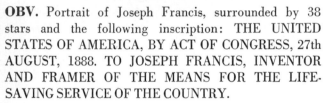

OBV. Portrait of Joseph Francis, surrounded by 38 stars and the following inscription: THE UNITED STATES OF AMERICA, BY ACT OF CONGRESS, 27th AUGUST, 1888. TO JOSEPH FRANCIS, INVENTOR AND FRAMER OF THE MEANS FOR THE LIFE-SAVING SERVICE OF THE COUNTRY.

REV. A ship distressed in heavy seas. In the rigging, figures are seen clinging; on the storm-beaten shore, the lifesaving crew is in full view; an extra lifesaving boat on wheels stands by for emergency use. To the right of the boat are seen three sturdy men with mortar and other appliances used in the Life-Saving Service. They have already shot a line to the ship and have made fast, and are hauling a life-car of the kind invented by Joseph Francis.

Zeleima Bruff Jackson designed the medal; the model was made by Augustus St. Gaudens.

Joseph Francis was presented a gold medal by President Harrison in 1890, in recognition of his services in the construction and perfection of lifesaving appliances. This medal, together with other medals and honors bestowed on Mr. Francis from nations all over the world, attest to the genius of this inventor whose efforts saved countless lives at sea.

Born in Boston, Mass., in 1801, Francis started early in life to develop lifesaving devices.

His earliest product was a small unsinkable boat with cork in its ends, which would hold four men. In 1838 he patented a wooden lifeboat to run back and forth on a hawser between ship and shore. When tests were run, it was found that the pounding of heavy seas was too much for this craft. Francis turned to molded iron plates which proved to be too heavy. After many years of tedious effort, he perfected dies for casting corrugated iron plates to be used in lifeboat construction. When put to the test in 1850, the success of this new craft was demonstrated by the saving of 199 out of 200 lives from a British ship which had foundered off the New Jersey coast. Ten years later, almost all ships leaving New York Harbor were equipped with Francis lifeboats. Francis also invented light-draft iron vessels that could be manufactured in sections, moved across mountains and plains, and reassembled at seaports. Through his efforts the American Shipwreck and Humane Society was organized; out of this grew the U.S. Life-Saving Service.

ABRAHAM LINCOLN, CENTENARY OF BIRTH, 1909

OBV. ABRAHAM LINCOLN. Bust of the President.

REV. 1809–1909 WITH MALICE TOWARD NONE WITH CHARITY FOR ALL. Palm and laurel branches.

By George T. Morgan.

WRIGHT BROTHERS

OBV. Busts of the Wright brothers and their names. Within a laurel wreath: the Great Seal of the United States. RESOLUTION OF CONGRESS MARCH 4, 1909. IN RECOGNITION AND APPRECIATION OF THEIR ABILITY COURAGE AND SUCCESS IN NAVIGATING THE AIR.

REV. SHALL MOUNT UP WITH WINGS AS EAGLES. A winged figure, the Genius of Aviation, with torch in flight.

By C. E. Barber.

This medal was awarded by the Congress "in recognition and in appreciation of the great service Orville Wright and Wilbur Wright of Ohio rendered the science of aerial navigation, in the invention of the Wright aeroplane, and for their ability, courage and success in navigating the air." The Wright plane was patented in 1906 as a result of 10 years of experimental work with gliders. The first successful flights in heavier-than-air mechanically propelled planes took place at Kill Devil Hill, 4 miles south of Kitty Hawk and one of the breeziest places in the country. At this place, on December 17, 1903, Orville Wright rose 120 feet from the base of Kill Devil Hill in 12 seconds; on the same day, Wilbur Wright rose 852 feet in 59 seconds. A flight of 24 miles was accomplished by Wilbur Wright in 1905, at a field near Dayton, Ohio. The War Department contracted for a plane to be built by the Wrights in 1904; successful tests were completed the following year. Wilbur Wright was born in Millville, Ind., in 1867; he died at Dayton, Ohio, in 1912. Orville Wright was born in Dayton in 1871 and died there in 1948.

ABRAHAM LINCOLN (INDIAN PEACE MEDAL)

(No. 640)

OBV. ABRAHAM LINCOLN, PRESIDENT OF THE UNITED STATES. Bust of the President, bearing the date of his second year in office.

By Salathiel Ellis.

REV. Within a circle, a rural scene; an Indian with feather bonnet, plowing, children playing. Above, an Indian warrior grasping another man by the hair, and holding a knife. Below, bust of an Indian woman, a bow and a calumet.

By J. Willson.

WOODROW WILSON

(No. 641)

OBV. Woodrow Wilson. Bust of the President.

REV. Eagle, with wings spread, holding in talons crossed branches of olive and oak. In the background, the Capitol of the United States. Inaugurated President of the United States March 4, 1913. Second term March 5, 1917.

By George T. Morgan.

This medal is identical in composition to the medal of Wilson in the Presidential Series, though it is reduced in size.

CHARLES A. LINDBERGH

(No. 645)

OBV. LINDBERGH. MEDAL OF THE CONGRESS. UNITED STATES OF AMERICA. Act of May 4, 1928. Bust of Brigadier General Lindbergh, wearing the helmet of an aviator.

REV. A lone eagle in flight; the sun and stars, symbolize the flight through day and night.

By Laura Gardin Fraser.

The act of December 14, 1927, authorized the President of the United States to present in the name of Congress, "a medal of honor to Colonel Charles A. Lindbergh, United States Army Air Reserve, for displaying heroic courage and skill as a navigator, at the risk of his life, by his non-stop flight in his plane, the Spirit of St. Louis, from New York City to Paris, France, on May 20, 1927, by which he not only achieved the greatest individual triumph of any American citizen, but demonstrated that travel across the ocean by aircraft was possible."

Lindbergh's flight to Paris started at 7:52 a.m. on the morning of May 20, 1927, at Roosevelt Field, Long Island, N.Y. The "Spirit of St. Louis" reached LeBourget Airfield, Paris, at 5:21 p.m. (10:21 p.m. Paris time) on May 21. Lindbergh had flown 3,610 miles in 33 hours, 29 minutes, and 30 seconds, and won the Raymond Orteig award of $25,000 for the first New York-Paris nonstop flight. Returned on the cruiser U.S.S. MEMPHIS, with his plane, Lindbergh was given a hero's welcome and promotion to the rank of colonel by President Coolidge in Washington on June 11. A tremendous demonstration was given him in New York 2 days later.

Following the award of the Congressional Medal of Honor and the Distinguished Flying Cross, the United States gave further recognition by directing that the Treasury Department strike a special medal in gold for presentation to Colonel Lindbergh and providing that bronze copies be made available to the public. This is the medal which is described.

Charles A. Lindbergh was born in Detroit, Mich., in 1902. After a brief period of study at the University of Wisconsin, he attended flying school. In 1924 he enlisted as a flying cadet in the air service, Department of War, and was stationed at Kelly Field, Tex. The following year he was commissioned first lieutenant in the U.S. Army; he became associated with the Missouri National Guard and was promoted to captain in the Officers Reserve Corps. On April 15, 1925, he became an airmail pilot on the Chicago-St. Louis route. Following his successful flight to Paris, Lindbergh undertook extensive good will missions to many parts of the world. An isolationist, Lindbergh resigned his commission in the Air Corps after war broke out in Europe. However, after the attack on Pearl Harbor, Lindbergh supported his country's war effort by serving as a civilian technician for aircraft companies in the United States and in the Pacific theater of operations. In 1954, Lindbergh was recommissioned as a brigadier general in the Air Force Reserve.

MOUNT VERNON

(No. 647)

OBV. View of Mount Vernon and bust of Washington. On left, 1732, and on right, 1932.

REV. Front portal of the United States Mint at Philadelphia.

By John Ray Sinnock.

BENJAMIN FRANKLIN

(No. 648)

OBV. Portrait of Benjamin Franklin, bearing the dates of his birth and death: 1706–1790.

REV. Four allegorical figures, or muses, representing Philosophy, Literature, Science and Patriotism, the names of which are inscribed in the field. The tablet bears the name, BENJAMIN FRANKLIN.

By John Ray Sinnock.

FRANKLIN D. ROOSEVELT

(No. 649)

OBV. FRANKLIN DELANO ROOSEVELT, PRESIDENT OF THE UNITED STATES. Bust of the President.

REV. An eagle with spread wings. INAUGURATED PRESIDENT. The dates are those of the President's four inaugurations.

By John Ray Sinnock.

ALBEN W. BARKLEY

OBV. AWARD OF CONGRESS TO ALBEN W. BARK-LEY. Aug. 12, 1949. Bust of the Vice President.

REV. IN RECOGNITION OF DISTINGUISHED PUB-LIC SERVICE. An eagle in flight, holding in its talons the olive branch of peace.

By Beatrice Fenton.

This is the first medal of a Vice President of the United States to be produced by the U.S. Mint. The jury which selected the design from a number of entries consisted of the President of the United States, the Chief Justice, the Speaker of the House of Representatives and the Majority Leader of the Senate.

In reporting favorably upon the resolution to award a gold medal to Vice President Barkley, Senator Maybank of the Senate Committee on Banking and Currency remarked:

"No medal could ever capture the humane spirit, the devotion to duty, and the sense of humor shown by the Honorable Alben W. Barkley in his long period of public service. The problems he has encountered in his brilliant career as a servant of the people have run the gamut of depression, war, and inflation. Yet, unpleasant as the task might have been, he always willingly shouldered the burdens of legislative action required to meet the grave national problems which arose. He is ever to be found in the vanguard of those fighting for the advancement of the great mass of citizens of the Nation which he so capably serves.

"His understanding of the problems of these people and his fearlessness in presenting their cause has won him the admiration and love not only of those who agree with his doctrines but even of those who hold differing views.

"The American people can never repay Alben Barkley for his extended, continuous, and meritorious service to the Nation. Yet, in heartfelt appreciation for public service so nobly performed over such a long span of years, a grateful populace as with a single voice urges recognition of that fact by providing for the striking of an appropriate medal as a token of their esteem."

Alben William Barkley was born in 1877 in Graves County, Ky. Son of a poor tobacco farmer, he graduated from Marvin College, Clinton, Ky.; attended Emory College, Oxford, Ga., and the University of Virginia Law School at Charlottesville, Va. After his admission to the bar in 1901, he commenced practice in Paducah, Ky., became a prosecuting attorney and later judge of Mc-Cracken County Court. He was first elected to the U.S. House of Representatives in 1912 where he served until entering the U.S. Senate in 1927. He served as Democratic majority leader of the Senate from 1937 to 1947 where he spearheaded the legislative programs of Presidents Roosevelt and Truman. Elected Vice President of the United States with President Harry S. Truman in 1948, he was inaugurated January 20, 1949. During his tenure the responsibilities of the Vice President were extended to include participation in the National Security Council as well as counseling to the President on foreign and domestic affairs. After leaving the Vice Presidency in 1953, Barkley regained his Senate seat in the following year's elections. He died suddenly in 1956 in Lexington, Va.

JONAS E. SALK

(No. 652)

OBV. Portrait of Doctor Salk

REV. An allegorical figure, with the aid of a shield bearing a caduceus, protecting two healthy children from the dread disease of infantile paralysis. Around the border: AWARD OF CONGRESS TO DOCTOR JONAS E. SALK IN RECOGNITION AND APPRECIATION OF HIS ACHIEVEMENT IN DEVELOPING A VACCINE FOR POLIO.

By Gilroy Roberts.

By joint resolution of the Congress, approved August 9, 1955, a gold medal was awarded "in recognition of the great achievement of Doctor Jonas E. Salk in the field of medicine by his discovery of a serum for the prevention of poliomyelitis."

Dr. Salk first entered the fight against polio in 1942 when he joined the staff of the University of Michigan as the recipient of a National Foundation for Infantile Paralysis fellowship. In 1951 he began his direct research at the virus research laboratories at the University of Pittsburgh on a polio vaccine.

The vaccine developed by Dr. Salk was the result of a painstaking and intensive research program. Live polio virus was treated by chemicals so that a delicate balance was struck in which the ability of the virus to cause disease was eliminated by meticulously calculated chemical additions but still leaving the virus with sufficient potency to stimulate antibody production.

In his tests at Pittsburgh, Dr. Salk proved that the vaccine which he produced was able to raise the antibody level. In the nationwide field trial held by the National Foundation for Infantile Paralysis held in 1954, Dr. Salk's vaccine was proved highly effective in preventing paralysis. Over 1.8 million children throughout the United States took part in this massive trial.

Dr. Salk was born in New York in 1914. After graduating from the College of the City of New York in 1934, he entered the College of Medicine, New York University where he was awarded an M.D. degree in 1939. From 1942 to 1947, he served at the University of Michigan, first as a research fellow and later as associate professor of epidemiology. During this period he also worked for the Army under his teacher, Dr. Thomas Francis, Jr., in an endeavor to develop a vaccine against influenza. In 1947 Dr. Salk became associated with the University of Pittsburgh School of Medicine, first as a research professor of bacteriology and head of the Virus Research Laboratory, and later as professor of medicine.

251

ROBERT H. GODDARD

OBV. ROBERT HUTCHINGS GODDARD 1882–1945. Bust of Dr. Goddard.

REV. Launching frame of Dr. Goddard's first liquid-propellant rocket. "The dream of yesterday is the hope of today and the reality of tomorrow." (sgd) Robert H. Goddard. Beneath frame: First Rocket March 16, 1926. Around border: IN HONOR OF ROBERT H. GODDARD BY ACT OF CONGRESS OF THE UNITED STATES OF AMERICA, 1959 IN RECOGNITION OF HIS PIONEERING RESEARCH IN ROCKET PROPULSION.

By Engelhardus von Hebel.

By joint resolution of the Congress, approved September 16, 1959, a gold medal was awarded to be struck "in recognition of the great, creative achievements of the late Doctor Robert H. Goddard, and his historic pioneering research on space rockets, missiles, and jet propulsion."

Dr. Goddard is generally recognized as the "father of modern rocketry." While still a student of physics in 1907 he prepared a manuscript outlining a scheme for using radioactive materials for jet propulsion in space, but, being ahead of his time, found no one willing to publish this pioneer document. As a physics instructor in 1914, he began actual experiments in rocketry which, together with technical papers he had prepared, led to grants from the Smithsonian Institution to assist him in his work.

During World War I, Dr. Goddard was assigned to explore the military possibilities of rockets and developed several promising rocket devices, including the forerunner of the modern bazooka. In the decade following World War I, he did pioneer work in the control of rocket flights by gyroscope, instrumentation to record conditions on rockets in flight, and in other important fields. In the period from 1929 to 1941, he made great strides in developing large rockets. In the mid-1930's Goddard rockets achieved speeds as great as 700 miles per hour and altitudes as high as 7,500 feet. His work was followed closely in Germany, and unquestionably contributed to the development of the V–2 rockets used by Germany in the closing months of World War II. From the beginning of World War II until his death in 1945, Dr. Goddard worked on important rocket projects for the Navy.

Dr. Goddard was born in Worcester, Mass. in 1882. He was graduated from Worcester Polytechnic Institute in 1908. Upon graduation he obtained a position as an instructor of physics at this institute, and at the same time began graduate work at Clark University. He received his M.A. from Clark in 1910, and his Ph. D. in 1911. He was a research fellow in physics at Princeton University in 1912–13, and the following year joined the faculty of Clark University where he became a full professor in 1919.

Writing about his graduation in 1904 from South High School in Worcester, Dr. Goddard remarked:

> "On graduating from the High School, I happened to be chosen from among the boys to give the oration in Mechanics Hall, Worcester. The subject I chose was "On Taking Things for Granted." After mentioning some of the mechanical and electrical developments that had at first seemed impossible, I gave at length Pickering's results which had shown the existence of vegetation on the moon. The oration closed with the thought that it is difficult to say just what is impossible, for 'the dream of yesterday is the hope of today and the reality of tomorrow.'"

ROBERT FROST

(No. 654)

OBV. ROBERT FROST. Bust of Mr. Frost.

REV. Around the border: IN THE NAME OF CONGRESS TO ROBERT FROST IN RECOGNITION OF HIS POETRY WHICH HAS ENRICHED THE CULTURE OF THE UNITED STATES AND THE PHILOSOPHY OF THE WORLD.

THE GIFT OUTRIGHT

The land was ours
Before we were the land's.
She was our land more than a hundred years
Before we were her people.

She was ours in Massachusetts, in Virginia.
But we were England's—still colonials.
Possessing what we still were unpossessed by.
Possessed by what we now no more possess.

Something we were withholding made us weak
Until we found out that it was ourselves we were withholding from our land of living.
And forthwith found salvation in surrender.

Such as we were we gave ourselves outright.
(The deed of gift was many deeds of war)
To the land vaguely realizing westward.
But still unstoried, artless, unenhanced.

Such as she was,
Such as she would become.

By Engelhardus von Hebel.

On September 13, 1960, the Congress authorized the presentation of a gold medal to Robert Frost "in recognition of his poetry, which has enriched the culture of the United

States and the philosophy of the world." Bronze copies of this medal were authorized for reproduction by the act of May 25, 1961.

Robert Frost was born in San Francisco, Calif., on March 26, 1874. After his father's death in 1895, Frost's family moved to Salem, N.H. Frost graduated from Lawrence High School in 1892 as valedictorian and class poet. He enrolled at Dartmouth College but left early in his freshman year. During the next 2 or 3 years he worked in mills in Lawrence, tried newspaper reporting, taught school and wrote some poetry. In 1895 he married Elinor White and for more than 2 years helped his mother manage a small private school in Lawrence. In 1897 he enrolled as a special student at Harvard, planning to qualify for college teaching and continued his studies there until 1899, when he made up his mind to abandon the academic career and establish himself in the business of raising hens and selling eggs.

In 1900 Frost moved to a farm in Derry, N.H., where he continued poultry farming, with ill success, until 1909. From 1906 to 1911 he taught English at Pinkerton Academy, in Derry, and for the academic year 1911–12 he was teacher of psychology at the State Normal School, Plymouth, N.H. In 1912 he decided to stake his future on his poetry, rather than on farming or teaching, and took his wife and four children to England. There he rented a house in Beaconsfield, Buckinghamshire, where they lived until their return to the United States, early in 1915.

It was during his English stay that Robert Frost achieved his first success, and laid the foundations for his lasting fame, in poetry. His first book of poems, "A Boy's Will" was accepted by the first publisher to whom it was offered, David Nutt, and published in 1913. Brought to immediate widespread notice among poets and critics by the enthusiastic support of Ezra Pound, the book was well received in England. "North of Boston," a book of dramatic dialogues was published in 1914, and achieved such success in England that by 1915 both books had been published in America by Henry Holt, and the Frost family returned to America to find that Robert Frost was firmly established as a poet.

Frost bought a small farm in Franconia, N.H., but found that for the support of his family it was necessary to accept speaking engagements and teaching positions. He traveled frequently and widely, speaking his poetry, and speaking about poetry, to student groups, to organizations and associations, and to general audiences. He was a professor of English at Amherst from 1916 to 1920, again from 1923 to 1925, and again from 1926 to 1938. At the University of Michigan, he was poet in residence from 1921 to 1923, and fellow in letters for the academic year 1925–26. In 1933, he was made associate fellow of Pierson College, Yale. In 1920 he was a cofounder of the Bread Loaf School of English, Middlebury College. Harvard made him a member of the board of overseers for 1938–39, Ralph Waldo Emerson fellow for 1942–43. He was a George Ticknor fellow in humanities, Dartmouth College; was a visiting lecturer in humanities at Dartmouth and Simpson lecturer in Literature at Amherst.

Apart from traveling for his lectures and various periods of college residence, Frost lived chiefly in Vermont from 1919 when he moved his family to South Shaftsbury to 1936, when, on doctor's orders, he began spending the most severe winter months in Florida. Mrs. Frost died in 1938. In 1940 Frost built a bungalow outside Coral Gables and also purchased an upland farm in Ripton, Vt.

For 1958–59 Frost occupied the post of Consultant in English Poetry of the Library of Congress. He later served as honorary Consultant in the Humanities of the Library of Congress for a 3-year term.

Over 40 honorary degrees were conferred on Frost. He spoke at the inauguration of President Kennedy in 1961, and met with Premier Kruschev in the Soviet Union in 1962. He died in Boston, Mass., on January 29, 1963.

DR. THOMAS A. DOOLEY III

(No. 655)

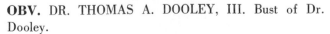

OBV. DR. THOMAS A. DOOLEY, III. Bust of Dr. Dooley.

REV. Dr. Dooley, holding a child, and surrounded by other youngsters; a map of the world in the background. IN RECOGNITION OF THE PUBLIC SERVICE TO ALLEVIATE SUFFERING AMONG PEOPLE OF THE WORLD. TO DR. THOMAS ANTHONY DOOLEY, III. AUTHORIZED BY CONGRESS MAY 27, 1961.

By Frank Gasparro.

The Congress, on May 27, 1961, authorized the presentation of a gold medal posthumously to Dr. Thomas Anthony Dooley III in recognition of the gallant and unselfish public service rendered by him "in serving the medical needs of the people of Laos, living in the remote areas of the Laotian jungles, and of peoples in other newly developing countries."

Dr. Thomas A. Dooley was born in St. Louis, Mo., on January 17, 1927. He was one of four sons born to Mr. and Mrs. Thomas A. Dooley. He selected medicine as his career while in high school. He had a year of premedical training at the University of Notre Dame in 1943–44, then served for 2 years, 1944–46, as a Navy corpsman, or medical aide, attached to the U.S. Marine Corps.

He then studied for a year at the Sorbonne, the famous Paris school. He was graduated from the St. Louis University School of Medicine in 1953.

He rejoined the Navy for his internship as a lieutenant, junior grade, and was at first assigned to the Naval Hospital at Camp Pendleton, Calif., and from there, was sent to Japan, where he received an assignment as medical officer aboard the attack transport U.S.S. MONTAGUE.

In May 1954, there began for young Dr. Tom Dooley an experience which was to change the whole course of his life. The MONTAGUE was one of four ships assigned to help in "Passage for Freedom," which comprised the evacuation agreed upon under terms of the Geneva Treaty after the French Indochina war was over.

This was the flight of those who wished to flee from Communist-held northern Vietnam to live in free South Vietnam. Dr. Dooley was assigned as a medical officer at an evacuee staging area set up at Haiphong. The main interest of this medical team was in preventing epidemics and the infestation of the ships being used in the evacuation.

More than 600,000 refugees were processed and cared for at this camp. When Communist demands forced reduction of the medical mission, Dr. Dooley was the only Navy doctor left behind. Enormous as it was, the medical problem involving the refugees was not the only one with which he had to cope.

> "I had to provide shelter and food, sanitation and some human solace to a flood of humanity, undernourished, exhausted, bewildered, and pitifully frightened,"

He wrote, later, in a book about his experiences:

> "My primary task was medical—to stamp out contagious diseases * * * but there was no ducking the huge problems of housekeeping and administration for the shifting camp population, normally between 10,000 and 15,000 persons."

For his extraordinary efforts in this operation, he was awarded the Legion of Merit, becoming the youngest officer in the history of the U.S. Medical Corps to receive it. President Ngo Dinh Diem of Vietnam also awarded him that nation's highest decoration, the National Order of Vietnam.

The assignment also brought a decision for young Dr. Dooley. After seeing the sick and dying in Southeast Asia, observing the amount of preventable disease which could be halted or cured, he felt that his place henceforth was with these people; that he must do what he could do to alleviate some of the suffering among countless millions of underprivileged peoples of the world who have scant hope of any medical care in their lifetime.

Dr. Dooley returned to the United States in 1956 and became a civilian. His book, "Deliver Us From Evil," about the work at Haiphong, became a bestseller. With the proceeds, plus generous help from pharmaceutical companies, he rounded up as his staff three former Navy corpsmen who had worked with him at Haiphong, returned to Southeast Asia and obtained permission from the new government of Laos to establish a small village hospital. It was located at Nam Tha, 5 miles from the border of Communist-held China.

Dr. Dooley turned the Nam Tha hospital over to the Laos Government in late 1957 and returned to the United States, planning to raise funds with which to start another such medical mission. He met with Dr. Peter D. Comanduras, a Washington specialist and medical professor who also had observed the medically underprivileged in other lands and had been working for the acceptance of an international program of direct physician-to-patient medical aid in areas where no facilities existed at all.

Together, these two physicians founded MEDICO (Medical International Cooperation Organization). This vountary, nonpolitical, nonsectarian organization was at first under auspices of the International Rescue Committee, but in late 1959 became a separate entity, incorporated as MEDICO, Inc.

Dr. Dooley's second bestseller book, "The Edge of Tomorrow," was published in May 1958. Proceeds from it, from other writings and a lecture tour went toward the financing of overseas operations begun by MEDICO.

The young doctor returned to Laos to establish another hospital, this one in the remote village of Muong Sing and the first under MEDICO auspices.

Less than 2 years later, by the end of 1960, MEDICO had 17 projects in operation in 12 countries. These included seven hospitals in Southeast Asia—in Laos, Cambodia, Vietnam, and Malaya—and Dr. Dooley had an important role in getting all of them underway. MEDICO established such projects only after the invitation of the host government, and in these instances it was Dr. Dooley who handled, for the most part, all of the necessary preliminary negotiations and the other details concerned with starting these projects.

In August 1959, Dr. Dooley learned that he had a highly malignant (melanoma) cancer of the chest wall and flew to New York to undergo major surgery for its removal at Memorial Hospital.

After a few weeks of convalescence, Dr. Dooley embarked on a nationwide lecture tour which raised nearly a million dollars for MEDICO. He then returned to his Muong Sing hospital and was soon working at his usual pace—which often kept him going 20 hours a day.

On two subsequent trips to the United States within the next 14 months he underwent checkups which showed no recurrence of cancer. On a trip in the spring of 1960 he gave 55 lectures in 30 cities in 34 days.

Then on November 30, 1960, Dr. Dooley entered a hospital in Hong Kong, suffering from what was described as "extreme fatigue and exhaustion." He also suffered severe pain in the lower spinal area but, wearing a brace—which he immediately characterized as his "Iron Maiden"— he left the hospital within a matter of days and attempted to resume his customary arduous schedule.

The pain, however, became progressively worse and he finally gave in to the persuasions of associates and relatives to come home for a new examination and any treatment which might be required.

He arrived on December 27, 1960, and entered a hospital. On January 10, 1961, the attending physician announced that extensive analytical examinations had proved without doubt that this was a recurrence of the previous primary cancer. On January 18, 1961, Dr. Dooley passed away, 1 day after his 34th birthday.

SAM RAYBURN

(No. 656)

OBV. SAM RAYBURN. A full-face likeness of Mr. Rayburn; in the background, the Capitol of the United States. Years of his birth and death: 1882–1961.

By Frank Gasparro.

REV. A gavel, symbol of the Speaker of the House of Representatives. A sprig of Blue Bonnets, the Texas State flower. FOR SERVICES RENDERED TO THE PEOPLE OF THE UNITED STATES.

By Phillip Fowler.

By joint resolution of the Congress, approved September 26, 1962, a gold medal was awarded posthumously to Sam Rayburn, Speaker of the House of Representatives, in recognition of his distinguished public service and outstanding contribution to the general welfare.

Sam Rayburn was born in Roane County, Tenn., on January 6, 1882. He was the eighth of 11 children born to the former Confederate cavalryman, William Marion Rayburn, and his wife, Martha Waller. Christened Samuel Taliaferro, he adopted the short form of his first name, and never used the middle name. When Sam was 5, his father moved the family to a 40-acre cotton farm in Fannin County, Tex., near Bonham. From that time on, Sam counted himself a farmer and a Texan. He attended a little one-room schoolhouse at Flag Springs, and worked on the farm with the rest of the family.

The political life of Sam Rayburn can be dated from the occasion when, at the age of 10, he rode the family horse 12 miles to Bonham to hear Senator Joseph Weldon Bailey speak. By the time he was 13, he had definitely decided on a political career. At 17, he entered East Texas Normal College (now East Texas State College), Commerce, Tex., with a stake of $25 contributed by his father. To pay his way through school, he swept floors, milked cows, and rang the college bell. He dropped out of college for 1 year, and taught, in order to raise enough money to continue and complete his college course, graduating with a B.S. degree.

Upon graduation, he returned to teaching, and then, in 1906, at the age of 24, entered politics by running for the State legislature, his family aiding his campaign. He won, and served in the Texas Legislature for 6 years, from 1907 to 1913, the last 2 years as speaker of the house of representatives. During sessions, he studied law at the University of Texas, and passed the bar examination. In 1912 he ran for office as U.S. Representative from his district in Texas, and was elected, taking his seat in the 63d Congress, which first met in 1913. Thereafter, he was elected to each succeeding Congress through the 87th. From 1931 to 1937 he was chairman of the Committee on Interstate

and Foreign Commerce. In the 75th and 76th Congresses, 1937 to 1940, he was majority leader. On September 16, 1940, he was elected Speaker to fill out the unexpired term of the late Speaker William B. Bankhead, in the 76th Congress, and was reelected Speaker of the 77th, 78th, and 79th Congresses, 1941 to 1947. In the 80th Congress, 1947 to 1949, he was minority leader. In the 81st and 82d Congresses, 1949 to 1953, he was Speaker. He was Democratic leader in the 83d Congress, 1953 to 1955. In the 84th, 85th, 86th, and 87th Congresses, from 1955 to 1961, he was Speaker.

Sam Rayburn served as permanent chairman of the Democratic National Conventions of 1948, 1952, and 1956. In the convention of 1960 he stepped aside in order to work for the nomination of Senator Lyndon Johnson. In his career, Sam Rayburn set many records. At 29, he was the youngest man ever elected speaker of the Texas House of Representatives. When he died, on November 16, 1961, he was 79 years old, and had served in the House of Representatives for 48 years and 8 months.

Rayburn was the author of the Federal Communications Act, the Securities Exchange Act, the Rayburn-Wheeler Holding Company Act, and the Rural Electrification Act.

THE UNITED STATES SECRET SERVICE
100th ANNIVERSARY

(No. 657)

OBV. In the center is displayed a replica of the official U.S. Secret Service badge. Around the border: CENTENNIAL; the anniversary dates 1865–1965; oak leaves separate the two inscriptions.

REV. In the center, the numeral 100; beneath is a shield upon which is shown the Scales of Justice; the wreath of oak leaves and laurel which surrounds the numeral signi-

fies protection and strength. Around the border; above, 1865–1965; below, U.S. SECRET SERVICE.

Designed by Secret Service Staff.

The U.S. Secret Service was created in 1865 as a bureau of the Treasury Department to suppress the counterfeiting of American currency. Since 1865 other duties have been added to the Secret Service jurisdiction, particularly the investigation of offenses against the laws of the United States relating to coins as well as all obligations and securities of the United States and of foreign governments.

The principal mission of the Secret Service today is safeguarding the life of the President of the United States and the members of his immediate family. In addition, protection is afforded by this agency to the President-elect, the Vice President and the Vice President-elect. The Service is also authorized to protect a former President and his wife during his lifetime and the person of a widow and minor children of a former President. In 1968 the Secret Service was directed to provide protection for major presidential and vice presidential candidates. Even more recently the Service has been authorized to protect the former Vice President. Further, in the interest of its protective responsibilities, the Service investigates those individuals and groups that threaten the President. The protective responsibilities of the U.S. Secret Service were assigned to this agency after the assassination of President McKinley in 1901.

The criminal investigative responsibilities of the U.S. Secret Service were first undertaken during the Civil War. At that time it was estimated that one-third of the paper money in circulation (United States Notes and National Bank Notes) was counterfeit. Counterfeiting plants were seized by the score. Counterfeiters ("boodlers" in those days) were caught, convicted and jailed. Respect for the new crime-fighting organization grew, not only in the underworld but also among various departments of the Government. Soon these other departments began to "borrow" Secret Service agents to investigate other crimes. Since there was then no other general Federal law-enforcement agency, it became common practice for the Treasury Department to lend Secret Service agents upon request.

In 1898, during the Spanish-American War, a ring of Spanish spies with headquarters in Canada directed espionage activities against the United States. Secret Service agents borrowed by the Department of Justice set up a counterespionage system and unearthed the enemy's hideout at Montreal. They exposed Lieutenant Roman Carranza, naval attaché of the Spanish legation, as the brains of the net, and Carranza was swiftly banished from the Dominion by its government.

In its early enforcement work the Secret Service was instrumental in smashing the gigantic "Louisiana Lottery," which began operation under a State charter but grew into a major crooked enterprise.

One of the most important assignments ever given the Secret Service was the investigation of extensive land frauds perpetrated upon the Government. By 1905, at the request of the Attorney General of the United States, some 32 Secret Service agents were lent to the Department of Justice to conduct this investigation. The Homestead

Act of 1862 had thrown western lands open to settlement. Through dummy entrymen, several cattle barons obtained rich grazing land intended for homesteaders. Others contrived to get lands rich in coal, oil, and timber, on the claim that the lands were to be used for agriculture. In the course of the investigation, Secret Service Agent Joseph A. Walker was shot in the back with 17 shotgun slugs while he was checking the suspected theft of coal from Government-owned land. Walker's killers were arrested and tried, but were acquitted.

The agents exposed countless frauds and recovered millions of acres of land for the Government, and in the course of their work they obtained indictments against many important and influential persons.

Congress, in 1907, restricted the work of the Secret Service to its Treasury Department duties and prohibited the lending of agents to other Government departments. At that time several Secret Service agents were permanently transferred to the Department of Justice and to other Government departments to form the nuclei around which separate investigative units were established.

With the approach of World War I, President Wilson lifted previous restrictions and directed that the Secret Service be employed to uncover violations of neutrality. Investigation led to George Sylvester Viereck and Dr. Heinrich F. Albert, German propaganda agents. Dr. Albert carried a mysterious brief case which he guarded most carefully. On July 24, 1915, Secret Service Agent Frank Burke followed Dr. Albert as he rode on a Sixth Avenue elevated train in New York City. At the 50th Street Station Albert left his seat to get off the train and forgot his brief case. In a flash Agent Burke grabbed the bag and fled from the train.

The case held papers showing elaborate German plots to influence American public opinion by buying newspapers and magazines. There were plans to organize strikes in munitions plants; to corner the supply of liquid chlorine used for poison gas; to acquire the Wright Aeroplane Co. and its patents for German use; to cut off the supply of cotton from England. One sheaf of papers revealed that Germany, through its secret agents, had actually bought a large munitions factory in Bridgeport, Conn., using dummy buyers. The plant accepted orders for ammunition from Great Britain and Russia without any intention of making deliveries.

In 1924, at the suggestion of President Coolidge, the Secret Service was assigned to investigate the Teapot Dome oil scandals, and its agents worked for some 3 years before their association with the investigation became known.

The Secret Service also supervises the White House Police and the Treasury Guard Force.

The White House Police Force is supervised and directed by the Director of the Secret Service. These uniformed officers are charged with the protection of the Executive Mansion and the grounds in the District of Columbia, also with any building in which White House offices are located and with the protection of the President and members of his immediate family. Members of the White House Police also receive special training in many fields.

The Treasury Guard Force is commanded by a Captain who is under the supervision of the Director of the United States Secret Service. The Guard Force is responsible for the safety of many billions of dollars in currency, bonds, and other securities in the Treasury Building and its vaults. These guards are trained in the use of all types of firearms, in self-defense, first aid and firefighting.

The Secret Service, in addition to protecting the President of the United States and others, has over the years protected priceless objects.

In December 1941 the Secret Service was chosen to safeguard the originals of America's priceless historical documents, including the Declaration of Independence, the Constitution of the United States, the Gutenberg Bible, Lincoln's Second Inaugural Address, and the Lincoln Cathedral copy of the Magna Carta. Under Secret Service protection these famous documents were taken from the Library of Congress in Washington to a place of safety and were returned to Washinton by the Secret Service near the war's end.

The Secret Service was also in charge of protecting the United Nations Charter when it was moved in April 1945 from San Francisco to the State Department in Washington, D.C.

The most recent protective assignment of this type, by request of the President of the United States, was safeguarding the priceless painting "Mona Lisa" by Leonardo Da Vinci, during its stay in the United States from December 1962 to March 1963.

KITTANNING DESTROYED

(No. 428)

OBV. KITTANNING DESTROYED BY COL. ARMSTRONG SEPTEMBER, 1756. Log cabin village in flames; to the right the Allegheny River; in foreground an officer accompanied by two men, points to a soldier firing under cover of a tree; an Indian falling on the bank of the river.

REV. THE GIFT OF THE CORPORATION OF THE CITY OF PHILADELPHIA. A shield consisting of four devices: a ship represented under full sail; an evenly balanced pair of scales; a sheaf of wheat; and two hands joined.

This medal was struck by the Corporation of the City of Philadelphia to commemorate Col. John Armstrong's destruction of Kittanning. Each of the commissioned officers in the engagement received one of these medals in silver. The dies were made by Edward Duffield, a clock and watchmaker of Philadelphia, and are now in the U.S. Mint where bronze restrikes are made.

Numerous raids upon white settlements originated from the Indian village of Kittanning, a headquarters for scalping parties. This settlement lies about 25 miles above Pittsburgh; it was ruled by a Chief Jacob. Determined to put an end to the attacks, a volunteer militia was organized by Benjamin Franklin, and a line of forts constructed to keep the Indians in check. Finally, Col. John Armstrong of Carlisle, Pa., with a force of 300 men marched to Kittanning on September 8, 1756. They surprised the village at 3 o'clock in the morning and offered quarter to the Indians, which was refused. Armstrong then ordered the village to be set on fire. Thirty or forty Indians were killed in the raid and 11 English prisoners were released.

Armstrong's successful attack on Kittanning was one of the few outstanding British successes in the early part of the French and Indian War. Henceforth, Armstrong was often styled the "Hero of Kittanning."

CORNELIUS VANDERBILT

(No. 523)

OBV. A GRATEFUL COUNTRY TO HER GENEROUS SON CORNELIUS VANDERBILT. Bust of Commodore Vanderbilt. By S. Ellis.

REV. America, with sword and shield of the United States, to whom a kneeling figure wearing a mural crown presents a trident and ship's prow. An American eagle, and a steamship. *In exergue:* BIS DAT QUI TEMPORE DAT (He gives twice who gives in time).

By S. Ellis (sculptor) and E. Leutze (designer).

By resolution of the Congress, approved March 17, 1862, a gold medal was awarded to Commodore Cornelius Vanderbilt "who did, during the spring of 1862, make a free gift to his imperilled country of his new and staunch steamship 'Vanderbilt' of five thousand tons burthen, built by him with the greatest care, of the best materials, at a cost of eight hundred thousand dollars, which steamship has ever since been actively employed in the service of the republic against the rebel devastations of her commerce."

In a letter of May 3, 1866, to the Secretary of War, Commodore Vanderbilt told of the circumstances which gave rise to the presentation of his vessel:

"On the 16th of March 1862, I received at my residence in this city (New York) a letter from the War Department enquiring if I would undertake to prevent the Confederate steamer "Merrimac" from coming out of the harbor of Norfolk, and urging my immediate attention, as the danger was most imminent and "there was no time to be lost." I answered by telegraph that I would go to Washington the next day. On the morning of the 17th of March I called at the War Department, where I saw for the first

time Mr. Stanton, the Secretary of War. He requested me to accompany him to the executive mansion, where I was introduced to Mr. Lincoln, to whom I was then personally a stranger. The President asked me if I thought I could, with the aid of my steamships, do anything to prevent the "Merrimac" from getting out of Hampton Roads. I replied to him that it was my opinion that if the steamship "Vanderbilt" was there properly manned, the "Merrimac" would not venture to come out, or if she did, the chances were ten to one that the "Vanderbilt" would sink and destroy her. Mr. Lincoln asked me to name the sum of money for which I would undertake the service; I replied to him that nothing would induce me to become a speculator upon the necessities of the government, and that I would not mention a sum as the value of her charter, but that I would make a gift of her to the government for the service proposed. The President replied, "I accept her." I left him promising that the "Vanderbilt" should be at Fortress Monroe properly equipped and officered under my direction within three or four days at the farthest, and she was there within the time. The requisite instrument of transfer was subsequently executed by me and transmitted to the War Department."

Cornelius Vanderbilt was born on Staten Island, N.Y., May 27, 1794, Living in New York City, he engaged in the shipping business, in which, by his energy and perseverance, he in time acquired wealth, and became owner of several lines of steamers, running from New York to places along the coast. In 1851 he established a line of steamers to California, and in 1855 another to Europe. He was made president of the New York & Harlem Railroad

Co. in May 1863; of the Hudson River Railroad Co. in June 1865; and of the New York Central Railroad Co. in December 1867. In November 1869, the two last were consolidated, with a joint capital of $90 million. He died in the city of New York, January 4, 1877. Cornelius Vanderbilt was, at the time of his death, one of the richest men in the world. Among his charities was a gift of $1 million to the "Central University of the Methodist Episcopal Church, South," in Nashville, Tenn., which, in consequence of this munificence, was named, in honor of him, Vanderbilt University. He was known by the sobriquet of "Commodore."

WRECK OF THE STEAMSHIP SAN FRANCISCO

(No. 525)

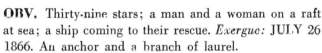

OBV. Thirty-nine stars; a man and a woman on a raft at sea; a ship coming to their rescue. *Exergue:* JULY 26 1866. An anchor and a branch of laurel.

REV. BY JOINT RESOLUTION OF CONGRESS TO THE RESCUERS OF THE PASSENGERS OFFICERS AND MEN OF STEAMSHIP SAN FRANCISCO WRECKED DEC. 1853. TESTIMONIAL OF NATIONAL GRATITUDE FOR HIS GALLANT CONDUCT.

America, personified as a female, seated, and with the eagle, fasces and shield at her left, crowns a sailor with a wreath of laurel; the U.S. Capitol and a ship at anchor.

By Anthony C. Paquet.

By resolution of the Congress, approved July 26, 1866, gold medals were awarded to Captain Creighton of the ship, THREE BELLS of Glasgow; one to Captain Low of the bark KILBY of Boston, and one to Captain Stouffer of the ship ANTARCTIC as testimonials of national gratitude "for their gallant conduct in rescuing about five hundred Americans from the wreck of the steamship San Francisco."

The SAN FRANCISCO, a new ship, left the Port of New York on December 22, 1853, under the command of Captain Watkins. Aboard the ship were about 550 U.S. troops of the 3d Regiment, U.S. Artillery, in addition to 150 other passengers.

While off Charleston, S.C., on December 24, the ship encountered a northwest wind which soon increased to gale force. The following evening, heavy seas washed about 150 of the troops overboard. The ship opened in the seams, over the wales a large portion of the quarterdeck was stove in, and it was only by the greatest exertion that she was kept afloat. On December 27, a disease resembling Asiatic cholera broke out. By this time the ship had drifted northward and was nearly opposite to Boston. On board, all was confusion and consternation.

The bark KILBY, from New Orleans, Captain Low, which, although herself suffering for lack of provisions, had remained by and relieved the SAN FRANCISCO of her lady passengers on December 29. A few days later the THREE BELLS, Captain Creighton, arrived and after rendering such assistance as it could, it took on as many extra passengers as it could. The remaining passengers were taken on board the ANTARCTIC, from New York, Captain Stouffer, which arrived on January 3, 1854. On board the ARCTIC was Captain Watkins of the ill-fated ship, who was the last to leave his vessel, and which, having been scuttled by his order, went down soon after they left her.

By this disaster and extreme suffering from exposure and starvation, nearly 200 persons perished.

METIS SHIPWRECK

(No. 527)

OBV. A boat engaged in rescue operations; the wreck of the "Metis" in the distance.

REV. BY RESOLUTION OF CONGRESS, FEBRUARY 24, 1843. Within a heavy oak wreath: TO _____ FOR COURAGE AND HUMANITY IN THE SAVING OF LIFE FROM THE WRECK OF THE STEAMER METIS LONG ISLAND SOUND. AUGUST 31, 1872.

By W. and C. Barber

In August 1872, the steamer METIS was passing Long Island Sound on its way up to Stonington when it was run into by a schooner. In the course of 15 or 20 minutes she went down, endangering the lives of all the passengers. The U.S. Revenue steamer MOCCASIN, in the neighborhood, immediately went to the distressed vessel's assistance. Its commanding officer, Capt. David Ritchie, received the thanks of Congress, and the privilege of appearing on the floor of Congress, by resolution of January 24, 1873, for "devoting himself with the most humane and earnest effort, confronted by danger and suffering, during the day to that work, and finally saving the lives of forty-two persons and rescuing a number of dead bodies."

By resolution of February 24, 1873, gold medals were awarded to Capt. Jared S. Crandall, Albert Crandall, Daniel F. Larkin, Frank Larkin, Byron Green, John D. Harvey, Courtland Gavitt, Eugene Nash, Edwin Nash, and William Nash of the town of Westerly, State of Rhode Island, "who so gallantly volunteered to man the lifeboat and a fishing boat, and saved the lives of thirty-two persons from the wreck of the steamer 'METIS'."

JOHN HORN

(No. 528)

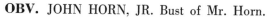

OBV. JOHN HORN, JR. Bust of Mr. Horn.

REV. BY ACT OF CONGRESS JUNE 20th, 1874. Within a wreath of laurel: IN RECOGNITION OF HIS HEROIC EXPLOITS IN RESCUING MEN WOMEN & CHILDREN FROM DROWNING IN DETROIT RIVER.

By C. Barber.

By act of Congress approved June 20, 1874, John Horn, Jr., of Detroit, Mich. was awarded a gold medal "in recognition and in commemoration of his heroic and humane exploits in rescuing men, women and children from drowning in the Detroit River."

In a letter of February 22, 1874, to Congressman Moses W. Field of Detroit, who introduced this legislation, Mr. Horn tells of his experiences, which at the time, made him the foremost lifesaver of the Nation:

"I have never desired a public statement of the service which, under God, I have been able to render in saving human life, but as you have asked me to send you a list of the men, women and children whom I have rescued from drowning, I will do so, so far as I can from memory. I have never kept a record of the names, and the number is so great that you will excuse me if I leave some unmentioned.

"I think I have altogether saved more than one hundred human beings, but I take no credit about this matter, and I have never regretted doing what I have done in any case, although I have had at times to keep my bed for many weeks on account of the exposure in the cold weather. It is well for me that I had a good mother to take care of me at such times of sickness. On the 21st of May, 1863, I saved Mr. Manning, of Windsor; on the 7th of July, 1865, I saved Mr. George Taylor, of New York State; he was very near dead when I got him on the wharf; October 10, 1865, I saved a child of Mr. T. Gorman of Adrian; she was about five years old, and was near drowned when I got her out; December 12, 1865, I saved a son of Mr. Yates,

who kept a clothing store on Jefferson avenue. The night was very cold, a high wind was blowing at the time, and he was very near dead when we reached the wharf.

"April 11, 1866, was the worst night I ever had. It will be ever memorable as the night of the great conflagration at the Detroit and Milwaukee Railroad depot, when sixteen poor fellows were drowned. I rescued nine, and then became so exhausted that I could not swim, and had to abandon them to their fate. I got a very bad cold and lay in bed two weeks, but that was nothing in comparison to the good accomplished. July 25, 1866, I saved Mr. Joseph Noble, of Windsor, and I believe you were there at the time. He was once engineer on the Great Western Railroad. You know he came near drowning me in his struggles in the water, at which time I received several internal injuries. April 7, 1867, I saved the son of Mr. C. Meyers, who lived in Mullet street. He was a boy about twelve years old. June 14, 1867, I saved the daughter of Mr. Andrew Nourse, of Cleveland. She was going on board the ferry-boat with her mother and some other ladies, when she fell off the plank. When I got to the wharf she was going out of sight for the last time, and I plunged in and brought her to the surface. September 15, 1867, I saved a colored man who was a deck hand on the propeller Meteor. He kicked me about in the water terribly, for drowning men are always crazy. November 2, 1867, I saved Mr. David Miller, the man who drove a wagon for Hull Brothers, storekeepers on Munroe avenue. May 10, 1868, I saved Mr. Robert Sinton, known as "Free Press Bob." You know he used to be a reporter for the "Free Press." And in his haste to get news, he fell in, and I got him out.

"A few nights after that I saved Mr. Steele, who used to keep a store on Michigan avenue. He was on the ferry-boat with his wife; he had a very spirited horse, and was holding him by the head when the boat struck the wharf. The horse jumped and threw him into the river, when the current swept him under the wharf. I jumped in and got him out all right. October 4, 1868, I saved a daughter of Mr. McDonald, of Windsor. May 11, 1869, I saved Mr. Flattery, one of the Flattery Brothers who kept a furniture store on Woodward avenue. He was a heavy man; when I got hold of him he was near gone, and I came near losing my own life in getting him out. June 21, 1870, I saved a man called Mr. George Brodier. I was eating dinner at the time, when some persons came running in after me, saying, "there is a man in the river." I ran out and jumped into the river, and as soon as I got near him he clutched me like a vice and took me under water twice. When I came to the top the last time my father handed me a large pole, which I caught and that saved me. He was a powerful man, and kicked and struggled so hard that he made my legs black and blue for many months.

"My mother goes to the edge of the wharf with me very often, when I jump in; but when she sees persons struggling in the water and drowning she never holds me back. August 24, 1871, I saved the daughter of Mr. A. Wilson of Milwaukee. March 4, 1872, I saved a colored man by the name of George Wilkes; he fell off the wharf while under the influence of liquor; but I think he has been a sober man ever since. July 4, 1873, I saved the daughter of Mr. F. Barlow, a butcher, who keeps a stall in the market. She was going on board the ferry-boat Detroit with her mother and some other ladies; the crowd was great, being the Fourth of July, and although her mother held her by the hand, the crowd surged, and she was crowded off the plank, and fell into the river. There were about five hundred people on the wharf at the time, and they were all staring at the poor girl struggling in the water, not one of them daring to go to her rescue. I was in the house when some one came to give the alarm, and when I got out there I could just see her dress as she was going out of sight, four or five feet below the surface. I jumped in and caught her, and when I got out on the top of the wharf with her the people gave me three cheers. March 6, 1873, I saved a young lady called Miss Louise McKenzie. This was the closest call I ever had for my life. I was in the water about seventeen minutes, and the river being full of floating ice at the time, I was nearer dead than alive when I got out. Four men carried me into the house, and they rubbed me with hot whisky for over four hours before circulation was restored to its normal condition. This severe exposure made me sick, and it was over three months before the right feeling was in my hand."

John Horn, Jr. was born at Sidmouth, Devonshire, England, on September 7, 1843. At the age of 11 he emigrated to America with his parents and settled in Detroit, Mich. He grew up on the docks at the foot of Woodward Avenue in Detroit, where his father had a ferry and tugboat business. After his father's death in 1897, he continued in this business. When the Congress approved the lifesaving medal in 1874, President Grant strongly favored pensioning Mr. Horn, saying that such heroism should not pass unrewarded. The pension was declined by Mr. Horn.

In later years, Mr. Horn was active in the civic life of Detroit; he served as deputy sheriff, alderman and as president of the Board of Health, and was prominent in fraternal circles, being a 32d degree Mason.

DWIGHT D. EISENHOWER

(No. 133)

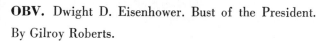

OBV. Dwight D. Eisenhower. Bust of the President.

By Gilroy Roberts.

REV. The figure of Freedom which stands on the dome of the U.S. Capitol. The scene to the right of the figure represents the eastern half of the United States, with the farmer plowing the soil and city buildings visible beyond the hills. To the left are the pioneering forefathers, blazing the westward trail in covered wagons, the Rocky Mountains in the background. Under the frieze is the inscription. United States of America; around the rim: Inaugurated President January 20, 1953.

By Frank Gasparro.

LYNDON B. JOHNSON

OBV. Bust of the President. LYNDON B. JOHNSON.

By Gilroy Roberts.

REV. An adaptation of the Seal of the President of the United States. PRESIDENT OF THE UNITED STATES. Beneath the eagle in the Presidential Seal, November 22, 1963, the date upon which the President took office. An inscription from the President's address before the Joint Session of Congress November 27, 1963: "WE WILL SERVE ALL THE NATION,—A UNITED PEOPLE WITH A UNITED PURPOSE. Lydon B. Johnson."

By Frank Gasparro.

HISTORY OF THE UNITED STATES
PRESIDENTIAL MEDAL SERIES

Many of the medals which are now included in the U.S. Mint's presidential series were made originally for presentation to American Indian chiefs and warriors. The Spanish, the French, and the British had presented medals to the Indians, and the British especially had produced large and magnificent silver medals, each bearing the likeness of the reigning monarch on one side and his coat of arms on the other. The British medals were solid silver, impressed in clear relief, and were given to the Indian chiefs as marks of friendship and special recognition. They were highly prized by the Indians, who not only delighted in the decorative aspects of the medals but who also esteemed the honor that was signified by possession of a medal bearing the likeness of the Great White Father.

When the United States replaced the British in dealing with the Indians, the new government found that it was necessary to continue the practice of presenting medals if it hoped to have peaceful relations with the tribes and influence with the chiefs. The Federal Government, then, began the production of Indian peace medals, which became a settled and extremely important part of American Indian policy.

As early as 1787, Henry Knox, the Secretary of War under the Articles of Confederation, urged Congress to comply with the request of the Indians for "medals, gorgets, wrist and arm bands with the arms of the United States impressed or engraved thereon." Congress was pressed for funds, but Knox noted that the Indians would turn in their British medals, which could be melted down to produce new ones. Thomas Jefferson, as Secretary of State, outlined the policy behind the distribution of medals to the Indians; he spoke of it as "an ancient custom from time immemorial." The medals, he said, "are considered as complimentary things, as marks of friendship to those who come to see us, or who do us good offices, conciliatory of their good will toward us, and not designed to produce a contrary disposition towards others. They confer no power, and seem to have taken their origin in the European practice, of giving medals or other marks of friendship to the negotiators of treaties and other diplomatic characters, or visitors of distinction."

Whatever the origin, the practice took firm hold in the United States. Medals were given to Indian chiefs on important occasions, such as the signing of a treaty, a visit of important Indians to the national capital, or a tour of the Indian country by some Federal official. Lewis and Clark on their famous exploratory expedition to the Pacific coast in 1804–06 carried along a large supply of medals, which they handed out with impressive ceremonies to important chiefs along the way. Indian agents on the frontier distributed the medals to their charges, in recognition of friendship and peace with the United States. These Indian agents or treaty negotiators used their own discretion in making the presentations, but they were guided by fixed norms. In 1829, in fact, Lewis Cass, Governor of Michigan Territory, and William Clark, Superintendent of Indian Affairs at St. Louis, drew up a series of regulations for the governing of the Indian Department, including rules for the presentation of medals. What these two experienced Indian agents set down in their proposed regulations represented the practice that they had observed on the frontier:

"In the distribution of medals and flags, the following rules will be observed:

"1. They will be given to influential persons only.

"2. The largest medals will be given to the principal village chiefs, those of the second size will be given to the principal war chiefs, and those of the third size to the less distinguished chiefs and warriors.

"3. They will be presented with proper formalities, and with an appropriate speech, so as to produce a proper impression upon the Indians.

"4. It is not intended that chiefs should be appointed by an officer of the department, but that they should confer these badges of authority upon such as are selected or recognized by the tribe, and as are worthy of them, in the manner heretofore practised.

"5. Whenever a foreign medal is worn, it will be replaced by an American medal, if the Agent should consider the person entitled to a medal."

The Indians expected to receive medals, and it was impossible to conduct Indian affairs without the use of them. Thomas L. McKenney, head of the Office of Indian Affairs, in 1829 wrote to the Secretary of War about the policy of distributing medals. "So important is its continuance esteemed to be," he said, "that without medals, any plan of operations among the Indians, be it what it may, is essentially enfeebled. This comes of the high value which the Indians set upon these tokens of Friendship. They are, besides this indication of the Government Friendship, badges of power to them, and trophies of renown. They will not consent to part from this ancient *right,* as they esteem it; and according to the value they set upon medals is the importance to the Government in having them to bestow."

The U.S. Government took great pains to produce medals for the Indians of real artistic merit. This cultural concern is surprising in a young nation trying to establish

335-478 O - 69 - 18

itself in a troubled world. Yet the medals which were made in the early years of the Nation's existence are collectors' items, not only because of the history associated with them, but also because of their artistic value. And this was a conscious policy. About one of the medals, McKenney wrote: "I am certainly anxious that these medals should be as perfect in their resemblance of the original, as the artist can make them. They are intended, not for the Indians, only, but for posterity."

The medals given to the Indians were supposed to bear the likeness of the President currently in office, and the medals can be traced administration by administration.

The Washington medals were unique. The Government presented a number of medals to Indian chiefs during Washington's term of office, but it did not mass produce the medals—undoubtedly because it did not command the technical means to do so. Instead, each medal was a separate production, hand engraved on oval plates of silver, the large ones roughly 4 by 6 inches in size. On one side was engraved the figure of Washington with that of an Indian in the peaceful gesture of throwing away his tomahawk. On the reverse was an eagle bearing the crest of the United States on its breast, with an olive branch in its right talon, a sheaf of arrows in its left. The plate was bound with a silver band and provided with a loop at the top by which it could be hung around the neck of the chief. The most famous of these Washington Indian medals was the one presented to the Seneca chief, Red Jacket, in 1792. The medal of Washington in today's presidental series, however, was designed to match later Indians medals and was not made until early in the 20th century.

No medals for Indians were made while John Adams was President. Medals distributed to the chiefs during his term of office were the so-called Seasons Medals, which had been produced in England during Washington's second administration. They showed scenes of a farmer sowing grain, women spinning and weaving, and domestic cattle, which were supposed to incite in the Indians a desire for white civilization. Later a John Adams medal similar in design to other Indian peace medals was struck in order to make the presidential series complete.

The production of Indian peace medals began to be regularized during the administration of President Thomas Jefferson. The pattern for the medals was more or less established, although the methods of manufacture were still not quite set. Medals in three sizes were ordered—large (4 inches in diameter), medium (3 inches), and small (2 inches). The medals were struck from dies cut by a special engraver who worked directly in the steel of the die, cutting out the features that would appear in relief on the finished medal. On the obverse was a bust of Jefferson in profile, with a legend which read: TH. JEFFERSON PRESIDENT OF THE U.S. A.D. 1801. On

the reverse were two hands clasped, one with a cuff showing three stripes and three buttons, the other wearing a bracelet engraved with a spread eagle. A crossed peace pipe and tomahawk and the words PEACE AND FRIENDSHIP completed the design.

One feature of the Jefferson medals distinguished them from later medals. They were hollow shells rather than solid medals. Possibly because there was no press in the country at the time powerful enough to strike the medals from solid discs of silver, two thin plates were used. The obverse and reverse of the medals were struck separately, then fastened together with a silver band to form a hollow medal. It was a satisfactory expedient as far as the appearance of the medal was concerned, but the Indians compared them unfavorably with the heavy medals they were accustomed to receive from the British. The Jefferson medal issued today by the mint in the presidential series is a solid medal which follows the 3-inch design of the original medals.

When James Madison succeeded Jefferson in 1809, new medals had to be designed and struck. The task of ordering the medals fell to John Mason, who held the office of Superintendent of Indian Trade. He turned to a friend in Philadelphia, John Vaughan, to engage an artist and to oversee the production of the medals at the mint. Mason insisted that the hollow medals be replaced by solid ones, and the mint undertook to strike such medals. The Madison medals, like the Jefferson ones, came in three sizes, although the diameters—3, 2½, and 2 inches—differed from those of the Jefferson medals. They were solid silver, and at the suggestion of Vaughan, the reverse had a slightly changed design. Vaughan objected to having both the wrists encuffed as they appeared on the Jefferson medals. This, he said, did not indicate the diversity of the races who were joined in the handclasp of friendship. He had the artist leave one of the arms bare, and this new design was used repeatedly until completely new designs were substituted for the reverse of the medals in the 1850's and later. Mason asked that the lettering on both sides of the medal be "so arranged that a small hole may be made through the medal exactly over the head of the President (so as to suspend it erect when worn by the Chiefs) without interfering with the letters." But for some unaccountable reason this wise advice was never heeded.

When it was time to have medals struck for President James Monroe, both the man directing the work and the artist-engraver were new. Thomas L. McKenney had replaced John Mason as Superintendent of Indian Trade, and Moritz Fürst was engaged in place of John Reich, who had engraved the Madison medals. The general form of the medals, nevertheless, followed the set formula. Fürst prepared satisfactory likenesses of Monroe on the three sizes of the medals, and the dies of the previous reverse were used again.

Fürst was engaged, also, to make the medals of Presidents John Quincy Adams, Andrew Jackson, and Martin Van Buren. These medals, like those that followed, were ordered by the head of the Indian Office (the Commissioner of Indian Affairs, after that office was created in 1832), who was the official responsible for the distribution of the medals to the chiefs. It was the custom to order 100 of each of the three sizes, although from time to time not all the medals were given out during the administration they represented. Rather than give the Indian chiefs medals of a previous administration, with the portrait of a Great White Father who was no longer in office, medals left over at the end of a President's tenure were regularly melted down to help provide the silver needed for the new medals.

As the series of medals progressed, they began to be considered as "Presidential Medals," quite apart from their original purpose as Indian peace medals. Franklin Peale, who became Chief Coiner at the mint in 1839, believed that the mint should be the depository of dies of all national medals, and he urged that medals missing from the presidential series (for example, one for John Adams) be supplied. He was supported by Robert M. Patterson, Director of the Mint, who in 1841 suggested making a medal of President William Henry Harrison, whose term had been too short to permit of making Indian medals bearing his portrait. Nothing came of the proposals at the time, however.

When it came time to prepare medals for President John Tyler, technical advances had taken some of the difficulties out of medal making. The invention in France of a "portrait lathe," a mechanical means of cutting dies did away with the need for the special engraver. A medallion of the President could now be modelled in wax, with full possibilities for making corrections until a suitable likeness was obtained. From this, by use of an intermediate plaster cast, a casting in fine iron was made of the medallion. With the use of the steam-powered lathe, reduced facsimilies were turned out in steel, and the lettering was then stamped in.

The new machine at the mint was used for making the dies of the President John Tyler Indian peace medal from a medallion modeled by Ferdinand Pettrich, the President James K. Polk medal from a model made by the artist John Gadsby Chapman, and the President Zachary Taylor medal from a medallion sculptured by Henry Kirke Brown. The portrait lathe was adjusted to make the various sizes of the dies from the same model, so that all three sizes of these medals are identical and do not show the variations that occurred in the earlier medals, when the dies were cut individually by hand.

The next medals were again made from dies cut by engravers, who signed contracts with the Commissioner of Indian Affairs to engrave the dies and strike the medals for presentation to the Indians. The two young New York artists who were engaged were Salathiel Ellis and Joseph Willson. Ellis engraved the dies for the portraits of Presidents Millard Fillmore, Franklin Pierce, James Buchanan, and Abraham Lincoln, while Willson made the reverses for the medals. The old peace and friendship design which had been used for so many years on the reverse of the medals was now laid aside, and scenes depicting the adoption of civilization were used instead. One such design was used on the reverse of the Fillmore and Pierce medals, another on the Buchanan and Lincoln Indian peace medals. For these medals only the large and medium size were made; the small size was discontinued.

Copies of the medals designed for presentation to the Indians from Jefferson to Buchanan are issued by the mint in bronze as part of the presidential series, uniformly now in the 3-inch size, although in past times the smaller sizes as well were reproduced. With President Buchanan, however, the presidential series begins to diverge from the Indian peace medal series. The Buchanan medal uses the reverse from the Fillmore and Pierce medals, instead of the one designed for it by Willson, and the Lincoln medal in the mint presidential series is an inaugural medal, not the one designed for presentation to the Indian chiefs.

The Indian peace medal for President Andrew Johnson's administration was engraved by Anthony Paquet. He had begun to make the medal for presentation to Indians during Lincoln's second administration and changed the obverse to show the bust of Johnson after Lincoln's assassination. The reverse was a completely new design, one suggested by the Commissioner of Indian Affairs to show the change from Indian culture to white civilization. This medal became part of the presidential series.

Although the presidential series for presidents following Andrew Johnson are not those made for the Indians, special peace medals continued to be produced for each administration up to and including that of President Benjamin Harrison. That for President Ulysses S. Grant was made by Paquet and was struck in only one size, $2\frac{1}{2}$ inches in diameter. Those for Presidents Rutherford B. Hayes, James A. Garfield, Chester A. Arthur, and Grover Cleveland were oval medals measuring 3 by $2\frac{1}{4}$ inches and on the reverse showed an Indian and a white man in a rural scene. They were designed by the engravers in the mint, Charles E. Barber and George T. Morgan. For Benjamin Harrison, both an oval and a round Indian peace medal were made. Only small numbers of these later medals were struck in silver, for the Indian tribes were no longer treated as sovereign nations, and the importance of the chiefs in dealings with the U.S. Government had declined. Bronze copies of all these Indian medals are available in the mint's miscellaneous series.

Many persons today who collect these medals do not realize that the medals are relics of our Indian policy and that the early medals were designed and produced exclusively to provide suitable symbols of peace and friendship for the Indian chiefs. But in a sense, Thomas L. McKenney's prophecy has come true. These medals were indeed designed "not for the Indians only, but for posterity."

ACKNOWLEDGMENTS

The Bureau of the Mint gratefully acknowledges the contribution of Michael Di Biase, American Numismatic Society, New York, who photographed the medals which appear in this catalogue, and whose society furnished the photographs as a public service to the Government.

To Phyllis H. Huie goes special thanks for typing and editing this catalogue.

Extensive aid in the preparation of the manuscript for the U.S. Navy medals was provided by the Department of the Navy. This was accomplished under the direction of Rear Admiral Ernest M. Eller, USN (Ret.), Director of the Division of Naval History, by Dr. William J. Morgan, Head of Historical Research, and his assistants, Lieutenant Patrick A. Lyons, USNR, and Lieutenant Commander Harold C. Wayte, USNR. Special appreciation goes, also, to Colonel H. A. Schmidt, Chief, Historical Services Division, Office of the Chief of Military History, Department of the Army for reviewing the manuscript on the U.S. Army medals.

Background material on the Revolutionary War was drawn from *Colonials and Patriots,* by Sarles and Shedd, published by the National Parks Service, and which is available from the Government Printing Office.

The chapter on the history of the Presidential Medal Series was prepared by The Reverend Francis Paul Prucha, S.J., Professor of History at Marquette University. Father Prucha is preparing a book-length historical study of U.S. Indian Peace Medals and their use in American Indian policy.

271

INDEX

Price List of Bronze Medals

For Sale by United States Mint, Philadelphia, Pa. 19106

The prices listed herein include all packing costs and shipping charges.

Remittance in the form of—
  U.S. money order
  Certified personal check
  Bank cashier's check

Express or bank money order must accompany all orders. Please make remittances payable to the "Superintendent, United States Mint, Philadephia."

All sales are final. Medals may not be returned for exchange or refund.

Presidential

No.		Price
☐ 101	George Washington	$3.00
☐ 102	John Adams	3.00
☐ 103	Thomas Jefferson	3.00
☐ 104	James Madison	3.00
☐ 105	James Monroe	3.00
☐ 106	John Quincy Adams	3.00
☐ 107	Andrew Jackson	3.00
☐ 108	Martin Van Buren	3.00
☐ 109	William Henry Harrison	3.00
☐ 110	John Tyler	3.00
☐ 111	James K. Polk	3.00
☐ 112	Zachary Taylor	3.00
☐ 113	Millard Fillmore	3.00
☐ 114	Franklin Pierce	3.00
☐ 115	James Buchanan	3.00
☐ 116	Abraham Lincoln	3.00
☐ 117	Andrew Johnson	3.00
☐ 118	Ulysses S. Grant	3.00
☐ 119	Rutherford B. Hayes	3.00
☐ 120	James A. Garfield	3.00
☐ 121	Chester A. Arthur	3.00
☐ 122	Grover Cleveland	3.00
☐ 123	Benjamin Harrison	3.00
☐ 124	William McKinley	3.00
☐ 125	Theodore Roosevelt	3.00
☐ 126	William H. Taft	3.00
☐ 127	Woodrow Wilson	3.00
☐ 128	Warren G. Harding	3.00
☐ 129	Calvin Coolidge	3.00
☐ 130	Herbert Hoover	3.00
☐ 131	Franklin D. Roosevelt	3.00
☐ 132	Harry S. Truman	3.00
☐ 134	Dwight D. Eisenhower	3.00
☐ 135	John F. Kennedy	3.00
☐ 137	Lyndon B. Johnson	3.00
☐ 138	Richard M. Nixon	3.00

Secretaries of the Treasury

No.		Price
☐ 201	Alexander Hamilton	3.00
☐ 202	William Windom	3.00
☐ 203	John G. Carlisle	3.00
☐ 204	Daniel Manning	3.00
☐ 205	Lyman J. Gage	3.00
☐ 206	Leslie M. Shaw	3.00
☐ 207	George B. Cortelyou	3.00
☐ 208	Franklin MacVeagh	3.00
☐ 209	William McAdoo	3.00
☐ 210	Carter Glass	3.00
☐ 211	Andrew W. Mellon	3.00

Secretaries of the Treasury—Con.

No.		Price
☐ 212	Ogden L. Mills	$3.00
☐ 213	William H. Woodin	3.00
☐ 214	Henry Morgenthau, Jr	3.00
☐ 215	Fred M. Vinson	3.00
☐ 216	John W. Snyder	3.00
☐ 217	George M. Humphrey	3.00
☐ 218	Robert B. Anderson	3.00
☐ 219	Douglas Dillon	3.00
☐ 220	Henry H. Fowler	3.00
☐ 221	Albert Gallatin	3.00
☐ 222	Joseph W. Barr	3.00

Directors of the Mint

No.		Price
☐ 301	David Rittenhouse, Philadelphia, Pa	3.00
☐ 302	Robert M. Patterson, Philadelphia, Pa	3.00
☐ 303	J. Ross Snowden, Philadelphia, Pa	3.00
☐ 304	James Pollock, Philadelphia, Pa	3.00
☐ 305	Henry R. Linderman, Washington, D.C	3.00
☐ 306	Horatio C. Burchard, Washington, D.C	3.00
☐ 307	James P. Kimball, Washington, D.C	3.00
☐ 308	Edward O. Leech, Washington, D.C	3.00
☐ 309	Robert E. Preston, Washington, D.C	3.00
☐ 310	George E. Roberts, Washington, D.C	3.00
☐ 311	F. J. H. vonEngelken, Washington, D.C	3.00
☐ 312	Robert W. Woolley, Washington, D.C	3.00
☐ 313	Raymond T. Baker, Washington, D.C	3.00
☐ 314	F. E. Scobey, Washington, D.C	3.00
☐ 315	R. J. Grant, Washington, D.C	3.00
☐ 316	Nellie Tayloe Ross, Washington, D.C	3.00
☐ 317	William H. Brett, Washington. D.C	3.00
☐ 319	Eva Adams, Washington, D.C	3.00

Army

No.		Price
☐ 401	Washington before Boston	$3.75
☐ 402	Maj. Gen. Gates, for Saratoga	3.75
☐ 403	Brig. Gen. Morgan, for Cowpens	3.75
☐ 404	Lt. Col. John E. Howard, for Cowpens	3.50
☐ 405	Lt. Col. W. A. Washington, for Cowpens	3.50
☐ 406	Count DeFleury, for Stony Point	3.50
☐ 407	Maj. Gen. Anthony Wayne, for Stony Point	3.75
☐ 408	Maj. Gen. Nathaniel Greene, for Eutaw Springs	3.75
☐ 409	Maj. Henry Lee, Paulus Hook	3.50
☐ 410	Maj. Gen. Scott, for Chippewa and Niagara	3.75
☐ 411	Maj. Gen. Gaines, for Fort Erie	3.75
☐ 412	Maj. Gen. Porter, for Chippewa, Niagara and Erie	3.75
☐ 413	Maj. Gen. Brown, for Chippewa, Niagara and Erie	3.75
☐ 414	Brig. Gen. Miller, for Chippewa, Niagara and Erie	3.75
☐ 415	Brig. Gen. Ripley, for Chippewa, Niagara and Erie	3.75
☐ 416	Maj. Gen. Macomb, Battle of Plattsburg	3.75
☐ 417	Maj. Gen. Jackson, Battle of New Orleans	3.75
☐ 418	Maj. Gen. Harrison, for Thames	3.75
☐ 419	Gov. Isaac Shelby, for Thames	3.75
☐ 420	Col. George Croghan, for Sandusky	3.75
☐ 421	Maj. Gen. Taylor, for Palo Alto	3.75
☐ 422	Maj. Gen. Taylor, for Monterey	3.75
☐ 423	Maj. Gen. Taylor, for Buena Vista	8.75
☐ 424	Maj. Gen. Scott, for battles in Mexico	8.75
☐ 425	Maj. Gen. Grant	5.00
☐ 427	Maj. Gen. Scott (Commonwealth of Virginia)	8.75

No.	Navy	Price
☐ 501	John Paul Jones, for Serapis	$3.75
☐ 502	Capt. Thomas Truxtun, for action with LaVengeance	3.75
☐ 503	Capt. Preble before Tripoli	3.75
☐ 504	Capt. Hull, for capture of Guerriere	3.75
☐ 505	Capt. Jacob Jones, for capture of Frolic	3.75
☐ 506	Capt. Decatur, for capture of Macedonian	3.75
☐ 507	Capt. Bainbridge, for capture of Java	3.75
☐ 508	Capt. Burrows, for capture of Boxer	3.75
☐ 509	Lt. McCall, for capture of Boxer	3.75
☐ 510	Capt. Perry, capture of British Fleet on Lake Erie	3.75
☐ 511	Capt. Elliott, capture of British Fleet on Lake Erie	3.75
☐ 512	Capt. Lawrence, capture of Peacock	3.75
☐ 513	Capt. Macdonough, capture of British Fleet on Lake Champlain	3.75
☐ 514	Capt. Henley, eagle, capture of British Fleet on Lake Champlain	3.75
☐ 515	Lt. Cassin, capture of British Fleet on Lake Champlain	3.75
☐ 516	Capt. Warrington, capture of Epervier	3.75
☐ 517	Capt. Blakely, capture of Reindeer	3.75
☐ 518	Capt. Biddle, capture of Penguin	3.75
☐ 519	Capt. Stewart, capture of Cyane & Levant	3.75
☐ 520	Rescue of officers and crew of brig Sommers	3.75
☐ 521	Capt. Ingraham	5.00

No.	Navy—Continued	Price
☐ 522	Capt. Perry (State of Pennsylvania) capture of fleet on Lake Erie	$3.50
☐ 522A	Pennsylvania Volunteers, action on Lake Erie	3.75
☐ 526	Commodore M. C. Perry, from merchants of Boston	3.75
☐ 529	Lt. Victor Blue (State of South Carolina)	3.50
☐ 532	Departure of American Fleet	3.50
☐ 533	Vice Adm. Hyman George Rickover	3.25

Miscellaneous

No.		Price
☐ 601	Time Increases His Fame	.65
☐ 602	Cabinet Medal	.45
☐ 603	Washington and Jackson	.45
☐ 604	Commencement of Coin Cabinet	2.50
☐ 605	Presidency Relinquished	2.00
☐ 606	Allegiance	.95
☐ 607	Washington and Lincoln	.45
☐ 608	Washington and Grant	.45
☐ 609	Washington Wreath	.45
☐ 610	Washington Bicentennial	2.50
☐ 611	James Garfield	.65
☐ 612	Lincoln and Garfield	.45
☐ 613	Pennsylvania Bicentennial	.65
☐ 614	Valley Forge Centennial	2.75
☐ 615	Lincoln and Grant	.45
☐ 616	Lincoln, Broken Column	.45
☐ 617	Japanese Embassy	4.50
☐ 618	Frederick Rose	4.50
☐ 619	Louis Agassiz	4.50
☐ 620	Indian Peace Medal (George II)	2.75
☐ 621	David Hosack	1.00
☐ 622	First Steam Coinage	.65
☐ 623	Union Pacific Railroad	2.75
☐ 624	Emancipation Proclamation	2.75

No.	Miscellaneous—Continued	Price
☐ 625	Cyrus W. Field	$5.00
☐ 626	Joseph Pancoast	4.50
☐ 627	Indian Peace (Grant)	4.00
☐ 628	Hayes, Indian Peace (oval)	4.50
☐ 629	Garfield, Indian Peace	4.50
☐ 630	Arthur, Indian Peace	4.50
☐ 631	Cleveland, Indian Peace	4.50
☐ 632	Harrison, Indian Peace	4.50
☐ 633	Let Us Have Peace (Grant)	2.75
☐ 634	Seward-Robinson	4.00
☐ 635	U.S. Diplomatic (July 4, 1776)	4.00
☐ 636	Great Seal Centennial Medal, 1782–1882	3.25
☐ 637	Joseph Francis	5.00
☐ 638	Lincoln Centennial	4.00
☐ 639	Wright Brothers	4.50
☐ 640	Abraham Lincoln	4.50
☐ 641	Woodrow Wilson	2.00
☐ 645	Charles A. Lindbergh	3.25
☐ 647	Mount Vernon	2.75
☐ 648	Benjamin Franklin	3.25
☐ 649	Franklin D. Roosevelt	3.00
☐ 651	Vice President Alben W. Barkley	3.00
☐ 652	Dr. Jonas E. Salk	3.00
☐ 653	Dr. Robert H. Goddard	3.00
☐ 654	Robert Frost	3.25
☐ 655	Dr. Thomas A. Dooley III	3.25
☐ 656	Sam Rayburn	3.00
☐ 657	U.S. Secret Service 100th Anniversary	3.00
☐ 428	Kittanning destroyed	3.50
☐ 523	Cornelius Vanderbilt	3.75
☐ 525	Wreck of the steamship San Francisco	4.00
☐ 527	Metis shipwreck	3.75
☐ 528	John Horn	2.75
☐ 133	Dwight D. Eisenhower	3.00
☐ 136	Lyndon B. Johnson	3.00

ORDER BLANK

Superintendent
United States Mint
Philadelphia, Pa. 19106

Please ship the bronze medals as marked on price list to:

_____
(Name)

_____
(Street number)

_____
(City)   (State)   (ZIP Code No.)

REMITTANCE ENCLOSED_____ $_____

Money orders or checks should be made payable to Superintendent, U.S. Mint, Philadelphia.
Medals are not necessarily numbered in chronological sequence.

Price List of Bronze Medals

For Sale by United States Mint, Philadelphia, Pa. 19106

The prices listed herein include all packing costs and shipping charges.

Remittance in the form of—

U.S. money order

Certified personal check

Bank cashier's check

Express or bank money order must accompany all orders. Please make remittances payable to the "Superintendent, United States Mint, Philadephia."

All sales are final. Medals may not be returned for exchange or refund.

Presidential

No.		Price
☐ 101	George Washington	$3.00
☐ 102	John Adams	3.00
☐ 103	Thomas Jefferson	3.00
☐ 104	James Madison	3.00
☐ 105	James Monroe	3.00
☐ 106	John Quincy Adams	3.00
☐ 107	Andrew Jackson	3.00
☐ 108	Martin Van Buren	3.00
☐ 109	William Henry Harrison	3.00
☐ 110	John Tyler	3.00
☐ 111	James K. Polk	3.00
☐ 112	Zachary Taylor	3.00
☐ 113	Millard Fillmore	3.00
☐ 114	Franklin Pierce	3.00
☐ 115	James Buchanan	3.00
☐ 116	Abraham Lincoln	3.00
☐ 117	Andrew Johnson	3.00
☐ 118	Ulysses S. Grant	3.00
☐ 119	Rutherford B. Hayes	3.00
☐ 120	James A. Garfield	3.00
☐ 121	Chester A. Arthur	3.00
☐ 122	Grover Cleveland	3.00
☐ 123	Benjamin Harrison	3.00
☐ 124	William McKinley	3.00
☐ 125	Theodore Roosevelt	3.00
☐ 126	William H. Taft	3.00
☐ 127	Woodrow Wilson	3.00
☐ 128	Warren G. Harding	3.00
☐ 129	Calvin Coolidge	3.00
☐ 130	Herbert Hoover	3.00
☐ 131	Franklin D. Roosevelt	3.00
☐ 132	Harry S. Truman	3.00
☐ 134	Dwight D. Eisenhower	3.00
☐ 135	John F. Kennedy	3.00
☐ 137	Lyndon B. Johnson	3.00
☐ 138	Richard M. Nixon	3.00

Secretaries of the Treasury

No.		Price
☐ 201	Alexander Hamilton	3.00
☐ 202	William Windom	3.00
☐ 203	John G. Carlisle	3.00
☐ 204	Daniel Manning	3.00
☐ 205	Lyman J. Gage	3.00
☐ 206	Leslie M. Shaw	3.00
☐ 207	George B. Cortelyou	3.00
☐ 208	Franklin MacVeagh	3.00
☐ 209	William McAdoo	3.00
☐ 210	Carter Glass	3.00
☐ 211	Andrew W. Mellon	3.00

Secretaries of the Treasury—Con.

No.		Price
☐ 212	Ogden L. Mills	$3.00
☐ 213	William H. Woodin	3.00
☐ 214	Henry Morgenthau, Jr	3.00
☐ 215	Fred M. Vinson	3.00
☐ 216	John W. Snyder	3.00
☐ 217	George M. Humphrey	3.00
☐ 218	Robert B. Anderson	3.00
☐ 219	Douglas Dillon	3.00
☐ 220	Henry H. Fowler	3.00
☐ 221	Albert Gallatin	3.00
☐ 222	Joseph W. Barr	3.00

Directors of the Mint

No.		Price
☐ 301	David Rittenhouse, Philadelphia, Pa	3.00
☐ 302	Robert M. Patterson, Philadelphia, Pa	3.00
☐ 303	J. Ross Snowden, Philadelphia, Pa	3.00
☐ 304	James Pollock, Philadelphia, Pa	3.00
☐ 305	Henry R. Linderman, Washington, D.C	3.00
☐ 306	Horatio C. Burchard, Washington, D.C	3.00
☐ 307	James P. Kimball, Washington, D.C	3.00
☐ 308	Edward O. Leech, Washington, D.C	3.00
☐ 309	Robert E. Preston, Washington, D.C	3.00
☐ 310	George E. Roberts, Washington, D.C	3.00
☐ 311	F. J. H. vonEngelken, Washington, D.C	3.00
☐ 312	Robert W. Woolley, Washington, D.C	3.00
☐ 313	Raymond T. Baker, Washington, D.C	3.00
☐ 314	F. E. Scobey, Washington, D.C	3.00
☐ 315	R. J. Grant, Washington, D.C	3.00
☐ 316	Nellie Tayloe Ross, Washington, D.C	3.00
☐ 317	William H. Brett, Washington. D.C	3.00
☐ 319	Eva Adams, Washington, D.C	3.00

Army

No.		Price
☐ 401	Washington before Boston	$3.75
☐ 402	Maj. Gen. Gates, for Saratoga	3.75
☐ 403	Brig. Gen. Morgan, for Cowpens	3.75
☐ 404	Lt. Col. John E. Howard, for Cowpens	3.50
☐ 405	Lt. Col. W. A. Washington, for Cowpens	3.50
☐ 406	Count DeFleury, for Stony Point	3.50
☐ 407	Maj. Gen. Anthony Wayne, for Stony Point	3.75
☐ 408	Maj. Gen. Nathaniel Greene, for Eutaw Springs	3.75
☐ 409	Maj. Henry Lee, Paulus Hook	3.50
☐ 410	Maj. Gen. Scott, for Chippewa and Niagara	3.75
☐ 411	Maj. Gen. Gaines, for Fort Erie	3.75
☐ 412	Maj. Gen. Porter, for Chippewa, Niagara and Erie	3.75
☐ 413	Maj. Gen. Brown, for Chippewa, Niagara and Erie	3.75
☐ 414	Brig. Gen. Miller, for Chippewa, Niagara and Erie	3.75
☐ 415	Brig. Gen. Ripley, for Chippewa, Niagara and Erie	3.75
☐ 416	Maj. Gen. Macomb, Battle of Plattsburg	3.75
☐ 417	Maj. Gen. Jackson, Battle of New Orleans	3.75
☐ 418	Maj. Gen. Harrison, for Thames	3.75
☐ 419	Gov. Isaac Shelby, for Thames	3.75
☐ 420	Col. George Croghan, for Sandusky	3.75
☐ 421	Maj. Gen. Taylor, for Palo Alto	3.75
☐ 422	Maj. Gen. Taylor, for Monterey	3.75
☐ 423	Maj. Gen. Taylor, for Buena Vista	8.75
☐ 424	Maj. Gen. Scott, for battles in Mexico	8.75
☐ 425	Maj. Gen. Grant	5.00
☐ 427	Maj. Gen. Scott (Commonwealth of Virginia)	8.75

Navy		
No.		Price
☐ 501	John Paul Jones, for Serapis	$3.75
☐ 502	Capt. Thomas Truxtun, for action with LaVengeance	3.75
☐ 503	Capt. Preble before Tripoli	3.75
☐ 504	Capt. Hull, for capture of Guerriere	3.75
☐ 505	Capt. Jacob Jones, for capture of Frolic	3.75
☐ 506	Capt. Decatur, for capture of Macedonian	3.75
☐ 507	Capt. Bainbridge, for capture of Java	3.75
☐ 508	Capt. Burrows, for capture of Boxer	3.75
☐ 509	Lt. McCall, for capture of Boxer	3.75
☐ 510	Capt. Perry, capture of British Fleet on Lake Erie	3.75
☐ 511	Capt. Elliott, capture of British Fleet on Lake Erie	3.75
☐ 512	Capt. Lawrence, capture of Peacock	3.75
☐ 513	Capt. Macdonough, capture of British Fleet on Lake Champlain	3.75
☐ 514	Capt. Henley, eagle, capture of British Fleet on Lake Champlain	3.75
☐ 515	Lt. Cassin, capture of British Fleet on Lake Champlain	3.75
☐ 516	Capt. Warrington, capture of Epervier	3.75
☐ 517	Capt. Blakely, capture of Reindeer	3.75
☐ 518	Capt. Biddle, capture of Penguin	3.75
☐ 519	Capt. Stewart, capture of Cyane & Levant	3.75
☐ 520	Rescue of officers and crew of brig Sommers	3.75
☐ 521	Capt. Ingraham	5.00

Navy—Continued		
No.		Price
☐ 522	Capt. Perry (State of Pennsylvania) capture of fleet on Lake Erie	$3.50
☐ 522A	Pennsylvania Volunteers, action on Lake Erie	3.75
☐ 526	Commodore M. C. Perry, from merchants of Boston	3.75
☐ 529	Lt. Victor Blue (State of South Carolina)	3.50
☐ 532	Departure of American Fleet	3.50
☐ 533	Vice Adm. Hyman George Rickover	3.25

Miscellaneous

No.		Price
☐ 601	Time Increases His Fame	.65
☐ 602	Cabinet Medal	.45
☐ 603	Washington and Jackson	.45
☐ 604	Commencement of Coin Cabinet	2.50
☐ 605	Presidency Relinquished	2.00
☐ 606	Allegiance	.95
☐ 607	Washington and Lincoln	.45
☐ 608	Washington and Grant	.45
☐ 609	Washington Wreath	.45
☐ 610	Washington Bicentennial	2.50
☐ 611	James Garfield	.65
☐ 612	Lincoln and Garfield	.45
☐ 613	Pennsylvania Bicentennial	.65
☐ 614	Valley Forge Centennial	2.75
☐ 615	Lincoln and Grant	.45
☐ 616	Lincoln, Broken Column	.45
☐ 617	Japanese Embassy	4.50
☐ 618	Frederick Rose	4.50
☐ 619	Louis Agassiz	4.50
☐ 620	Indian Peace Medal (George II)	2.75
☐ 621	David Hosack	1.00
☐ 622	First Steam Coinage	.65
☐ 623	Union Pacific Railroad	2.75
☐ 624	Emancipation Proclamation	2.75

Miscellaneous—Continued		
No.		Price
☐ 625	Cyrus W. Field	$5.00
☐ 626	Joseph Pancoast	4.50
☐ 627	Indian Peace (Grant)	4.00
☐ 628	Hayes, Indian Peace (oval)	4.50
☐ 629	Garfield, Indian Peace	4.50
☐ 630	Arthur, Indian Peace	4.50
☐ 631	Cleveland, Indian Peace	4.50
☐ 632	Harrison, Indian Peace	4.50
☐ 633	Let Us Have Peace (Grant)	2.75
☐ 634	Seward-Robinson	4.00
☐ 635	U.S. Diplomatic (July 4, 1776)	4.00
☐ 636	Great Seal Centennial Medal, 1782–1882	3.25
☐ 637	Joseph Francis	5.00
☐ 638	Lincoln Centennial	4.00
☐ 639	Wright Brothers	4.50
☐ 640	Abraham Lincoln	4.50
☐ 641	Woodrow Wilson	2.00
☐ 645	Charles A. Lindbergh	3.25
☐ 647	Mount Vernon	2.75
☐ 648	Benjamin Franklin	3.25
☐ 649	Franklin D. Roosevelt	3.00
☐ 651	Vice President Alben W. Barkley	3.00
☐ 652	Dr. Jonas E. Salk	3.00
☐ 653	Dr. Robert H. Goddard	3.00
☐ 654	Robert Frost	3.25
☐ 655	Dr. Thomas A. Dooley III	3.25
☐ 656	Sam Rayburn	3.00
☐ 657	U.S. Secret Service 100th Anniversary	3.00
☐ 428	Kittanning destroyed	3.50
☐ 523	Cornelius Vanderbilt	3.75
☐ 525	Wreck of the steamship San Francisco	4.00
☐ 527	Metis shipwreck	3.75
☐ 528	John Horn	2.75
☐ 133	Dwight D. Eisenhower	3.00
☐ 136	Lyndon B. Johnson	3.00

ORDER BLANK

Superintendent
United States Mint
Philadelphia, Pa. 19106

Please ship the bronze medals as marked on price list to:

_____
(Name)

_____
(Street number)

_____
(City)   (State)   (ZIP Code No.)

REMITTANCE ENCLOSED_____ $_____

Money orders or checks should be made payable to Superintendent, U.S. Mint, Philadelphia.
Medals are not necessarily numbered in chronological sequence.

p.243